MEETINGS
WITH
THE MADONNA

Copyright © 1979 by Jan Dobraczyński.
© English language translation copyright
1988 by Polonia Publishers, Warsaw, Poland.

FIRST EDITION

Revised and edited for the American reader
by W. S. Kuniczak and Lawrence Lockhart

Photographs by
Jan Morek, Janusz Rosikoń,
Andrzej Szypowski, Lech Zielaskowski
and Polonia Publishers

Designed by Andrzej Przygodzki

Printed in Poland
ISBN 83-7021-066-X

PG
7158
.D6313
1979

Jan Dobraczyński

MEETINGS
WITH
THE MADONNA

Translated from the Polish
by
Piotr Goc

SALZMANN LIBRARY
St. Francis Seminary
3257 South Lake Drive
St. Francis, Wis. 53235

POLONIA PUBLISHERS
Warsaw

61432

Jan Dobraczyński, born in Warsaw, April 20, 1910. Wrote for the Catholic press since 1933. Fought in the 1939 Campaign and in World War II resistance movement, including the Warsaw Uprising; editor of World War II underground press, Home Army psychological warfare section; inmate of Nazi POW camp.

Winner of several Catholic and State literary awards.

His most renowned books include: *W rozwalonym domu* (In a Ruined House), 1946; *Najeźdźcy* (Invaders), 1946–1947; *Święty miecz* (Holy Sword), 1949; *Klucz mądrości* (Key of Wisdom), 1951; *Listy Nikodema* (Nikodem's Letters), 1952; *Kościół w Chochołowie* (Church of Chochołów), 1954; *Pustynia* (The Desert), 1955; *A znak nie będzie mu dany* (And There Shall Be No Sign for Him), 1957; *Dłonie na murze* (Palms on Wall), 1960; *Piąty akt* (Fifth Act); 1962; *Spalone mosty* (Burned Bridges), 1969; *Truciciele* (Poisoners), 1974; *Bramy Lipska* (Gates of Leipzig), 1976; *Cień ojca* (The Shadow of Father), 1977; *Samson i Dalila* (Samson and Delilah), 1979; *Małżeństwo Anny* (The Marriage of Anne), 1981; *Dzieci Anny* (The Children of Anne), 1983.

Many of Dobraczyński's books, plays, treatises have been published internationaly.

*To the Memory
of Stefan Wyszyński,
the Primate of Poland*

Warszawa, dnia 5 listopada 1975 r.

N 2612/75/P.

Drogi Panie Janie,

Dziękuję za "Żółty Zeszyt", który doręczyłeś mi. Pragnę
powiedzieć, że jest to najmilsza książka, którą dałeś polskie-
mu czytelnikowi. Bardzo dziękuję.

Przyszła mi myśl, związana z rozpoczynającym się od
1.I.1976 sześciowiecznem przybycie Obrazu Matki Bożej na Jas-
ną Górę. Różni ludzie podejmują próby pisania szkiców histo-
rycznych. Już kilka opracowań istnieje.

Boję się jednak, że dzieje pobytu obrazu na Jasnej Górze,
choćby napisane najbardziej wiernie jeszcze nie odtworzą tej
mocy oddziaływania na duchową formację małych czy wielkich
Polaków.

Tu trzeba czegoś więcej. Trzeba wniknąć w przedziwne
misterium trwania Pani Jasnogórskiej. Myślę, że w kraju tylko
Twoje pióro zdołałoby sprostać zadaniu.

Gdybyś, Panie Janie chciał się tego podjąć, ufam, że
praca ta przyczyniłaby się do przezwyciężenia deflacji spo-
łecznej, jaka opanowywuje coraz to szersze kręgi naszej inte-
ligencji.

Proszę nad tym pomyśleć. A gdyby projekt odpowiadał chęt-
nie porozmawiałbym n.t. - jak to rozumiem.

Ale za wiele nie powiedziałbym. Idzie przecież o auten-
tyczność tego przeżycia na własną miarę.

Ślę słowa oddania w Chrystusie i błogosławię.

+ Stefan Kard Wyszyński

+ Stefan Kardynał Wyszyński
Prymas Polski

Szanowny Pan
Jan DOBRACZYŃSKI
ul. Hetmańska 42
04-305 W a r s z a w a

Warsaw, November 5, 1975

PRIMATE OF POLAND   No 2612/75/P.

My dear Mr. Jan,

Thank you for the "Yellow Notebook" you gave me. I would
like to say that this is the finest book you have given Polish
readers. Thank you very much indeed.

A certain idea has occured to me in connection with the six-
-hundredth anniversary of the arrival of the Miraculous Painting
of Our Lady at Jasna Góra, the celebrations of which begin on
January 1, 1976. Various people have attempted to write historical
essays about the Icon. Some such essays already exist.

However, I am afraid that even the most accurate historical
account of the Icon's presence at Jasna Góra will not be able
to reproduce the powerful influence which it exerts on spiritual
formations of Poles, both the mighty and the humble.

The occasion calls for something more. It is necessary to grasp
the mysterious endurance of Our Lady of Jasna Góra. I believe you
alone in Poland measure up to this task.

If you were to agree to take on this project, my dear Mr. Jan,
I am confident that this work would contribute to overcoming
the social disenchantment that has been infecting ever broader
sections of our intelligentsia.

Please think this over. Should you accept this project, I would
be glad to talk it over with you and explain how I see it.

But I would not interfere excessively. After all, this has
to be written from someone's own experience.

I remain, Dear Sir, your servant in Jesus. God bless you.

                                    † Stefan Cardinal Wyszyński
                                      Primate of Poland

Mr. Jan DOBRACZYŃSKI
ul. Hetmańska 42
04-305 W a r s z a w a

Contents

CHAPTER 1

QUEEN JADWIGA

The small party of riders that approached the inn greatly aroused the curiosity of the innkeeper, a man named Kurek. People of that kind were not often seen in Lejów. They came from the direction of the river, a seldom used route, with their belongings in packs. Ordering supper and rooms for the night, they sat down around the table waiting for Kurek's wife to prepare the meal: three women, several men who looked like knights, one priest, and one monk. An armed escort of a dozen or so men attended to the horses. Although they wore ordinary clothes, Kurek's experienced eye told him that these were not ordinary people.

Two of the women were young; one of them very young. Both had a pleasing appearance. The elder of the pair laughed all the time, showing her white teeth, and her black eyes darted around the room, contrasting with the shock of golden hair escaping from under her pearl-studded coronet. The younger one differed in every respect: taller than the men accompanying her, she had a dark complexion, dark hair, and dark eyes. She wore a sorrowful expression on her face and evidently had been biting her pale lips. She hardly uttered a word, yet seemed to be held in the highest esteem by the whole company. Seated in the best place, with a soft rug spread on the bench under her, she was the first to have her cup filled when Kurek brought her beer.

When the innkeeper was not in the kitchen urging his wife to hurry with the supper, he stood in the doorway of the dining room and surveyed his guests, who talked to each other mostly in a foreign tongue. But only the ladies could have been foreigners, he thought, for the knights spoke Polish.

The soldiers waiting for their meal in another room also spoke the native tongue. Kurek tried to talk to them, and ask who they were, but he was quickly told he would be better off seeing to the beer instead of chattering.

The priest sat beside the tall girl and she was listening attentively to what he was saying. As Kurek looked at her, he gradually became convinced that she was not even twelve years old. Her coloring and height made her appear older, but the eyes and lips, twisted in an expression of dismay, betrayed the helplessness of a child. Meanwhile the golden-haired beauty talked merrily to the young man beside her, the one who gave the orders and seemed to be in charge.

At last Kurek heard his wife announce that supper was ready. When they brought the dishes of meat into the room, the young man gestured for them to pass the first to him. Taking it, he knelt in courtly fashion before the tall girl and offered it to her. She thanked him with a graceful nod of her head, but even now she did not smile. Having set down the platters, Kurek and his woman stood at the door awaiting further orders. His wife whispered: "This lady must be greatly troubled. She's so young, not much older than our little Jagnieszka, and of noble brith no doubt, and yet she's pained by something. Oh Holy Virgin of Stara Góra, what misfortunes there are in this world!"

The travelers ate their supper quickly. They looked weary from their journey. As soon as they finished, the knight summoned Kurek and told him to prepare the bedchambers, explaining that they wanted to rest at once and be up before dawn.

The ladies' chamber was upstairs, so Kurek's wife lit a piece of tarred wood to show them the way. The younger of the Kurek daughters, just four years old, peeked out from behind her mother's skirts. The chubby, bright-eyed girl's curiosity had not let her stay in the kitchen as she was supposed to – she had run into the hall to see the guests. At the sight of the child, the first trace of a smile appeared on the tall girl's face. She bent down and stretched out her hands.

"Come on," she said in Polish, pronouncing the words a bit too hard. "What's your name?"

"Magda."

"Come with me, show us where we're going to sleep."

Holding the little girl by the hand, she followed Kurek's wife. The other women also got up, although the golden-haired beauty was clearly unwilling to end her conversation with her knight.

The bedchamber was small. A low elevation piled with hay and enclosed by planks along one of the walls formed a wide bed. A linen sheet covered the hay. Outside the narrow window, with the shutter open to let in the fragrance of ripe apples, was a warm October night.

The other two women approached the tall girl to help her out of her clothes. Dressed for the night in a long white shift, she kept talking to Magda as if to make amends for her silence during the meal. Then, as though even that not enough, she said to the little girl: "Do you want to sleep with me?"

"Oh yes, yes!" the girl said happily. "I do!"

"She'll disturb you, Your Ladyship," protested Kurek's wife. "She's very restless in her sleep, kicking about the whole bed like a colt."

"We'll get along fine," the tall girl answered. She lifted Magda up and put her in the bed.

Her companions undressed as well. The elder of the pair had brought in an oil lamp with her, which she lit from the tarred stick. Before going to bed, the women knelt down to pray. The tall girl read prayers aloud from a book bound in red leather, illustrated with beautiful paintings. The two women gave the responses. The prayers went on for some time and when they had finished, the two older women went to bed. The young girl indicated that they should sleep, while she herself returned to her prayers. Now she put her book aside, praying with her hands gripped tightly together and her forehead resting on the table. Finally, she was overcome by fatigue. She lay down and put her arm around the sleeping child.

Downstairs, Kurek kept bringing food and beer to the servants, who sat at the table long into the night, until finally one of them, weary of the innkeeper's insistent questioning, motioned him aside and placing a finger on his lips said: "Look, I'll tell you, but you're to keep it to yourself. The Cracow castellan warned that if anyone talked, he'd put him on the stocks and rip out his tongue. It's the Queen herself who's sleeping under your roof tonight. So now you know – and keep your mouth shut! Remember what I told you. You'll be in real trouble if you talk! You're not to tell anybody, not even your own wife. Remember, now!"

The party left early the following morning, vanishing immediately into the woods. They must have had a guide who knew every road and path in the area.

Kurek and his wife stood on the inn's doorstep watching the travelers depart. He clutched a generous purse the knight had given him for his services. Little Magda danced about with joy: the young lady had presented her with a beautiful crucifix.

The sun was setting when they finally emerged from the woods and rode to the top of a hill which marked the beginning of a long ridge that forked out in the distance to flank the river below. There was a settlement on the bank, but the travelers turned in the opposite direction. A lone peak of bare white rock towered above the ridge, surrounded by black woods. It resembled the shaven head of a monk, surrounded by a ring of hair. As they drew closer, the riders saw buildings at the end of a road that wound between the trees.

Jadwiga rode in front. The gentle wind blew her hair back from her forehead and from under her hood. The horse seemed to sense that the end of the trip was near, for he put his exhaustion behind him and cantered forward confidently. The girl held the reins firmly in her hand and sat in the saddle with grace. She was strong and nimble, fond of riding, skilled in archery; she knew how to hurl a spear, and had even learned the rudiments of swordsmanship. Her mother had ordered her to learn these things, believing that a sovereign should be able to serve as a knight, even if that sovereign was a woman. There were many things she would have liked to teach her daughter, although she herself had not mastered half of them.

Jadwiga loved the long chase after an animal fleeing a pack of barking hounds as much as she loved dancing, singing, and merrymaking in the company of other joyful youngsters. She took delight in listening to music and the tales of wandering minstrels. But that had been back in Hungary.

She had been missing the fun and joy since coming to Poland. The Wawel Castle was gloomy. She lived alone there, surrounded by maids of honor she had brought with her. Instead of her beloved mother, it was the serious and elderly members of the council who took care of her. For them, she was simply a monarch whom they expected to carry out her regal duties; the rest of her life was of no interest to them. She longed for her mother, wrote letters begging her to come and join her, and tried to find some entertainment for herself. Her joyous disposition could not be reconciled to a life devoid of gaiety.

This thirst for joy was matched by the profound faith in which she had been brought up by her grandmother and mother. Jadwiga's devoutness was full of radiant trust. Jesus Christ and His Mother seemed to smile at her from every picture. She dreamed of happiness, but that happiness required the blessing of the Son and the Mother. She felt that God was joy, especially when she was among the friars minor. She did not like the murky, empty chapel at the Wawel, but gladly went to the Franciscan church nearby which resounded with singing.

When the cavalcade had approached the top of the hill, Jadwiga noted that the path had been trodden wide on both sides, as if many people walked that way. This seemed strange to her. She knew that the friars who had been sent to Poland by her father and then settled on this hilltop by Prince Władysław were eremites who avoided any noise and bustle. King Louis cherished a great deal of respect for the White Friars. He helped them in every way he could and had gone to a great deal of effort to obtain the body of the founder of their Order from the Venetian republic, laying it to rest with immense reverence in a church near Buda.

The monastery was a place of silence, and only the royal visits occasionally disturbed the monks' peaceful life. But if Jadwiga was riding to the eremites' monastery today, it was less to show her respect for the monks, like her father used to do, than to plead for help. After the experiences of her recent months in the Wawel Castle, she had sought, in vain, the assistance of others. She had felt lonely ever since coming to Poland, but recently this loneliness had become simply horrifying. Her rebellious feelings were suppressed, but stayed in her like a wound that bled afresh every day. Outwardly, she had surrendered, but in her heart the resistance remained as firm as ever.

She remembered what a Franciscan monk had told her about a strange

15

Icon before which miracles occurred. In fact, the story had been told earlier by the Paulite friars who came to Poland with her party a year ago to join a smaller group previously sent by King Louis. But, when she expressed a desire to visit the monastery, the council vetoed the idea. Stubbornly she repeated her demand again and again, but they remained impervious to her pleas, convinced that there was some devious stratagem involved.

She knew what they had talked about at their meeting. "She wants to run away and put herself in the custody of Prince Władysław," they had shouted. "We can't trust either her or him. He's made many promises before, only to do something else!"

Dymitr of Goraj always defended Jadwiga: "No, no – I trust her."

But that was countered by another argument: "Even if we trust her, nobody can trust that sly manipulator!"

Archbishop Bodzanta had been the last to speak. Formally not a member of the council, he had been invited to Cracow and attended all the debates.

"I think, my lords," he said, "that if at this difficult moment of her life the Queen wishes to seek the assistance of the Virgin Mary, we should put no obstacles in her way. He who bars access to Christ's Mother is opposing Jesus himself. Whatever we may think about human affairs, we cannot forget about the cause of God."

Silence had followed.

The Archbishop of Gniezno was not greatly liked in Cracow. They knew that he had first supported the royal candidacy of Sigismund of Luxembourg and then that of Ziemowit of Mazovia. But now, in the face of the proposed marriage between the child-queen and the aging prince of Lithuania, the lords of Cracow needed the support of the highest Church authority in the kingdom.

Bishop Radlica supported the Archbishop: "After all, there will be no harm in allowing the Queen to make the pilgrimage."

Dobiesław opposed that view at once. "I wouldn't be so sure. After all, these are the lands of the Duke of Opole. Even if the Queen herself is sincere about her pilgrimage, this backer of the Duke of Austria may try some new tricks. You keep forgetting, my lords, that the Queen is still only a child!"

Then the voivode of Cracow had joined the dispute. "The Queen is indeed a child, and for that reason we must look after her, but that's not to say that we should oppose her every wish. Besides, she doesn't have to travel to Stara Góra so that everybody knows about her pilgrimage. If she goes there secretly and be in good hands, I'm sure she'll get there and back unharmed."

"You talk about her being in good hands," someone had said, "but who exactly would protect her?"

"With your consent, my lords, I myself am ready to accompany the Queen," Spytek had declared.

The others had stayed silent for a moment, but then old Dobiesław chuckled: "No doubt the beautiful daughter of Starost Emeryk will be going too, won't she?" At this, everybody had begun to laugh and the young voivode blushed.

Jadwiga had learned from Elżbieta that she owed the consent for her trip to Spytek of Melsztyn, or, to be more precise, to his passion for one of her maids of honor.

"But please, Your Highness," said Bishop Radlica who had come to the Queen to tell her about the council's decision. "Keep your departure a secret. The servants must think you're unwell and staying in your chambers for a few days. You can only confide this to the most faithful of your maids of honor. You must also travel without the normal retinue of servants and carts."

"I will do whatever you tell me, Bishop," Jadwiga had replied. "I only want to pay homage to the Holy Mother and place myself in her care. And I don't need to tell you how fond I am of riding."

The path become increasingly steep as they climbed the hill. The woods were now behind them and they rode onto the open, rocky hilltop where they stopped outside the heavy gates of a stockade that surrounded a small yard. At Spytek's orders, one of the riders pounded on the gates. This went on until a friar dressed in white peered over the stockade.

"Who, in God's name, is making that racket at this time of day?"

"Open the gates, brother, I'm the lord of Melsztyn and Governor of Cracow," Spytek said. "We've come to pay tribute to the Miraculous Icon of the Mother of God."

The friar did not answer. He was in no hurry to open the gates and eyed the small armed party distrustfully. He seemed to be counting the riders and making a note of their clothing. At last he disappeared, but the gates stayed closed. The friar had to go to the prior and consult with him. The riders waited patiently, accustomed to such distrust. Finally they heard the noise of a wooden bar being drawn back and the gates opened narrowly, so that the riders could enter the yard only one at a time.

Spytek ordered two archers to ride in first and followed them himself. At his signal, the soldiers dismounted and, shoving the friars aside, took charge of the gates which they closed and barred as soon as the whole party had entered the yard.

A group of friars, including the prior, looked on in amazement as Spytek dismounted and strode over to them. The prior, a short, bald-headed man with terror written all over his face, was sure that the riders had used the governor's name as a ruse to get inside the stockade.

He stood in silence in front of Spytek who summoned a man who could speak Hungarian. He spoke while the other translated: "Don't be afraid, Reverend Prior, I really am the Governor of Cracow and I'm not here to raid your holy monastery. I am only accompanying our gracious sovereign and beloved Queen..."

He gestured toward Jadwiga, who had dismounted and was approaching the prior, accompanied by her chaplain and maids of honor.

The terror on the friars' faces instantly gave way to joy. Most of the Paulites knew by sight the daughter of the protector of their Order, and some of them had actually arrived in Poland with her entourage. They moved forward and bowed to the ground before her, crying out: "Greetings, Your Majesty! We're happy to receive you here!"

"Greetings, fathers and brethren," she said softly, "Forgive me for arriving unexpectedly and unannounced."

"But why weren't we told to expect your arrival, Majesty?" the prior asked. "Ours is a poor monastery and we are not prepared to host such an exalted visitor."

"There are reasons why nobody should know about Her Majesty's stay here," Spytek interjected. "My men will be guarding the gates until the Queen departs. Do not be offended by this, Reverend Prior, our sovereign's safety is at stake. And don't worry about how to receive the Queen. Her Highness expects no luxuries and views this trip as a holy pilgrimage to the Icon of Our Lady. Tell your friars to take meat and wine from my men and let the cook prepare supper for all of us. Tomorrow we'll be setting off right after Mass."

Bowing all the time, the prior led the Queen to the refectory. The monastery was modest and small. It had been the parish priest's house before the hilltop church was handed over to the friars, and the new residents had not done much to develop the monastery.

"Please excuse me, Your Majesty," the prior was pleading. "This is a poor place. We are eremites and have no need of anything more. But when such distinguished visitors arrive..."

"Neither do we have need of anything more," Jadwiga replied. "We don't want to disturb your prayer and meditation."

"Your Majesty's visit won't disturb anybody's paryer," the prior assured her. "Besides, we owe so much to your father... Although," he went on, sighing, "it's true that not everybody is sensitive to our need for peace. The crowds coming here to pay homage to the Icon grow greater all the time!"

"That should gladden your hearts," Jadwiga suggested.

The visitors seated themselves around the refectory table and the friars brought in jugs of beer. The exhausted travelers were silent then, with the exception of the golden-haired Elżbieta who chattered happily, eyeing her handsome suitor.

The young Queen had barely wetted her lips when she nodded to the prior. They rose and left the refectory. The prior led the way to the chapel holding an oil lamp in his hand. The corridor, built of thick fir logs, was drafty and the flame in the lamp died down every now and then. When this happened, their pace slowed.

"Yes, Your Majesty," the prior began. "The Duke of Opole was very kind to leave this holy painting with us. But those huge crowds that besiege us here are so ignorant..."

"Would you prefer that the picture wasn't here?"

"Oh, no! Of course not!" he denied hurriedly. "The only thing that disturbs me is that we, the followers of the saintly eremite Paul, are denied our silence."

"Perhaps that is how it has to be? Perhaps that's the Lord's will?"

"You're probably right, Your Majesty," he said. "God wants to test us, poor sinners that we are."

She did not answer. They walked on, the only sounds being the heavy footsteps of the prior contrasting with the gentle ones of the Queen. The church was built of timber, on a foundation of white boulders. The wind whistled somewhere through a gap between logs.

At last they reached a heavy, ironclad door. The prior removed a wrought iron bar. The lock grated and the door creaked. A chilly wind blew in from the darkness before them. The prior stopped and held the light aloft for Jadwiga to cross the high threshold. He put the lamp down and lit two thick candles. The light pushed back the darkness. They went along a side aisle between the walls of the church and the wooden pillars supporting the roof.

The Icon she had come to see was on a low altar. She approached it slowly, her hand clutched to her breast. Her heart pounded. The prior stepped slightly to one side, still holding the burning candles in his raised hands.

The Icon was surrounded – as if framed – by a thick wreath of votive offerings nailed to the boards on which it was painted: chains, beads, rings, earrings, coins. People had brought their gifts for decades, if not centuries. The wreath got larger and thicker, covering more and more of the painting until only the faces of Mary and Her Son could be seen, seeming to look up from the bottom of a deep well at those who had come to pay homage.

The prior held the candles in such a way as to let the light fall on the two faces.

Jadwiga's eyes followed the light. When they reached Our Lady's face, the Queen realized that the Mother of God was looking at her. The narrow, almond-shaped eyes appeared to be alive. There was so much life in them that one might have thought they had long been waiting to meet the eyes of the child-queen. Now that they had done so, they held Jadwiga captive. She would not be able to free herself from the Virgin's gaze.

Slowly, she sank to her knees. The light of the candles trembled and the flitting shadows filled the dark face with life. How desperately she'd wanted to come here! The things the friar minor had told her had convinced her that this was the place where she would find the answer to her questions. Could she possibly have been expected? The eyes in the Icon were strangely commanding, as if saying: "Speak!"

She lowered her head, then raised it at once. Exhausted from what she had gone through, she feared she would not find the strength to tell her story again. But the eyes before her seemed insistent, and she had to surrender to them.

She'd asked the council to allow this trip for no other reason than to beg for deliverance. Who had she talked to? The Archbishop, the bishops, the father confessor? They all used noble words, but – and this was worst of all – their words did not always have the same meaning. Some told her about the enormous responsibility of being a queen and the great tasks facing her as a Christian, others talked about sacred duties and the superiority of the God-fearing Christian over the bloodthirsty pagan. These were not the words she needed. She was a child separated from her mother, cast among strangers, crowned, and yet treated as an object. Nobody asked her about anything, nobody ever consulted her. Others made the decisions for her. The servants knew more than she and learned about everything sooner than she did. Nobody was bothered by any misgivings she might have; they appeared to understand what God wanted her to do, while she did not.

She had not wanted to come to Poland. The crown had not tempted her. Her sisters had more thirst for power than she. She was interested only in games, singing, music, dancing and rejoicing. She loved her mother, her lenient confessors, her servants and maids of honor. As for her father, she hardly knew him. When she was only four, she had been taken to Vienna. She'd been plunged into despair by leaving her mother despite the promises made to her that she would find nothing but happiness at the court of Austria. She had wept for a year, her heart filled with longing, and then her mother took her back to Buda.

Elizabeth had taken advantage of her husband's grave illness to be reunited with her most beloved child. She was deeply attached to her youngest daughter, and by no means pleased at her being married off as a child to the Duke of Austria. This Bosnian princess had no friendly feelings toward Germans. The Hapsburgs recognized the false. French pope, while she was full of admiration for the short-tempered but magnificent Urban, who had decided to halt the exile in Avignon. When it became obvious that Louis would not recover from his disease, Elizabeth realized that she was the real ruler now. Until then, her husband and mother-in-law had made all the decisions, a fact which made Elizabeth suffer greatly. With the blood of the Piasts of Gniewkowo flowing in her veins, she was not accustomed to giving up her rights.

From the moment of her return to Buda, her mother had meant

everything to Jadwiga. Her father died shortly afterwards. Both Jadwiga and Elizabeth were determined never to part again.

The youngest daughter was to succeed to the Hungarian throne. However, the Hungarian magnates would not accept any ruler other than one chosen by themselves, and their choice was Mary. Jadwiga was to sit on the throne of Poland. Elizabeth consented to this, but assured her daughter that they would go to Poland together. This later proved to be impossible; problems arose which prevented Elizabeth from leaving Mary, while Poland was impatient to have Jadwiga in Cracow. The ten-year-old Queen had to travel there alone. Elizabeth hoped that after the coronation she would be able to take her daughter back to Buda for a time, but even that plan went awry. Jadwiga was left in the gloomy Wawel Castle, far from her mother, among strangers who needed her only to further their own schemes.

"We only feel true happiness", thought Jadwiga, "when we are able to share it with those we love the most. How badly she missed being able to run to her mother and tell her about everything that gave her joy, and about all that filled her with horror."

The Franciscan church in Cracow had seemed to be the only place in Poland that offered an escape to something that was dear to her, something that resembled a family home. The good monks there spoke Hungarian, and there was the joyous worship of the Blessed Virgin. Next to the cloisters, the youth of Cracow lived its merry life: rich German burghers and young Polish noblemen who kept their courts within the city walls. On Saturdays, they would sing the Angelus on their knees to obtain indulgence, after which they gathered in the cloister refectory to amuse themselves. The kind-hearted friars did not object. The young people listened to the minstrels and then sang and danced.

Jadwiga's maids of honor had learned about these gatherings and informed their mistress. The servants intimated to the young Queen that it was possible to reach the monastery without leaving the castle by the main gate, which would have meant going with a suite and observing the requirements of protocol. While a small gate in the southern wall seemed to be locked, in reality its lock had long since been eaten away by rust. Few people knew about the gate and hardly anybody ever used it. It led straight out into a district called Okoł, outside the city walls. All one had to do then was cross a small bridge over the moat and enter the gardens. From there, a path between the bushes growing along the city walls led to the back of the Franciscans' garden. Here was another gate, equipped with a bell, and a friar posted nearby would open the gate whenever the bell was rung. Jadwiga had no qualms about using this route. Her father confessors had themselves encouraged her to do so. Besides, she was not doing anything wrong, while the very thought of seeking the consent of the old and severe members of the Royal Council was awful.

Not that Jadwiga's secret expeditions to the Franciscans had escaped the notice of the councilors. But they decided neither to oppose the Queen nor to give her official permission to sneak out of the castle. As old Dobiesław said when the council debated the matter: "Let the child have some fun. It won't last long anyway. Let's pretend we don't know anything about it but keep her under observation."

Governor Spytek had quickly made a protective arrangement with his beloved Elżbieta: on the days when Jadwiga visited the Franciscans, he sent out his men to protect her little group as it made for the city. When Elżbieta admitted betraying the secret, the Queen only laughed, realizing that both sides were guilty of deception. Watching the terror on the faces of their companions, when they spotted some burly male silhouette slipping past in the bushes during their night excursions, Jadwiga and Elżbieta would shake with hidden laughter.

Jadwiga had first heard about the picture, donated by Duke Władysław to the friars of Stara Góra, from the Paulites who'd accompanied her on her journey to Poland. The friars could not tell her much as they had not yet seen it themselves. But the Franciscans knew much more. Traveling all over the country to teach, they met various people and listened to what they had to say. And so they had heard about huge groups of people walking from remote places to the Paulite monastery, in order to kneel and pray before the Holy Icon.

Barely a year had passed since the Duke had sent it to Stara Góra and its fame had already spread for miles around. It attracted even bigger crowds than Łysa Góra with its relic of the Holy Cross, once stolen but recently returned by the Lithuanians. As Jadwiga discovered, the Paulites were not happy with this state of affairs. She was also told that Władysław himself was equally displeased, as he would have preferred to conceal his treasure rather than publicize it.

This Duke of Opole was a strange man; Jadwiga had known him since her childhood as one of her father's closest advisers. He showed great ambition, which consumed him and for which he would have been prepared to commit the gravest sin, yet at the same time there was a strange softness in him that made him hold back at decisive moments.

Now, praying before the painting which Duke Władysław had found hidden in a secret niche in Belz castle, Jadwiga was full of questions: how did it get to Belz in eastern Ruthenia? Was it true that the old Duke Lev had gotten it from the Emperor of Byzantium as a reward for his services? But why had nothing been heard for so many decades about this unusual Icon, which had became famous in the Kingdom of Poland within just a year? Why was it that only here in Stara Góra, it had begun to attract pilgrims who came to seek that extraordinary grace that the Holy Mother bestowed upon them in return?

When Jadwiga asked the Duke about this, he had only shrugged.

"I can't answer your questions, Your Majesty," he replied. "It wasn't for a picture that I searched the castle, but for a treasure that some people had been fantasizing about. When I was leaving Ruthenia, as your father asked me to, I ordered the Icon shipped to Opole. But the horses went lame and we had to stop the carts near Stara Góra. I left the painting with the friars for safekeeping until I could collect it. But the horses didn't recover for weeks, not until I ordered the eremites to hide the painting and told my men to return home. Then the horses got well at once, to everyone's complete amazement, and the friars put the Icon on display in their church instead of hiding it. And that's how it all began".

The painting was hung low on its wall so that the pilgrims could attach their votive offerings to it and to kiss its edges.

Jadwiga inched forward on her knees, stretched out her fingertips, and gently touched the boards on which this holy image had been painted. Brother Jakub assured her that they had once been part of the tabletop that St. Joseph had fashioned for his wife. If that were so, then Her hands must have touched them often, perhaps to pick up breadcrumbs or to brush the table clean with a damp cloth. Now, as her fingers brushed against the wood, Jadwiga had the feeling that she was touching the hand of God's Mother.

"Oh Mother," she whispered. "Oh Mother, does it have to be this way? Does it really have to be? Why?"

The decision that was expected of her was too terrible for the child-queen to make on her own, and yet her own mother could neither help her nor advise her then.

She prayed. As a small child, she had been pledged in marriage to a handsome lad, Prince Wilhelm of Austria, even though her mother had opposed the alliance with a German. The unexpected recent reappearance of the golden-haired young man in Cracow had been a brilliant moment in her sad, dull life, but it wasn't really Wilhelm of whom she was thinking as she touched the Icon. She was remembering all those joyful things she had lost when she came to Poland: her family home, her mother and sisters, the relaxed life in the Hungarian royal castle on St. Gellert's Hill. She had liked Wilhelm. Her cousin, Władysław of Opole, had praised his piety and courage, and everyone at court seemed to admire him as well. But the prospect of marriage, arranged by her father, had been so remote! Becoming Wilhelm's wife in some distant future hadn't troubled her heart. She was too close to nature not to know about the physical side of marriage, even though she had never been attracted to those matters that made men laugh uproariously while the women giggled and hid their faces in their hands. She knew about the consummation of marriage but she was sure her mother would prepare her for it. Everything could be understood when her mother was near.

But now another suitor had sent emissaries to Cracow, asking for her hand, a man of whom she thought with horror and revulsion as a Lithuanian savage, an enemy of Christianity and thief of holy relics. Duke Jagiełło, ruler of the Lithuanians and Ruthenians, was an old, cunning and bloodthirsty tyrant, and when her councilors told her why his envoys had come, she had screamed: "Never! Never! I'd sooner die!"

The lords of the council had said nothing then. They had merely looked at each other, making their own plans. Soothed and advised by the kindly Bishop Radlica, the young Queen had hidden her revulsion from Jagiełło's envoys. She told them that she was still too young to make such decisions and that it would be up to her mother in Hungary to choose a husband for her, and when they left her court to journey to the Hungarian capital of Buda she had sighed with relief. But uneasiness lingered. She couldn't forget their mission, nor the friendliness with which they had been received by her councilors who clearly wanted this dynastic union with the

Lithuanians. Bishop Radlica had told her how Christianity itself would benefit from the baptism of Jagiełło's people which might take place if she became the wife of their ruler. But she refused to listen to his exhortations, insisting that she was a Christian and that she would marry only a Christian man whom her mother would choose.

And then one day, as if to save her from the horror, her cousin, the Duke Władysław of Opole, arrived at the court to tell her that her handsome Austrian prince was also in Cracow. Wilhelm had come to be united with her, as Władysław put it, but the council had barred him from Jadwiga's castle.

"How dare they? Who gave them the right?" she had cried out in fury.

Like her strongwilled grandmother and mother, the young Queen was impulsive and easy to anger.

"They have no right," Władysław said smoothly. He called them disobedient, feeding Jadwiga's anger. He told her that Wilhelm was her rightful husband. "I'm here by your mother's wish to unite you with him."

She was surprised. She knew her mother's feelings about Germans. She also knew that she was not yet completely a woman and certainly not old enough to consummate a marriage. But Władysław set her doubts at rest. He told her that her mother and the bishops could approve such an early wedding, and that Elizabeth of Hungary would hurry to her daughter's side as soon as she could. He pointed out that her sister Mary had become the wife of the Margrave Sigismund still a young girl. "It had been necessary to resort to subterfuge, Your Majesty," he reminded her. "The Hungarian magnates had opposed your sister's marriage to the Margrave."

"Am I to become Wilhelm's wife by a trick?" she demanded. And, once again, Władysław of Opole soothed her.

"There is no other way," he said with assurance. "As soon as you've been united with Prince Wilhelm in fact as in name, then you attain maturity under the law and the council won't be able to oppose your wishes."

Should she have trusted the words of her cousin? Later, her councilors told her that her mother's approval of Wilhelm had been extorted under pressure... that she opposed that marriage. But the young Queen distrusted the lords of her council even more. Anything would seem better than what they wanted for her: marriage to the man whose greedy hands were reaching out for her even then. The palace servants told awful tales about him. They said he was short, almost like a dwarf, and that he was hairy. He was old, they said, and had a herd of wives. Cunning and treacherous, he trusted no one. He had slain his own uncle and murdered the missionary friars who'd come to preach in Lithuania.

The handsome, well-formed, splendidly dressed Wilhelm couldn't have presented a better contrast to the Lithuanian. He seemed to have come like St. George to save her from a dragon. Her friends the Franciscans arranged the meetings in their cloisters, and she knew the way. Remembering everything that Władysław told her, she went there without hesitation and, at first, Wilhelm had seemed to be everything that she hoped he would be. He was kind and attentive. He sang well and he danced gracefully, and it had pleased her when he waited on her at the table, eating from the same dish and sharing her cup. But then she noted that his foot landed on hers repeatedly and that his knee was touching her too often. She knew about such things but she didn't like them. She had expected something different from the man who had hurried to her rescue like St. George. She had rather hoped that all that would come to her wrapped delicately in gentleness and affection. She was dismayed to discover that the boy whom she remembered more as a brother than a "husband" was now whispering hot words of desire into her ear.

She hadn't known what to do. She would have been untroubled if it had been only a choice between suitors but there were other persons and opinions involved in the choosing. Her father had promised her to Wilhelm and her council urged her to accept Jagiełło. In some views, her father's choice had the weight of a promise made to God. Others argued that the council's choice accorded with the wishes of the Lord, the Church and the nation. Nobody had ever asked her what she wanted, and no one was there to tell her what was true. Her mother was far away, whom else could she believe? Władysław assured her that her mother wanted Wilhelm for Jadwiga's husband. "Where, oh Blessed Mother," she prayed every day, "where is the truth?"

When they met at the Franciscans' for the third time, Wilhelm had asked Jadwiga outright whether it was true that the council wanted to marry her off "to that mad Lithuanian dog." She told him what she thought: that although the council had agreed to wait until they'd had word from Hungary, she was afraid that they might do what they wanted anyway. It was then that Wilhelm confided to the girl-queen the plan that he and Władysław had devised. The Duke had his supporters in the city, and in the castle too. Wilhelm was to be secreted into the castle with their help so that the marriage vows exchanged in Hamburg many years ago could be consummated. Then, after the Prince had spent some days in Jadwiga's chambers, the matter would be allowed to come into the open and the council would be powerless to do anything about it. Even if Wilhelm were forced to leave the castle afterwards – as had happened to the Margrave Sigismund in Hungary – no one would be able to question the marriage nor his title to the Polish crown. Help would come, if needed, from the Teutonic Knights who had revered her father, and from the Margrave Sigismund and the King of Bohemia. There were many others who'd come to their aid.

She tried to listen to him with calmness but a great burden rested on her shoulders. She was eleven years old, and she had to make her decision alone. One thing was certain in her heart and mind: she would do anything to save herself from marriage to a savage pagan! If her mother was at Mary's side, she reasoned, and if she had consented to her sister's marriage to the German margrave, then that must have been the right thing to do. And that, Jadwiga told herself, is what she'd do herself.

"Do what you've said you will," she told Wilhelm. "I will join your plan."

His reply was fierce. He clutched her hands tightly and pushed his knee against hers again.

But when the night came, and she and Wilhelm and their guests sat down to their wedding supper, and when the armed guards had rushed, shouting, into the chamber and the guests fled in terror, it had been she, not Wilhem, who had leaped up, enraged, and seized a sword hanging on a wall.

"Stand!" she had cried. "You're facing your monarch! Stand, I order you."

But they ignored her orders, she remembered as she knelt before the Icon in the gloomy chapel.

She had prayed much that summer, her prayers becoming increasingly desperate. Although it was a beautiful season that changed into a warm and fragrant autumn, Jadwiga's days had become sad and gray. Wilhelm had been spared. His retinue had also been set free. Władysław of Opole had changed his allegiance and now held the same opinions as the councilors. Her maids of honor whispered that Wilhelm had not fled from Poland but was in hiding near Cracow, and that a meeting could be arranged between them. But she declined the offers.

All summer she had waited for a clear sign of her mother's will. She felt lost in Cracow, despite the secret support she received from the city's German burghers who supported Wilhelm's designs on the Polish throne. But she saw many persons who had once wished him to be her husband now turning to Jagiełło. "That repulsive pagan, polygamist and murderer seemed to be winning everybody to his side," she thought.

"Oh Blessed Virgin," she prayed through long hours before her many paintings of the Mother of God. "Save me. I'm so alone. My mother is far away and I don't know what she expects from me. She may not even know the danger that I face! And what shall I do if she consents to their plans for me?"

She knew now that her lords and nobles would never accept a German as ruler in Poland; they had told her so that night when she faced them sword in hand, and she had finally thrown that sword to clatter at their feet while her own cries were stifled in her throat.

"Help me to die," she prayed, "rather than sin by marriage to a man I loathe. Make my mother reject the offers of Jagiełło. They say the marriage would make a Christian of him, but can't you make him a Christian in some other way? I'd gladly give my life to bring him to You, but not as his wife."

But the only answer she received was from her councilors who came to tell her that the Lithuanian envoys had returned from Hungary, and that they had brought her mother's consent to the Lithuanian marriage.

"This marriage will accomplish much for Christianity," Bishop Radlica had tried to console her. "It will bring the whole Lithuanian nation into the Church and unite it with ours..."

"Not God himself can ask me to make such a sacrifice!" she had cried. "I cannot marry a man who disgusts me! You'd do better to take away my crown and send me back to my family and my mother..."

"Kings and queens, Your Majesty, do not renounce their crowns," the Bishop had told her. "The crown is an annointment and it comes from

God. Your life is not your own, you live for His purpose. Would you really refuse to answer His call?"

She had wept and argued but they wouldn't listen. The Bishop left her alone with her dispair. During the days that followed, she lost her love of gaiety, the desire for joy that had been the frame of her life until then. She knew now that she had been deserted by everyone, including her mother.

She now had no one to turn to for help and understanding... except, perhaps Wilhelm. And so she told the people who whispered to her about him that she wished to see him. She'd meet him in two days' time at the Franciscan cloister. She would renounce her crown and they would flee from Poland. If he loved her as much as he claimed he did, they'd find a simpler life together, away from royal honors and distinctions, a life that didn't put such terrible demands on a human being. She was sure that Wilhelm would agree.

But when she and a few trusted maids of honor arrived at the familiar little gate that led beyond the walls, they found it locked and guarded by a soldier.

"The keys had been taken by the castellan", he said.

"Then give me your battle-axe!" she had cried.

He had not dared to refuse her. He knelt and offered the heavy weapon to her, and she clutched it and lifted it in both hands. She struck the padlock again and again. The iron-rimmed gate clanged as if sounding an alarm. But just as she was about to bring down her axe for the final blow, the one that would shatter the padlock into pieces, she saw a head of silvery hair between her and the gate.

"Move aside!" she shouted at the kneeling man.

But he said he would not.

In the dim starlight she recognized the face of Dymitr of Goraj, a member of the council and one of the most trusted of her father's advisors. He had a daughter of Jadwiga's age whom he often brought to the castle.

"Get away, my lord," she hissed through clenched teeth. "I want to leave here and I will! No one will stand in my way!"

"I beg you, Your Highness, think again," he pleaded. "I'm begging you as I would my own daughter."

"You wouldn't condemn your daughter to a fate like mine!" she had cried. "I don't want the man you're forcing upon me. I want to be free!"

"But you're our queen, Your Highness! You took an oath..."

"Then I don't want to be your queen. I also gave my oath to Wilhelm and you want me to break it. Stand aside, my lord!"

But the old man refused.

"You are our sovereign," he said, "and you cannot leave us. You knew what we were like before you came here. The wars... the quarrels... The people love you, Your Majesty, you remember the welcome that they gave you when you come here. They see hope in you, they've begun to breathe again. You have brought them peace. Order and justice returned to us with your coming. You've said so often that you want your people to be happy, and, for them, you are their happiness..."

"And it's for that you want me to sacrifice myself?" Jadwiga demanded.

"If that's what God wills..." he nodded.

Slowly, she lowered the axe.

"Get up, my lord," she said in a hollow voice. "I don't want to see you on your knees."

"Change your mind, Your Majesty, I beg you," he had pleaded.

"Get up," was all she said.

He rose. She dropped the axe on the paving stones. It rang once, thinly, like a bell tolling someone's death. She turned around but all her maids had fled. She was alone in her defeat and started walking slowly towards the stairs that led into the castle. But then she motioned to Dymitr to come up.

"Do one thing for me," she said and slid a ring from her finger. "Return this to Whilhelm. It's... my betrothal ring. Tell him that I'm returning it under no coercion, of my own free will. Then let him ride away and forget about me."

"I am your servant, Your Majesty," the old man replied.

Even slower than before, she had climbed the stairs and turned towards her chambers.

"If that's what God wills..."

Those words remained in her memory, as she prayed for guidance before the Holy Icon. Dymitr of Goraj had known her since she was quite small and she, too, remembered him from her earliest years. She liked his daughter, a girl of rare beauty, almost as lovely as her Elżbieta, her favorite maid of honor. He had shaken her profoundly when he had dropped to his knees and exposed his head to the blade of her axe. This, perhaps, was why his words had spoken louder to her than all those spoken by Bishop Radlica and the others.

If God so willed, could she refuse? She remembered childhood moments when her grandmother, the Dowager Queen Elizabeth, once a Polish Princess, would take her to a huge cross hanging in the chapel of the castle in Buda. They would both press their lips against the pierced feet. The bloodied, tortured body hung limply above their heads. Although she was only a child, she knew what pain meant. She had seen the condemned, prisoners in the stocks, thieves whose hands were cut off... Pain had always awakened compassion in her. She often cried at the sight of suffering.

"You've inherited that from your great-grandmother," her grandmother told her. "My mother's mother, Duchess Jolanta of Kalisz, was famous for her charitable acts. The memory of her deeds lives on in Kalisz to this day."

A cross similar to the one in Buda hung in Wawel Cathedral. More and more often, she came to pray in front of it. Here, too, Christ's head hung low. Jadwiga felt that it was not only the suffering of the body that had broken the heart of Him who was crucified, He must have been hurt even more by the terrible disillusionment He met among His people. He brought them salvation and the word of love that is all-forgiving, and they responded with hatred, condemning Him to a cruel death. Hate for love. Yet He continued to love them, and still wanted their joy and happiness. For them He had renounced not only heaven, but also all the human joys that could have been His: a quiet life, His own home, wife, children, friends... He had rejected all that in order to tell them of God's love. And still people scoffed at His promises. They nailed Him to the Cross, as if afraid that He might follow them with arms outstretched. And there He stayed, spread out in a gesture of undying love, as if waiting for someone to do for Him – at least in some small human measure – what He had done for mankind.

If God so wills...

"Oh Blessed Virgin," Jadwiga prayed, "is it possible that this is what He wants? Bishop Radlica is right: I only know Jagiełło from my fears. But even if what they say about him is true, the bandit on the Cross was a murderer and yet he went straight to heaven. Mary Magdalene knew many men, and yet He accepted her into the circle of His closest servants. The Roman centurion was a pagan, yet He healed him. Lepers, the lame, the possessed came to Him and He made them well. Before it had become the most fiercely Catholic monarchy in Europe, the Hungarian kingdom was a land of Mongol invaders, sowing death and destruction among the worshippers of Christ. Why shouldn't the Lithuanian plunderers become a nation which, like Paul, will take the name of the Lord to pagans and kings? And here am I, disgusted by a man whom He might use as His tool..."

One day as she prayed, she thought she heard the words: "Mother will help you".

She had looked around the empty church. Dusk was creeping in, clinging to the pillars like webs. In the darkness loomed the tombs of her great-grandfather, Władysław the Short, and King Kazimierz the Great. In grief, she pressed her face to the prayer bench and whispered: "I'd like to go to her, but my mother is far away..."

Again she seemed to hear: "Go to Mother, then. She will help you".

And so her pilgrimage to Stara Góra had begun.

And now she knelt in front of the mysterious picture of Our Lady. Nobody knew for certain how this Icon had surfaced from the tides of history. No one knew how much truth there was in the tales people told about it. It had appeared and began to shine unexpectedly, as if it had to shine here, and to shine now. As if it were needed here, and needed now.

"Oh Blessed Virgin," she whispered. "I have no one, so I've come to You. I bring You my humility. I don't want to defend my joys, pleasures and dreams. I want whatever He asks of me."

The narrow eyes looked at her from below the wreath of votive offerings. Jadwiga saw great calm and great love in them. Neither days nor years nor centuries had affected them. Jadwiga also saw things that had been born of pain and accepted in faith.

"Do you think, My child," the eyes said, "that I did not foresee His departure? His torment and death? That My heart did not rebel, too? Do you think that I didn't want to protect Him, and with Him My peace, My joy? But He... My Son, My Child... taught that it's only when we add our blood to His that something great and eternal can be born. Your time may seem long and your cross too heavy. But have courage, My child. When your pain reaches its utmost, you will know that He is allowing you to touch His Cross. Fear not. What seems to be more than your mortal shoulders can bear today, you will then bear together with Him..."

Jadwiga heard footsteps then. The prior, worried by her long absence, had entered the chapel. The candles were dying out, icebergs melting into white, rippled lakes. She had to lean hard on the faldstool to rise from her aching knees.

"Your Majesty", the monk said, "let me now show you where you will be able to rest. Your chamberlain already awaits you there."

Kurek and his wife saw the party from a distance and ran to meet them, bowing low to the tall, black-haired girl sitting gracefully on a beautiful horse. Jadwiga smiled at little Magda, who clutched her hand and would not let go. Entering the inn, she lifted the girl in her arms, and Magda threw her tiny hands around her neck.

"Chase her away, Your Ladyship," Kurek's wife said, embarrassed by her daughter's daring. "She's such a disobedient child, but she'll regret having taken the liberty to bother you so."

"Don't spank her," Jadwiga said, "I'm glad she's showing me so much affection. Let her stay with me until we leave."

Magda did not leave the Queen for one moment. When everybody sat down to supper, she sat on the bench next to Jadwiga, dangling her legs. Her hand reached out to the Queen's dish.

"Shove her away, Your Highness," said the chief servant. "She won't let you eat your meal in peace."

"An impudent child," observed one of the courtiers. "She needs a good spanking."

"She's dirty," offered another. "She'll soil your robes."

"Enough," Jadwiga said firmly, embracing the girl. For a moment, she stopped smiling and gazed into space.

"Do you remember, Father Piotr," she asked the priest, "how the apostles argued when Mary, the sister of Lazarus, poured precious ointment on Jesus's feet? And Jesus silenced them, saying she had done it for His burial. Perhaps this little child..."

She broke off and went back to feeding Magda.

Nobody uttered a word.

Father Wysz turned to Governor Spytek and whispered: "Have you noticed, Your Honor, how serious our Queen has suddenly become? It's as if she's matured overnight."

CHAPTER 2

THE WOODCARVER

A young priest appeared at the top of the stairs, framed in the arch of the stone doorway. Noticing someone on a bench in the semi-darkness, he called out: "Hey, good man! Are you Łukasz of Rogi?"

The man sat holding his head in his hands. His elbows rested on his knees and his legs were spread apart. He slowly raised his head and looked at the priest.

"I am," he replied.

"Come up here."

The old man got up, reached for a bundle lying on the bench, and unhurriedly mounted the stairs. He had short, graying hair and an ash-gray growth on his cheeks and chin. His weary face was deeply furrowed. His clothes were well-worn. His huge hands hung like leaves burdened by the first snows of autumn. Reaching the top of the stairs, he stopped in front of the priest.

"Are you the one who brought the letter from the Duchess of Niemodlin?"

"I am."

"And you're a painter?"

"I do lots of things. I carve, I paint..."

"Have you done any paintings or carvings for churches?"

"Yes. Sometimes the good priests wanted a holy figure or icon... Sometimes I'd repaint pictures that had been damaged."

"Don't you do that anymore?"

"It's been a long time since I did."

"Where do you get your paints from?"

"I mix them myself."

"You know what we want?"

"Yes, Her Ladyship the Duchess told me."

The priest studied the man carefully. He seemed to be thinking something over. This fellow looked nothing like the artists who'd recently been received at the castle. They had come wearing fine clothes, gold chains around their necks, fancy shoes, and with laboriously curled hair and rings on their fingers. Their servants carried their bags and boxes. They spoke eloquently, mouthing promises and assurances, and demanded respect. They wanted gold in advance, good food and the proper comforts. But this man looked like a simple craftsman who'd found himself within the walls of the royal castle for the first time in his life.

"You should be aware," the priest cautioned, "that this in an extremely important task. His Majesty the King is seeing to it personally. There have been famous artists here before you, sent by the Roman and Greek emperors. All of them tried... Nobody would be talking to you now, were it not for the Duchess's letter."

The man listened in silence. His face remained expressionless.

"Do you know the Duchess?"

"Yes. I was summoned to her castle to repaint an old picture of Elisabeth, the patron saint of the Duchess's mother. Her Ladyship was pleased with my work. She wanted to see other things I'd done. She came to my house and asked to have one of my carvings."

"What carving?"

"One I did a long time ago. Of our saintly Queen."

"Queen Jadwiga?"

"Yes."

"And how could you portray her? You can't have ever seen her."

"But I have."

"Where? When?"

"Long ago. As a young lad, I helped build the church at Piasek. One day the Queen came to see how the work was going. That's when she left her footprint in the mortar. Master Mikołaj ordered us to carve that footprint in stone and mount it in the church wall. Now people come and kiss it."

"I take it you're getting on in years."

"I am..."

The priest eyed the man one more time.

"Listen to what I tell you now," he said. "I'm going to take you to His Majesty. If he allows you to try your hand, then that's his royal will. But I tell you: be careful. If – God forbid – you were to spoil anything, then you'd be better not starting work at all. To His Majesty, that Icon is sacred. He'll reward generously the person who repairs it, but if anyone were to ruin it beyond repair, a terrible punishment would await him. Well, then? Perhaps you've had second thoughts?"

The man shook his head slowly.

"No, I'll have a try."

The priest surveyed him one last time and then jerked his head, motioning him to follow.

They walked a long way through dim corridors until finally reaching a low door. A guard armed with a spear was posted outside it. He bowed before the priest and opened the door.

The chamber was dark. Although it was daytime, a thick wax candle burned on the table. The King sat in a huge chair, a wizened old man with sunken cheeks and colorless hair matted on his temples and neck. It was May, but he wore a shabby sheepskin coat.

Jagiełło turned his head towards them as they entered, fixing his eyes on them. The royal secretary bowed deeply, while Łukasz fell to his knees.

"Who's this?" the King inquired, pointing a bony finger.

"It's the woodcarver, Your Majesty," the priest explained. "The man sent by Jadwiga, Duchess of Niemodlin."

"Read me what she wrote about him again."

The King's secretary lifted a crucifix on the table and pulled out a letter. He walked to the candle and read aloud: "I am sending Your Majesty one of our subjects, a man known in these parts for his carvings and paintings of people and Our Lord's saints. He has produced many figurines and icons, some of which adorn churches and chapels. They are painted in beautiful and lasting colors. Other people hold a different opinion, but I consider him an honest man, although one whose life has been hard. He greatly reveres the memory of our Holy Queen, my godmother."

The secretary broke off and looked at Jagiełło, who sat hunched in his chair. His long fingers clutched at the strands of his hair, placing them behind his ears.

"So he's to be trusted, eh?" he asked at last.

"Her Grace says she considers him an honest man."

"Didn't I ask you to ask Duke Witold what he thought about all this?"

"I went to see him, Your Majesty, and showed him the letter from the Duchess. But he wouldn't even listen to me. He said he wasn't in the least interested."

"And the Bishop – what did he say?"

"His Lordship said that, in his opinion, we should try."

Jagiełło asked his secretary no more questions. His eyes were on the kneeling figure of the woodcarver, his restless fingers played with his hair.

"Come here!" he ordered.

Łukasz shuffled toward the King's chair on his knees.

"Your Duchess writes that you are a good man," said the King, speaking slowly, more accustomed to Ruthenian than Polish. "She says you greatly revere my dead wife. But she also says there are people who speak ill of you. Why?" He raised a finger in warning. "No lies!"

"I don't know why they speak badly of me. Perhaps because I fought under Prince Zygmunt Korybutowicz."

"Did you return when the order was given?"

"Not at once. But I returned."

"Did you accept their faith?"

"I didn't want to desert them when everybody had turned against them."

The King accepted the words in silence. His eyes, partly covered by the huge brows, never left the woodcarver. He clenched his jaw so hard that a spasm ran across his sunken cheeks.

"You know why you've been sent here, don't you?"

"Yes."

"Are you up to it?"

"I don't know..."

There was another moment of silence, then the King stretched out a hand. The hard fingers rested on the woodcarver's shoulder. Leaning on the kneeling man, Jagiełło rose to his feet. Standing, he seemed even smaller, an ungainly figure with long, dangling arms. His thin legs, and feet clad in fur slippers, showed from under his belted sheepsking coat.

"Rise," he commanded. Then, turning to his secretary, he said, "Lead the way."

Leaning on Łukasz, Jagiełło followed the priest, who opened the doors as they went. Before they left the chamber, Jagiełło turned three times to spit behind him, an old habit dating back to his pagan past. His secretary looked on in silence, although disapproval could be seen in his eyes.

The room they entered was brighter than the others in the castle. It was in a corner tower and had windows on three sides. Down to the right, behind the miserable dwellings of Stradom, the Vistula glittered in the sunlight. The window on the left looked out onto the waterlogged meadows, overgrown with rushes and bushes, known as Żabi Kruk.

The room was sparsely furnished. In the center stood a huge table, and there was a bed in one corner. On the table, which was covered by a thick cloth, lay the Icon, or rather what little was left of it: three thick boards bearing the traces of a brutal assault. Mere patches of the canvas on which the Icon was painted were left on the boards. Torn pieces had been stuck back on, but the dark, cracked boards showed through. The picture was not only damaged, but also discolored, cloaked in a grayness resembling a layer of dust.

On the center board, the face of the Virgin Mary remained recognizable, although it had been hacked by a sword or an axe. One cheek had been slashed in several places. The Blessed Virgin's small lips were contracted as if in an effort to conceal the pain. The sides of the boards looked as though they'd been bitten by a beast. This must have been the work of hands greedily clawing at the votive offerings, pulling out the nails which held them to the Icon. The remains of the picture lay on the table like a body on a bier, presenting a pitiful sight.

"Look at what they did," said the King.

Łukasz lowered his head and made no reply. He looked as if he were witnessing a death for which he himself was responsible.

"Whoever repairs the painting will be well rewarded," continued Jagiełło. "Money is of no importance here. I've called in craftsmen from all over – Vienna, Prague, Kiev, Constantinople, Bamberg, Nuremberg... But they couldn't do a thing. Each laughed at his predecessors and boasted that he'd succeed where the other had failed, and then he had to pack up and leave in embarrassment. Now, the Duchess says that you're a master of your trade. Take a good look and tell me: can you restore the Icon?"

Łukasz spread his hands.

"Well, tell me!"

"I don't know, Your Majesty. I'll try..."

"Try, then. You'll live here and be given whatever you need for your work. This picture has to look as it once did. It has to make people come to it again, pray before it, and have their prayers answered. It has to heal people. A land that possesses a Holy Icon such as this will be powerful, invincible."

Łukasz stared at the floor, listening to the rapid stream of almost unintelligible words. Jagiełło's withered hand held his arm like an iron vice. Had it not been for this painful grip, he would have fallen to his knees. The shattered Icon lay in front of him like some dreadful reproach.

"Do what you can", Jagiełło resumed. "Succeed, and you'll have everything you want. But remember" – his fingers dug even deeper into Łukasz's arm – "if you damage the picture even more..." His small face darkened menacingly, like that of a lynx caught in a snare. He lifted his hand slowly from Łukasz's shoulder and leaned on his secretary instead.

"You won't leave the castle until you complete your work or concede that the job is beyond you." He said to his secretary: "Give him a servant to see to his needs. And another to keep an eye on him."

The King stared at Łukasz for a moment, then he left the chamber with the priest, dragging his feet.

Left alone, Łukasz dropped slowly to his knees. He rested his forehead on the edge of the table, then, after a while, he raised his head and surveyed the painting.

The sight of the damage filled him with horror and despair. During his years in Bohemia he'd seen a great many burned churches, smashed crosses and damaged icons, but none could compare with what he now saw before him. The damage seemed to constitute the ruination of everything, his own life included.

When he was still a young carpenter's apprentice and worked building churches, somebody had noticed that he had a talent for carving holy figures. Priests learned of this and told the Bishop of Cracow about him. Bishop Wysz provided the money to send him to study with the master craftsmen who decorated churches. Łukasz honed his skills in Cracow and Wrocław before returning to his native Silesia. His carvings and paintings adorned various churches, large and small. One parish priest recommended him to the next. He soon became famous, and with fame came prosperity.

But when he'd gained both fame and riches, his misfortunes started. His beloved wife Agnieszka fell seriously ill and died after two years of immense suffering, leaving two sons and a daughter. Łukasz was plunged into despair. Work was his only consolation. He carved and painted furiously, with his efforts arousing greater admiration than ever.

Immersed in his work, Łukasz neglected his home and children. His house fell into disrepair and his children ran wild. So he decided to marry again. He did not have to look far, as by now he was known all over Silesia. He found a pretty, healthy girl, but their marriage was not a happy one. The girl was too young and too keen on merriment; she did not understand her husband's craft, and did not accept his children by Agnieszka. The atmosphere in the house became unbearable, with interminable quarrels between his adolescent children and their stepmother. Łukasz could barely stand it. He was constantly on edge. He put less heart into his work, producing only enough to fulfill obligations undertaken earlier. However, he was not satisfied with the results, which made him even angrier, and he could not tolerate criticism from others. His quarrelsome nature lost one order after another. In the end, he'd had enough of everything. All he felt was resentment. The priests, he claimed, paid him too little and did not appreciate his work.

Finally he discovered that his wife was being unfaithful, and drove her out of the house. She took her children with her and he was left with his own, a source of never-ending trouble. His sons, Jakub and Maciej, loafed around, loath to take on any work at all. His daughter, given away in marriage against her will, deserted her husband. Later, Łukasz learned that she had gone to Wrocław and ended up in a bawdyhouse. Crippled by all these misfortunes, he became angry at the whole world and, taking his sons with him, joined the army that Zygmunt Korybutowicz was forming to seize the throne of Bohemia for Witold.

In Bohemia, Łukasz had been drawn into the atmosphere of a religious war and the idea of the rebirth of the Church. The resentment that had built up within him led him to join a rebellion started by Bohemian Christians driven to despair by the perfidious German emperor. Demanding obedience to the Church, he had imposed the German language and customs on them. Even when Korybutowicz – at Jagiełło's request – left Bohemia, Łukasz stayed on with the Hussites and joined Jan Žižka. His elder son was killed and the younger badly wounded fighting a crusade mounted by Friedrich of Brandenburg. Then Korybutowicz returned to Bohemia, this time without his King's consent. Fierce fighting erupted once more. Žižka, the Taborites' blind leader, died near Pribislav. The Kingdom of Poland no longer supported the edict of Wieluń and imposed harsh penalties on all who had joined them. People started drifting back to Poland, an additional factor being that the mood in Bohemia was turning against the Poles. Łukasz would not have returned even then, but the younger son had lost an eye and a leg in combat and had to be looked after, so he took him back to Rogi and they stayed there together.

Now he was even lonelier than before. Everybody had deserted him. He was believed to be a Hussite, and hatred of the Hussites was growing in Silesia as news of their attacks on churches and monasteries spread. Trzebnica and Lubiąż fell victim to these attacks. The Hussite movement had evolved into a bellicose heresy, supported by all the heretics of Europe. Those who wanted to reform the Church had been replaced by those who saw the Church as their enemy. Silesia, a deeply religious land, opposed all things Hussite. No parish priest would now order carvings or paintings from a man tainted by the stigma of heresy. Even his neighbors broke off all contacts with him. Whenever Łukasz walked along the road, children threw stones and mud at him. The villagers said that the woodcarver had been punished by God for his connections with heretics.

He was astounded when one day he saw a party of horsemen in knights' attire ride up to his neglected home. The next moment the Duchess of

Niemodlin herself was coming toward the house, accompanied by her courtiers. He rushed to the porch to greet her.

The Duchess was a beautiful fair-haired woman, although some insisted that her mother, the widow of Spytek of Melsztyn, had been even lovelier.

"Greetings, good fellow", she said, nodding graciously. "I come as an old acquaintance. You once did splendid work in renovating a picture of Saint Elisabeth, remember? I'm told that you also sculptured a figure of King Władysław's first wife."

"Forgive the disorder of my home, Your Grace," said Łukasz, embarrassed. "I'm a poor man and my son is a cripple. It's true that I once carved holy figures and painted icons, but I haven't done anything in a long time. I have just a few old carvings left."

"Show them to me."

In the other room, which had been fouled by chickens, a few dustcovered figures stood by the wall.

"Which is the Queen?"

"This one, Your Grace." He picked up a figure, wiped off the dust, and passed it to the Duchess. "I carved her as I remembered her, from the time she came to see a church I was helping to build."

"It's very beautiful. Queen Jadwiga was my godmother, but I don't remember her. I will buy this from you... Have you heard that the Miraculous Picture of Our Lady of Jasna Góra has been desecrated by outlaws?"

"I have, Your Grace." Łukasz lowered his head. Youths had made several attempts to set fire to his house since the vicious attack. Stones whistled by his head when he walked along the road, and at Sunday Mass the priest stared angrily at him. The people had not closed the church door to him, but they avoided him as if he were a leper. "I know who they were. Everyone says they were not merely out to plunder."

The Duchess smiled understandingly.

"I hear you spent many years in Bohemia with the followers of John Huss. But you've made so many exquisite carvings, you wouldn't raise your hand against the Icon of the Blessed Virgin... Would you?"

"Nobody trusts me," he muttered.

"I do. My chaplain knows you well from the old days. He knows that fate has not been kind to you. Have you ever made a pilgrimage to Jasna Góra?"

"Yes, several times."

"They hacked up the Icon and threw it in the mud," the Duchess went on. "A horrible sacrilege and a great misfortune. Everyone is greatly alarmed, claiming that the Blessed Virgin will be angry at us, and will deny us Her protection. The Teutonic Knights are already triumphantly telling the world that the King himself despatched those bandits to Jasna Góra. When the King was still a pagan, he once raised his hand against a holy relic of the Cross. Later he did penance and sent offerings to atone for his sin. Now he's desperate to have the painting restored to its former glory. Many have tried, but their paints trickled off the boards like water... Perhaps you could help? What do you think?"

He raised his head in astonishment.

"But Your Grace, who would let me touch the Miraculous Image of Our Lady?"

"If you manage to repair it –"

"I don't know if I could. Maybe the Mother of God doesn't want the Icon to be repaired – after all, She has allowed the work of so many artists to be ruined."

"But She may allow you to repair it."

"Why me? I was a Hussite."

"Why not? My chaplain says Her Grace is greatest for those who repent and suffer."

He was silent for a while.

"Nobody will ever let me try."

"If you wish, I'll write a letter to the King. Go there, my man, and try your skills. How much do you ask for the carving?"

"Nothing, Your Grace. Your faith in me is more precious than gold."

"And may She trust you, too. Go to Cracow, waste no time."

And now the damaged Icon lay before him. Our Lady's eyes seemed to look out from Her gashed face with a strangely penetrating force. Could She be angry, he thought, because I have dared to come here? I who have fought against knights sent by the Pope and the Emperor on a crusade to defend the faith? This must be a punishment for my daring to carve and paint holy objects with these sinful hands, for my false pride, and for pursuing fame so blindly that I allowed Agnieszka to die.

The thoughts had been taking shape for years, although he hadn't wanted to admit their presence. But now, as he faced the vandalized Icon, he had to let them burst free. Could the Blessed Virgin permit him to succeed where others had failed? Weren't Her half-closed eyes accusing him of once more succumbing to the sin of pride?

He knew why those men had destroyed the Icon. He'd heard various views when he was in Tabor, the rallying point for rebels from all over Europe, followers of the strangest faiths, enemies of the Church and the Pope. Some argued that creating images of God and His saints with human hands turned hearts away from the Creator, that this earthly beauty overshadowed the true beauty of God.

And yet crowds of people took their pleas and supplications to the Icon, but not because they were attracted by its beauty as a work of art. He recalled that during one of his pilgrimages he'd stood amidst a group of blind people; they would never see the Madonna painted by an anonymous master, yet their hands reached out to Her.

Now the Icon was ruined. Even if a man were to fall on the ground before it, what help could he expect? Had the destruction of the Blessed Virgin's likeness destroyed the mysterious force that drew people to it? Would the strength return if the painting were restored? Those who'd defaced it may have destroyed more than the ancient painting itself.

"But", he thought, "I am here and I will try my best. There was a time when I carved and painted thinking more of my own glory than of my subject. Today fame no longer interests me. I wouldn't be able to enjoy it. Can a man be happy when he has nobody to share his joy with?"

Łukasz rose from his knees and bent over the painting. Shyly, he touched the Icon with his fingertips. The boards were very old and rough with borer holes here and there. Scraps of thin canvas with the gray outlines of the Virgin's face still clung to the pitted wood. The face of Jesus had been obliterated. In their attempts to renovate the painting, his predecessors had removed the wax-based varnish from Mary's face and Her once-dusky complexion was now bright, as if some glare from the background shone through it. A lock of hair escaped from underneath the wrinkled headscarf onto Her shoulder; it was golden now, like the hair of village children around Niemodlin.

He reached for his bundle and removed the pots of paint. He mixed some navy blue and applied it to the hem of Mary's dress, but it trickled off like a drop of water on a glazed surface. He tried again, then again, with the same result.

I'll have to give up like the others, he thought later. He was sure his paints were not inferior to theirs. He'd painted and repainted icons more times than he could remember, but nothing like that had ever happened.

Łukasz decided that he would not give up yet. He mustered all his skill and experience. Over the years he'd learned how to use various leaves, flowers and roots to increase the adhesive qualities of paint. He began pounding and mixing. Preoccupied with what he was doing, he did not hear the door open and turned only when a voice said: "So how is it going, woodcarver?"

Although he had never seen the man before, Łukasz immediately guessed who he was. He wore a cross on his chest and a bishop's chain. He was tall, in the prime of life, and well built. He looked more like a knight than a member of the Church hierarchy. His clean-shaven face showed wisdom, but also betrayed ambition.

Łukasz bowed to kiss Bishop Oleśnicki's ring.

"I have not got anywhere yet, Your Lordship. And I really don't know if I will."

Oleśnicki graciously laid his hand on Łukasz's arm. "Come, come, don't lose heart. And don't be in such a hurry to give up. Gather all your strength and knowledge."

"The others failed."

"They were interested primarily in their fee. That's why they gave up at the first sign of difficulty. But I hear you haven't even said how much you would want."

"If I only knew what to do."

"If you succeed, the King will shower you with gold. He's very anxious to get the work done. Impatient, in fact. However, I've asked him not to press you. Take all the time you need."

"I'll do what I can. But I have to admit it has occurred to me that it may be the Lord's Will that we shouldn't repair the horrible crime that's been committed."

Queen Jadwiga.
Fragment from Jan Matejko's painting
Establishment of Collegium Maius, 1888

King Władysław Jagiełło with prince Witold
praying before the Grunwald battle.
Fragment from J. Matejko's painting, 1855

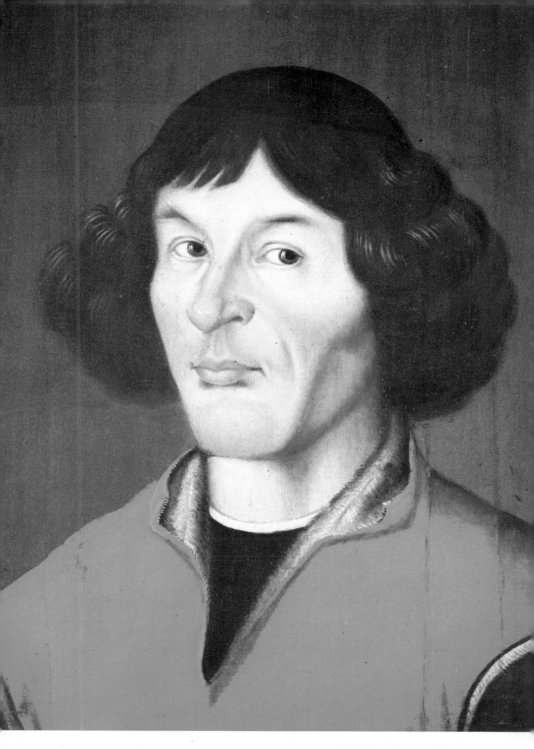

Nicholas Copernicus.
Toruń portrait, XVI cent.

King Jan III Sobieski.
Fragment from Matejko's painting
Sobieski during the relief of Vienna, 1853

From the Paulite Monastery collections:

Quiver and arrows, said
the have been bequeathed
by Jan III Sobieski, 17th cent.

Bunchuk
(Tartar horse-tailed
insignia off an officer),
17th cent.

Detail of a Turkish tent,
17th cent.

Casimir Pulaski.
Fragment from an oil-portrait,
early XIX cent., from
Antoni Oleszczyński's steel engraving

Prince Józef Poniatowski,
early XIX cent. copy.

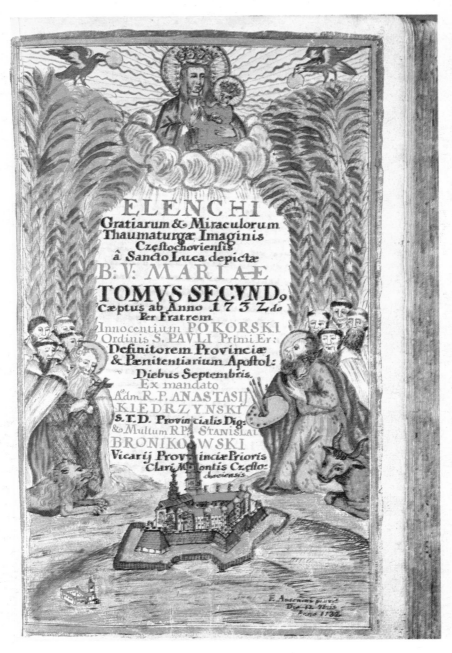

Title page of the second volume of the *Elenchi Gratiarum et Miraculorum... B. V: Mariae* (The Book of Miracles) with representation of SS. Paul and Luke, Paulites, the Madonna and Child and a view of the monastery, 1732

The Bishop looked at Łukasz carefully. "It's a good thing you're of that opinion, and call a crime a crime. You were once a Hussite."

"I admit to that sin, Your Lordship."

"Maybe it wasn't a sin. Huss sought to improve the Church, it was the others who added the evil to his fervor. And the crime they've committed had to be atoned for. We have to pray. Have you prayed to Her, woodcarver, that She might help you in your work?"

"No," he answered, shifting uneasily from one foot to the other.

"Start, then. God forgave man the crime committed on the Flesh of His Son, so He can also forgive a crime against the image of the Virgin. She, too, treats human madness with mercy. Come and pray with me."

Łukasz made the sign of the cross. Standing beside the Bishop, he repeated after him: "Oh Mary, assist us, weak and wretched that we are, in wanting to fulfill the Will of Your Son. Be with us in our deeds, our desires, and our sacrifices. Straighten our paths, correct our mistakes, keep up our spirits. Oh Blessed Virgin, who intercedes for us before God, do not reject us, your children, nor ask us to wait too long for your assistance. Knowing how badly we need You, let Your image, which revives our love and our will, regain its splendor and strength."

The May evening was turning to night over the city which spread out below the castle. Łukasz looked at the red glare of the setting sun reflected on the steep roofs. His eyes wandered along the city walls and beyond the Vistula towards the Carmelite Church of the Blessed Virgin at Piasek, hidden behind a bend in the river, the church he had helped build during his apprenticeship. That was where it had all begun, where the world had suddenly smiled on the son of a Silesian peasant. Then love came along... Agnieszka was the daughter of a master carpenter who would not have given her away to any mediocre apprentice. But when it turned out that this particular apprentice was becoming a successful carver of holy figures, and that his services were sought by priests and priors, he readily accepted the suitor. They had loved each other very much until Agnieszka's health deteriorated, and she sometimes complained that Łukasz was so busy with his work that he had no time for her. Then she died, and from that time on everything had gone wrong. Nothing was left now except an embittered and crippled son who grumbled at home, and a daughter steeped in sin somewhere.

He turned slowly away from the window and went to the table. The pink glow of sunlight skimmed over the Icon's surface. The Madonna's eyes seemed to be fixed on his face.

After sunset, the young servant assigned to him brought supper – a basket filled with bread, cheese, honey, and a jug of beer. Łukasz told the lad that he would need a number of items the following morning: wax, resin, oil, and certain herbs. He also ordered him to find a little stove for heating the mixtures. He was determined to keep trying.

When dusk fell the church bells rang the Angelus, their peals coming from all directions: St. Stanisław in Skałka, the Church of St. Jadwiga, little old St. Idzi at the foot of Wawel Hill, the Franciscan and Dominican churches, the Church of Our Lady in Market Square, St. Nicholas on Wesoła Street, the Church of the Blessed Virgin at Piasek, and from St. Floryan in Kleparz. The bell of Wawel Cathedral was the last to join in.

Looking through the window at the resting city and the star-specked sky, Łukasz prayed for Agnieszka. She had suffered a long time. For two years he'd kept a vigil by her bed, deprived of all hope, not daring to pray for deliverance, sensing that death was the only deliverance there could be. But death had come unexpectedly, when he no longer believed it would arrive. He was left with the bitter feeling that he had not received it the way he should have, and that Agnieszka had died as if weary of his weariness.

Before going to sleep, he returned to the table and surveyed the Icon once more by the light of an oil lamp. Our Lady's eyes still looked at him as if through a mist, and he had the impression they were trying to tell him something.

Łukasz blew out the flame and stretched out on his bed, but sleep would not come. The wind carried the fragrance of flowers from the gardens in Stradom. He heard the guards call out to one another. Somewhere in the distance a dog howled pitifully. Rattling and rustling sounds echoed around the thick walls of the castle. He could not forget for a single moment that the Icon was so near. It was like a living being, keeping watch reassuringly so that others could sleep in peace.

Dawn greeted him with pink blotches of sunshine on the wall. The roosters in town did their best to outcrow one another. He walked down to the well to wash.

The boy brought him a bowl of gruel with curds floating on top. Both the servant and the guard glanced at the table with pious fear each time they entered the room.

"Aren't you afraid to sleep so near such a holy object?" the guard asked Łukasz.

"I wouldn't sleep here," the boy said, crossing himself. "She looks at a man as if She were calling him. I know She's good, very good. She's the Mother of our Lord. But they've hurt Her so badly."

Łukasz resumed his work. With the tip of a knife he removed a tiny piece of canvas from the edge of the painting. He examined it thoroughly. It was lovely fine canvas, very old, but otherwise quite ordinary. He'd put his paint on such material many times. There was no reason why his fresh paint would not stick to the old.

The King's secretary came in while he was mulling over the problem.

"Well, have you tried anything yet?"

"I have."

"And?"

"The paint won't hold."

"Oh, Saint Floryan, worker of miracles! So you can't repair it either?"

"I'll try a few other things."

"Yes, yes, do! Do everything you can. The King is impatient."

"There's nothing I can do about that, Father."

"I'll keep reassuring him. And you, man, you keep on trying. You must understand that the King is terribly anxious to have the Icon restored. He's promised you'll be rewarded generously. He might give you land, a title... He could knight you, perhaps. Do your best and you won't regret the effort. Our enemies are rejoicing that the Holy Icon is damaged. The Teutonic Kinghts are sending letters all over the world saying that the Mother of God has been insulted in Poland and we've reverted to pagan ways. Do you understand what all this means?" Łukasz nodded his head. The priest went on. "When Prince Ostrogski raided Jasna Góra, he must have conspired with Prokop the Bald. Did you ever meet Prokop?"

"Yes."

"They said he was rebel monk."

"So they did."

The priest left the chamber and Łukasz began to prepare more tests.

The lad brought the materials he had asked for. Together they started a fire in the stove. A pungent mixture was set to boil in a small cauldron hanging above the fire. The boy watched over it, looking at Łukasz in awe.

"Are you going to use witchcraft?"

"Stupid lad, I'm just preparing the paints and the ground."

"Ay! The other fellows claimed this Icon couldn't be repaired without magic spells."

At the end of the day, the Bishop looked into the room.

"How are your tests going, woodcarver?" he asked but Łukasz spread his hands in a gesture of helplessness. "Keep going, don't give up. It's immensely important that this Icon be returned to Jasna Góra. Many people are waiting for it. They come here to pray from every place imaginable – Bohemia, Moravia, Lusatia, Hungary, Ruthenia, the land of the Szczecin dukes, even from Dalmatia, Denmark, Sweden... Whoever needs Our Lady's help."

"I'm doing all I can, Your Lordship."

"Don't stop. I've said Mass for your efforts and have asked the nuns to pray that your hands be blessed with grace. I'll also order a procession and ask the faithful to make offerings. We'll hold a novena to all the patron saints of Cracow and the Kingdom. Have you been praying too?"

"As best I know how."

"Dedicate yourself to Our Lady, understand? Vow that your whole life will be devoted to Her alone from now on."

"To Her alone?"

"If you really want to receive Her Grace... Take this rosary of olive stones. The trees grow on the mountain where our Savior prayed the night before His death. My predecessor, Bishop Wysz, brought it from his travels to the Holy Land. I want you to keep it."

Kneeling before the Icon that night, he recited time after time: "Hail Mary, full of grace, the Lord is with Thee. Blessed art Thou amongst women and blessed is the fruit of Thy womb, Jesus."

The next day he tried his hand repeatedly, and failed each time. An entire workshop had been set up in a corner of the room, with countless jars, brushes, scrapers, and pots of paint. The boy had run many errands to the market outside the Cloth Merchants' Hall to buy the necessary ingredients. Whatever Łukasz asked for, he received at once. Yet he'd achieved nothing. Worst of all, he was beginning to run short of ideas. Just two more possibilities, maybe three, he thought, and then he'd have to admit that he wasn't able to restore the Icon.

But when he prayed that evening, holding the rosary given to him by the Bishop, he did not feel the pain of defeat. By now he was quite sure that the reconstruction of the painting did not depend on human skills alone. Only the Virgin Herself, by Her own Will, could return the Icon to its former beauty.

Would She allow him to do it? He was determined to carry out his attempts to the very end, but he was losing confidence. Who was he to be chosen as the one to succeed? Hadn't he once been associated with those who'd damaged the Icon? And although he'd broken off that association, did his heart not perhaps still share their hopes and longings? The others had wandered astray, lost amid anger, rebellions, and quarrels. But he remembered how at the beginning they sought the reform of the Church; how they believed that only a genuine, reborn Christianity could save the world.

What did it matter, he thought, whether he was the one to restore the Icon? His life was drawing to an end. He felt old, but most of all he felt terribly exhausted. More and more often he found himself viewing death as the start of great rest. He no longer sought gold – who would he pass it on to? If there was one thing he desired, it was that the Icon return to Jasna Góra for people to kneel before and beg Mary for salvation.

He stayed on his knees long into the night, moving the smooth olive stones between his fingers. If She allowed him to repair the Icon, he would take that as a sign of forgiveness. But even that would not be the most important thing.

He woke many times during the night and returned to his prayers. Perhaps someone else would come tomorrow and repair the Icon? He would then have to leave in humiliation. And yet, as soon as the picture returned to Jasna Góra, he would go there on a pilgrimage as he had in the past: on foot in a crowd of the lame, the blind, and the afflicted. He had gone to ask salvation before, but his prayers had not been answered. Now he would go only to pray in thanksgiving.

Perhaps, he thought, perhaps Agnieszka is praying for me? She left so suddenly, like someone in such a hurry he has no time to agree on a date for another meeting. He had often been tormented by the thought that his work had destroyed their love. But perhaps that had changed; perhaps they were united again in a desire they both shared?

In the morning, black clouds hung above Cracow like heavily laden sacks. Again and again they emptied torrents of water onto the steep-sided roofs, where it streamed from gargoyles into the middle of the streets and flowed off down the narrow gutters.

Łukasz was back at his work at dawn and by noon he had tried everything he knew. He sat doing nothing when Oleśnicki appeared.

"Why aren't you working?"

"There's nothing more I can do, Your Lordship. All my ideas have failed. It's time for me to go."

"Have you prayed?"

"I have."

"But have you prayed enough?"

He spread his arms.

"Can there ever be enough prayer? I prayed as long as I still had hope of achieving something. Maybe somebody else will come now –"

"How do you know you've done all you can?" interrupted the Bishop. "One of the prophets sent down by the Lord was so weary and hungry that he could go no further. He fell down and said, 'Lord, I can go on no more. I will stay here and die.' But the Lord does not retract His orders. He sent a raven with a piece of bread, and when the man had eaten, He told him to go on. The prophet got up and went, and arrived at his destination."

"I'm no prophet."

"Who can say what role has been assigned to him? I'll tell you this: the Icon must return to Jasna Góra. Thousands of people are waiting for it, thousands more will need it. Through Her image, Our Lady wants to comfort us. Don't you want to fulfill Her wish?"

"I do – but how?"

"Pray. A great many people will be praying with you. I have ordered prayers said in all the churches. Wherever you see a cross from your window, people are praying that She tell you what to do."

The Bishop left him alone again.

Łukasz fell to his knees, but prayer did not come easily. It flowed like a mountain stream forcing its way through a ragged landslide. Thoughts fled his brain and words died on his lips. Still the eyes of the Black Madonna looked at him as if trying to communicate something. But what?

The King's secretary entered the room at dusk.

"Are you praying?"

"I am."

"And how is your work going?"

"I've already tried all I know."

"Do you intend to give up? Perhaps you'll still think of something? Make the effort. The King inquires about your progress."

Łukasz was quiet for a while.

"I thought somebody else would come and do what I have been unable to do. But if there's no one else, then I may as well try one more thing."

"You may indeed!"

"Give me three more days. And for those three days don't disturb me."

"What are you going to do?"

"I can't tell you now, Father. To tell the truth, I don't really know myself."

"I'll try to explain that to His Majesty. Very well, I won't even look in to see you. But tell me one thing – you're not planning some kind of sorcery, are you?"

"I'll only do what the Blessed Virgin tells me."

"If you need anything, just tell the boy and he'll fetch it."

"Why did I ask for three days?" he asked himself when the secretary left. "I've already tried everything. I don't have any more ideas."

It was as though somebody had told him to mention those three days, as though a daring idea that had been on his mind since the previous night had met with unexpected encouragement.

The idea had come to him when he was looking at the Icon by the light of the oil lamp. At first he rejected it angrily. How could he dare do such a thing? The painting was sacred. Only a saint could have produced such a work; only a saint would have been allowed to paint the Icon on boards taken from Our Lady's table. That person must have had Her in front of him, must have heard Her words and seen Her smile as he painted.

Yet the idea gave him no rest. He tried vainly to fend it off like a sinful temptation. But he was increasingly certain that this was what he had to do.

He did not rest that night. He took a roll of fine canvas out of his bundle and stretched it on a frame, making sure that the frame matched precisely the boards on which the Icon was painted. Then he meticulously grounded the canvas. It was past midnight when he finished and the short May night enveloped the city.

He let himself snatch a little sleep, but before dawn he was on his feet again. He knelt down to pray, begging the Lord to cast him free of the thought which appeared so sinful in its boldness. But his prayers did not relieve him from the inner command that demanded to be carried out. He placed the Icon in front of him, and beside it the framed canvas.

He reached for his paints.

With reverent concentration, he began to copy the Icon.

When the boy brought his breakfast he covered his work quickly and took only bread and water from the basket, and told the servant to take the rest away.

He painted and prayed, prayed and painted. Every stroke of the brush was a word of prayer. Standing in one position his body was numbed and began to hurt, but he did not break off his work nor did he notice the passage of time. He painted faster than he ever had before. The work advanced at unbelievable speed.

The Icon was so badly mutilated that he virtually had to paint the face of Jesus in Mary's lap without the original. But it was Her face that presented the greatest difficulty. He reproduced every feature exactly, no matter how minute. He spent hours on the eyes. Narrow, half-shut, they always looked at whoever stood in front of the Icon. They seemed to speak. He was certain he could never reproduce the mystery contained in those eyes.

When the servant brought his dinner he said he would not eat and ordered the guard not to allow anyone into the chamber. Several times during the day he heard voices behind the door, but nobody disturbed his concentration.

By sunset Łukasz was indescribably weary and his legs no longer supported him, yet the picture was to all intents and purposes finished. That was something he could not understand. He had always worked quickly, but he'd never managed to paint so large a canvas in one day.

He fell on the bed and instantly plunged down into sleep as if thrown into a river with a boulder around his neck. Even as he slept, the painting remained before his eyes. He noticed mistakes, and details he'd overlooked. As soon as he awoke, he rushed back to work.

He could not tear himself away from the Icon the entire day. He repainted some areas, improved others. Then he sketched out the fleurs-de-lis on Mary's robe. During the previous days he'd prepared so much paint that he had no need to stop.

Again all he ate was a piece of dry bread, yet he was not hungry. He burned with the fever of creative inspiration and was determined not to lose a single minute. His body ached but he took no notice. He no longer thought about anything, he just kept repeating the words of the Hail Mary.

Although no one came into the chamber that day either, several times he heard voices and footsteps outside the door. The servant boy and the guard must have spread the word that the woodcarver was not to be disturbed, which only made people doubly curious.

Before evening the painting was finished except for the Madonna's face. Now Łukasz concentrated all his attention. He was not satisfied with his work. Everything he'd painted was an exact replica of the old Icon, but that face...

Again he slept heavily, but anxiety accompanied him even in sleep. The extraordinary effort he'd undertaken was like an escape from mortal danger. The only way he could survive was by immersing himself in his work. He saw no future for himself if his present efforts were to prove futile.

On the third day the sun shone fully, and as soon as he stepped in front of his canvas Łukasz realized the difference between the Madonna's face as he had painted it and the image on the boards: the face on his canvas bore no scars. It was as if the wounds distended the cheek, making the lips twist downward to one side; when the wounds were visible the swelling appeared natural and the face did not lose its proportions. Without the scars, it was simply not the same.

"So what had it looked like before?" he asked himself. "It could not possibly have been distorted from the beginning. The sword that slashed the Madonna's face had left the stigma of suffering on it, something that neither the King's gold nor the prayers ordered by Bishop Oleśnicki could remove. Could it be that She Herself wanted the scars to stay?"

He dropped to his knees and spread his arms and fell to the floor before the Icon. He prayed fervently, begging for help to properly understand the Blessed Virgin's Will, and he rose from the floor only when the Angelus bells sounded at noon.

He removed the cloth cover from the painting and he studied it for a while. Finally, with a firm stroke, he drew scars on Her cheek with a piece of charcoal. The distortion vanished. He could scarcely believe it, but the face he'd painted and the original were identical.

Trembling, he placed the Icon on the table. Fear mingled with conviction as he applied a coat of glue to the tattered remains of the original canvas. For the last time, he looked at the face that some great artist and saint had painted centuries ago. Then he carefully laid his own canvas across the holy boards.

Now there was only one Madonna of Jasna Góra – one that was both old and new.

Using a burin, he gently pressed the scars into the canvas along the charcoal lines. After he finished he placed the painting upright and knelt down before it. This is no longer my work, he thought. He had done what She had asked. What he saw in front of him was Her work and Hers alone.

Łukasz was filled with tremendous joy but at the same time he felt a gnawing emptiness. He seemed to regret that the time spent painting and struggling to understand Her wishes had finally come to an end. It had been difficult, but magnificent, too. He would never again be as close to Our Lady as he had been during those long hours of endeavoring to understand Her Will.

He had no desire to hear what people would say about his work. He wanted no praise, no rewards, no words of appreciation. What he'd done was meant for others. All that was left for him was to long for what had filled his life for three days.

"Before death claims me," he thought, "I must attend to my unfulfilled duties. I have to comfort my crippled son and find my errant daughter. I have to repay the great privilege I have been accorded by my love for others. He knew that he could never repay it in full. But how could anyone refuse to pay until the very last minute of his life, knowing what great love awaited him?"

Łukasz prayed till sunset, then he tied his things in his bundle and quietly pushed the door ajar. The guard, bored with his uneventful duties, sat on the floor asleep. Łukasz slipped past him soundlessly. The lad who'd been his servant had told him about a small gate in the castle walls that was neither guarded nor locked, and which opened onto the marshes of Żabi Kruk.

The moon was out, so he moved stealthily to avoid being spotted by the soldiers guarding the walls. He crept from one shadow to another until at last he found the gate. The boy had been right – it was unlocked, and it was unguarded.

Before passing through it he took a last look at the castle that towered above him like a mountain of sheer rock. He located the window of the chamber in which he'd lived and worked. The Icon was there. There, too, was all of his previous life, which he'd discarded like a butterfly sheds its cocoon. Back there were his rebellions, grievances and objections.

Łukasz of Rogi left a free man, his only possession the Grace that had been bestowed on him.

CHAPTER 3

NICHOLAS COPERNICUS

The Paulite friars were informed a day before his arrival that the Bishop of Warmia was coming to Jasna Góra to pay homage to the Sacred Icon of Our Lady. They had been expecting him since early morning.

The day was cold and windy, and it seemed more like winter than April. Spring was long in coming that year. Sleet fell all day long. The oaks were bare of leaves, and the fir branches waving in the wind were covered with rusty needles. Here and there, clumps of fresh grass were covered by patches of snow that was soon washed away by the rain.

The Bishop's cortege arrived late in the day, appearing at the foot of the hill and, after a while, approached the gate. The first rider held the Bishop's crosier in his cold-stiffened arm as if it were the pennant of a sovereign. All of the entourage wore sheepskin coats with fur caps or heavy hoods that only revealed noses red from the cold.

The friars surrounded their guests, welcoming the Bishop with great respect. Watzenrode was short and stocky, yet quick and energetic. His square face betrayed obstinacy and a quick temper, and his gray eyes were set deep below bushy brows. They seemed as cold as steel.

His predecessor, Bishop Tungen, installed in the Warmia See after years of work in papal offices and chancelleries, had been on friendly terms with the Teutonic Knights. When the Order was defeated, the Bishop, too, humbled himself to the King, something he certainly did not do of his own accord. It was expected that Tungen's coadjutor, hastily appointed to succeed him by the Curia immediately after his death, would be much like his late superior and would carry on the tradition of good relations with the Order. But events took a different course. Although Watzenrode, like Tungen, had been educated in Italy and spent some time working in papal chancelleries, he took an altogether different view of the Knights. His appointment was approved by King Jan Olbracht only after the death of King Kazimierz Jagiellończyk. Shortly afterwards, he became a counselor to the young monarch. It was he who persuaded Jan Olbracht to prepare for war against his treacherous vassals, who refused to obey the provisions of the peace of Toruń. In the end, the war did not occur. The King suddenly died, but the Bishop of Warmia remained as an advisor to his successor. But getting the dull and sluggish Aleksander to act was not easy. Yet, before long, Aleksander was also dead. The young Jagiellonians were evidently men of poor health. Only the youngest brother looked strong and healthy. Even before he was crowned, plans were made to appoint Prince Zygmunt administrator of Prussia and Grand Master of the Teutonic Order, which would then cease to be a foreign growth on the soil of Pomerania. These plans came to nothing. The Knights defended themselves skillfully, hiding under the Emperor's apron or scheming in Rome. The position of Grand Master was now held by a Saxon duke who considered himself more a German prince than the superior of the Order, and sought the assistance of other German princes against the Polish King.

Zygmunt had already been on the throne for two years, but the first problem he had to settle was the war with Moscow. It was only when the Sejm convened in Piotrków that Watzenrode had a chance to discuss with the King his plans for taming the Knights. It was certainly time to do something. When the Teutonic Knights realized who was out to destroy them, they sent raiding parties to Warmia, plundering and burning the Bishop's villages and farms, robbing merchants, and posing a threat to towns. The Sejm's debates lazily dragged on. When a recess was announced, Bishop Watzenrode took the opportunity to visit Jasna Góra.

The friars led their visitor into the refectory. Huge logs burned in the fireplace, exuding a pleasant warmth. The guests removed their furs and coats and the Bishop was offered a comfortable chair. Servants brough mulled beer and various meats. The prior sat next to the Bishop.

"How are the debates going?" he asked.

"Very slowly. There're hundred things to discuss. I brought quite a few questions from our Prussian land myself."

"I've heard that the Teutonic Knights have been raiding Your Excellency's lands."

"Not personally. They train bands of robbers, arm them, and send them out to burn and destroy anything they can lay their hands on. They abduct our women and steal our cattle. Tell us, Nicholas, how many farms did they burn this winter?"

He addressed the question to a tall, slim canon who sat in silence not far from the Bishop. He was modestly dressed, his dark attire tailored according to the latest Italian fashions. His behavior displayed the manners and refinement that can only be acquired at a great court. He answered at once: "Seventeen, Your Excellency."

"So you see, Father, how much we have to put up with. Unless the King helps us, we won't be able to get rid of those bandits. And this," he said pointing at his young escort, "is Nicholas Copernicus, my secretary and nephew, a Warmia canon and a scholastic at the Holy Cross Church in Wrocław. He recently returned to Poland after studying in Italy for six years. Now the Curia has assigned him to me. He helps me administer the land and I must admit he's become really valuable. He remembers everything and gives me an answer at once. I never have to check him, as I've had to do with others. What's more, he's also a physician, so when my health fails he knows how to prepare the right remedy."

The prior and the canon bowed their heads toward each other in silence.

"We caught a few of those Teutonic scoundrels recently," the Bishop went on. "They're in our dungeons. One of them is a knight, their commander. They all deserve the gallows, whether knight or common bandit, but we're keeping them alive to show them to the papal legate. Let him see for himself how the Order is misbehaving. How many do we have now, Nicholas?" Once more he turned to Copernicus, as if trying to impress his hosts with his secretary's depth of knowledge.

"Five in chains in Olsztyn, seven in Lidzbark, and three at Braniewo. There might be one or two more somewhere."

"There'll be no end to this plundering as long as the Order is located where it is now!" thundered Watzenrode, banging his fist on the arm of his chair. "Christendom in threatened by heathens and the Hungarian kingdom is having to fend off Turkish invasions. Constantinople is in pagan hands. Moldavia is in jeopardy, the Tartars are attacking Podolia. And here we've got the Teutonic Knights living on Christian territory, attacking and robbing Christians. A holy Order!" he exclaimed. "The Knights of the Virgin Mary! They've long since forgotten that they pledged to serve the Lord with sword and prayer. And since this Saxon duke become Grand Master, they've forgotten what little of monastic life they had left. Now it's an ordinary duchy, whose knights spend their time in merrymaking, lewdness, drinking, and robbing. I said the same to King Jan, I said it to King Aleksander, and now I'm saying it to you: there's only one way to deal with them. We have to do what Paweł Włodkowic once advocated – get the Order out of Prussia and settle it in Podolia. That's the place for them. Let them defend Christianity from the Tartars. For the sake of their own souls!"

"Or give them to the King of Hungary, let them shield his land from the Turks," the prior said.

"That's a good idea, too. I'm glad to see that the relations between our King and the King of Hungary are getting better all the time. Brothers should support one another. It would be wise to seal this union by marriage. Our King is past forty and still not married. He's living in concubinage. No debauchery, as they say, but it's sin all the same. And he's the last of his line. High time to get him married and unite the two kingdoms. There would be great strength in that union. You, the brothers here, have long had good relations with the Hungarians. Would you have any suggestions as to a suitable candidate for queen?"

"It seems to me, My Lord Bishop, that there is one such lady. The Countess Zapolya. She's beautiful, young, and very pious."

"That might be a fine match."

"I hope our gracious King will not be deaf to good counsel. We need an heir to the throne. The King's brothers haven't left anyone. Strange, how the Jagiellons have become such a sickly family."

"The brothers here must know our King well from the time he ruled Silesia."

"No, I'm afraid not, My Lord. It's true that he spent many years in the castles of Głogów and Budzin, but he never visited here."

"Pity. He needs a wife all the more then, she'll teach him to look to the Virgin Mary for protection and assistance. I hope he's willing to come here now. Ah, and I also tried to persuade the legate to come, His Lordship Bishop de Grassis, but the chill of this spring has caused him so much discomfort that he just sits by the fireside and grumbles, refusing to venture out anywhere. And he won't go to Prussia, althought I'm going to keep pressing him on that. I'm determined to show him the plight of our people, suffering the attacks of the Teutonic Knigths."

* * *

Copernicus listened attentively, ready to supply any additional information his uncle might need, but he did not join in the conversation. He had already wearied of the matters Watzenrode had asked him to attend to, which took up all of his spare time. His uncle treated him as his closest assistant and introduced him to all the intricacies of the office. He suspected that the Bishop was grooming him as his successor, wanting his nephew to be versed in everything involved in ruling the land, down to the minutest detail. These ambitions were by no means matched by Copernicus' own aspirations. Sunny Italy had drawn the student from the misty north too deeply into totally different affairs, both challenging and shocking. Watzenrode had grimaced as he listened to Nicholas tell of his interest in astronomy, his discoveries and his successes.

"My dear boy," he had said. "I hold nothing against your having fun discovering the paths of the stars and working out horoscopes. Everybody needs some entertainment and this is certainly a better way of passing your time than hunting or feasting. However, this is not what I expect from you. It wasn't for this that I paid the cost of your stay in Italy. Warmia needs people who will safeguard its independence, its peace and its real nature. I've often argued in Rome that a province of the Church ought to be established here, and I expect you to further that cause. Yet now I see you didn't raise the matter with anybody."

He hadn't, that was true. He'd been looking for entirely different things while in Italy. He followed the footsteps of the great Pomponius, whose works he had studied at the Academy in Cracow under the guidance of Wojciech of Brudzewo and Jan Ursinus Baher. In doing so, he was inspired to study the stars. While in Bologna he observed Aldebaran and Saturn, and their conjunctions with the moon. When he later arrived in Rome, in the spring of the jubilee year, 1500, he already enjoyed the reputation of an expert on the heavens. The Holy Father later kindly asked him to deliver a lecture in the Roman Sapienzia on the movements of the stars.

Copernicus remembered the Pope well: an elegant, cultured man, always smiling and ready with a pleasing compliment. The young visitor from distant Warmia was treated in a most friendly manner. As he knelt at Alexander's feet, Copernicus looked at him with greedy curiosity. So many good and bad things were said in Italy about this charming man. Some people claimed that after his son was murdered, he decided to make good his previous trespasses and became an ardent Christian. However, he changed under the exceptionally strong influence of his younger son. Cesare Borgia had the reputation of being a monster whose savagery and cruelty betrayed the family's Marran origin. One day, Copernicus met Cesare as well. The youngster was in an excellent mood. He debated vigorously with the humanists around him, complimenting them, charming everybody with his refined behavior. He was exactly like his father. Only the grim brave Michelotto, who did not leave his side for a minute, served as a reminder that ordering someone killed was as easy for Cesare as making a quip in good company.

Copernicus's lecture was attended by the creme of the papal court, a crowd of the poets, scholars, and artists of Rome. In a small box sat none other than the Duchess Lucrezia; youthful, beautiful, with black eyes and hair dyed a ligh shade of gold. At the end of his lecture, Copernicus received huge applause and a purse of gold coins from the marshal of the papal court. Thanks to this generosity, the two Copernicus brothers – Nicholas was accompanied by his brother Andrzej – were able to pay the debts they'd incurred back in Bologna, which their uncle had promised to meet only in part. Copernicus felt wonderfully dizzy as he left the hall. People whose names were known all over Italy greeted him and said nice things. They encouraged him to continue his studies and were particularly eager to hear some daring hypotheses. In Rome, nobody was afraid to attack established laws and Christian dogmas. In fact, it was hard to say if Rome was still Christendom. Epicurus reigned supreme among philosophers while Socrates was the accepted guide to morality. Imitation of classical Greek and Roman artists was the dominant trend. Encouraged by a poet he'd met, Copernicus began translating "Ethical, Bucolic and Love Letters," by Theophylactus Simocattes from Greek into Virgilian Latin.

The simple faith Copernicus had brought with him from Poland began to crack under the scorching Italian sun. The humanists of Rome hid their contempt for Christianity in order not to antagonize the popes from whom they got their money, but among themselves they confessed to worshiping Jupiter, Apollo, Juno and Venus. The churches of Rome had once been built of stone and columns, recovered from ancient temples. Now one got the impression that the zealous advocates of humanism were prepared to pull the old stones from church walls and erect new temples dedicated to the ancient gods. They also tried to overthrow what Christianity had built. By putting the ancient gods of Greece and Rome on their altars, the humanists in reality saw in them a personification of man. Man now knew everything and could do everything – he was like the Gods.

After returning from Bologna, Rome, Padua and Ferrara, Copernicus was not all that eager to take the priestly vows required of a canon of a chapter and a scholastic. But his uncle would tolerate no dissent. Watzenrode had different things in mind for his two nephews and he was not in the habit of abandoning plans he had laid. Therefore both had to consent to his wishes, take the vows, and pay for the paramenta.

So he became a priest and carried out his priestly duties. In addition he was assigned to the Bishop, to accompany him to congresses and meetings, help administer his land, carry out orders and supply him with information. It was in secrecy while at Lidzbark that Copernicus wrote a small book in which for the first time he presented his discoveries regarding the movement of heavenly bodies. These discoveries were stunning and terrifying. He didn't dare show his book to anyone. His findings suggested that it was not the Sun that circled the Earth – the Earth, obeying the law of submissiveness toward bodies larger than itself, was in fact circling the Sun. His discoveries amounted to heresy.

He took his work with him when he traveled to Piotrków with his uncle. A copy, neatly written and provided with numerous illustrations, was hidden in his luggage. Serving Watzenrode as best as he could, he begged to be allowed to go to Cracow when the Sejm debates ended. He gave the idea of publishing Theophylactus' "Letters," which he had translated, as the reason for the trip. This was not a matter which displeased the Bishop, who saw nothing wrong with translating literary works from Greek to Latin. This did not divert his nephew's attention from work in the Curia chancelleries and improved his knowledge of languages. He therefore consented to the excursion.

In reality, Copernicus wanted to meet his friend, the Cracow canon Bernard Wapowski, and show his work to him. Both had studied under Wojciech of Brudzewo. He wanted Wapowski's advice as to whether his unorthodox hypotheses about the Earth's movements, which contradicted the Holy Scriptures, could be disclosed without risking excommunication. While there he also wished to observe an eclipse of the moon, which, according to his calculations, should occur in June.

The Sejm debates were drawing to an end. It was certain that the present recess would be the last. His departure for Cracow was getting closer and as time went by, Copernicus' anxiety rose: How would Wapowski react to his discovery? He returned to his calculations again and again, checking them endlessly. He was increasingly certain about the correctness of his theory, but at the same time could see no solution to the contradiction between his conviction that the Scriptures could not be wrong and the truth revealed by his discoveries. When his ideas had been applauded in Rome, he'd had no doubt that they were right. Here, however, he felt the bony fingers of Uncle Watzenrode on his shoulder, like a threatening hand reached out by the Church.

* * *

As soon as he had warmed himself, the Bishop said he would like to see the picture of Our Lady which enjoyed such wide reverence. The Paulites rose and led Watzenrode to the chapel, full of respect for the influential royal counselor. The Bishop was accompanied by the canons who had arrived with him.

Watzenrode sank to his knees in front of the painting. The friars opened the wings of the triptych, which portrayed St. Catherine and St. Barbara paying homage to Our Lady. On the Virgin Mary's radiant face he saw swollen red weals left by sword strokes.

Copernicus knelt behind the Bishop. After his return from Italy, his uncle, whose cool eyes rarely missed anything, had noticed that the young canon was hesitant about taking holy orders, so he told him to go to Kwidzyń. "Go there," he said, "and pray in front of the cell of the venerable Dorota, our patron saint. It's she who protects Warmia and Prussia. Let her pray for the return of our erstwhile fervor. Let her tell you where you should go to seek help."

Yet the trip had been delayed for years. His uncle kept him busy with new matters and it looked as though he wanted to entrust him with the post of chancellor of the chapter. It had been only recently, when a congress convened in Elbląg to approve new taxes needed to defend the country from the Teutonic raiders, that Copernicus had finally visited Kwidzyń. Next to the church was a small cell in which the saintly recluse had lived immured for many years. Countless pilgrims from all over Prussia, Poland, Germany, and Bohemia came to the tiny window. The daughter of a colonist and a local woman, Dorota had become a genuine representative of a land inhabited by a mixture of Prussians, Poles, and Germans, a land that could not fuse itself into one whole because of the Order.

Copernicus prayed at the grated window of the cell, and then said Mass. But although he'd fulfilled his uncle's wish, the visit to Kwidzyń had not produced the desired result. In Italy there were many graves of saints, both famous and unknown, but only common people ever prayed before them. Cultured men preferred to pay tribute before monuments to poets and scholars, revered both in life and in death. They were acclaimed as magnificent and divine, and their poems were recited widely.

Now he was on his knees at Jasna Góra. From the empty cell of the Prussian hermit his path had taken him to a painting which, so it was said, had been destroyed eighty years ago but then miraculously returned to its former splendor. Many of those who prayed before it had been cured of illness. Even more people came here with problems they could not comprehend, yet, gazing at the scarred face, they began to understand.

This face bore no trace of the pride of Juno, nor the authoritativeness of Minerva, nor the flirtatiousness of Venus. The Roman goddesses had very human features, dominated by various traits of human nature. Conceit lurked underneath pride, rapacity underneath charity, lust underneath piety. The Madonna's face looked quite ordinary. Everyone could find something in it that was dear to him. There was more than just goodness and immense inner peace: some other element attracted those who looked at it, and made them long for Her and remember Her.

As if prodded by something, Copernicus began to pray, forcing himself through a great effort of willpower like a man rowing a boat against a strong current. He was disturbed by the anxiety that he felt.

While on his knees, he realized once again that what he'd discovered and described in his book was terrifying, something that might shake the whole world. There had been so much talk recently about thinkers who announced the results of their investigations, toppling ideas that had been taken as absolute truths. Doctrines shook on their foundations. The world of dogma was not alien to Copernicus, nor altogether irrelevant. He was inseparably bound up with it, not because Watzenrode was a despot or that he happened to owe everything he had achieved to him. The captivating promises held out by Italy could turn out to be mere temptations once his fascination had waned, and Copernicus was not prepared to renounce his faith. In the bright south this was not so easy to perceive, but in the grey, dark Warmia, under a canopy of clouds, he felt that faith was like a mound of solid ground amid the Żuławy marshes. If one did not stand on the mound, one sank in the bog with no hope or rescue. He would not be able to abandon his faith, despite his frequent irritation at his uncle's firm demands.

And so, he wondered, should he now forget about his theories, close his eyes, and bury himself for the rest of his days in administrative work? Adjudicate disputes between peasants and colonists, count the revenues from the Bishop's estates, and organize defenses against hired robbers? Reject the intoxicating mysteries of the heavens once and for all? Stop talking about them? That seemed impossible. And yet the stars rose up to oppose his faith. After all, didn't the Scriptures say Joshua stopped the sun? But his calculations showed beyond dispute that it was the sun that stood still, while the Earth circled it. Could that be possible for a tiny particle cast out into space and left to the blind forces of masses far more powerful than itself?

How Copernicus envied his uncle! At one time, he too must have been tempted by the world of Italy's humanists. Nevertheless he had left that behind, concentrating on the needs of the homeland and sacrificing everything for it. True, he might not be a perfect bishop. Copernicus knew his uncle too well. He was not immune to honors, glory, wealth, or power, and he could be hard, even ruthless. Watzenrode, who was more a duke than a bishop, required his canons not only to serve him and assist in administrative matters, but also to be model priests. He tolerated no indiscretions. If he learned that one of his subordinates had too young a housekeeper he went there himself and threw the woman out, and there could be no question of clemency.

Copernicus often grumbled and rebelled inwardly, but he obeyed his uncle nevertheless. Often subject to temptations, he fought against them and, gradually, they disappeared. But the stars were the one temptation he could not resist, the one from which he was powerless to free himself. They appeared invincible. They were part of his life, his eternal hope and remorse.

Suddenly a fresh thought occurred to him: maybe it was no accident that he was there? Maybe he should ask the Blessed Virgin to help him? If she, the Lady of the Stars, could not free him from the stars and their epicycles, then he would never be liberated.

He mustered all his strength to continue praying. He felt that there, before this unusual painting, the most important decisions of his life would be made. His brain, accustomed to mathematics and the study of causality, was not easily forced to engage in humble supplications. Yet he repeated stubbornly: "Hear me, answer me, explain, help me..."

Later he sensed the Virgin's gaze upon him.

"Are you afraid of your temptations?" he thought he heard Her say. "Don't be. There are temptations that hide a calling. You can always suppress a calling with a temptation. But you have trusted me and I will watch over you. I will not let you perish. You can discover the truth about them. Their truth is the truth of God. He wants you to discover His truths. What you discover out of His Will, you will not be discovering for personal glory. People will not crown you with laurels for the work to which you will dedicate your whole life. No rewards will be bestowed upon you. Until your death you shall remain an unknown canon from Frombork. You will face many hardships and objections. Again and again your work will be interrupted by other matters. Then, in the end, a disease will cripple you and you will die an old and lonely priest. You will not see your book in the hands of other people. But trust in Me, it will be better for you this way. Your death will be your deliverance.

"For your work will triumph. Not now, but in many years' time. It will triumph not only in revealing the truth about the stars, but also by disclosing another, much more important truth. The day has arrived when Man is being declared a God. He believes that he knows everything about good and evil. But the day will come when Man will learn that he is not above good and evil. Your work will show that the Earth is but a speck of dust in the hand of My Son, and if Man, living on this speck of dust, is nonetheless of immeasurable value, it is only because he is loved beyond the limits of comprehension.

"Do not fear those who dismiss as blasphemy the truth that the Earth is but a tiny particle in the universe. My Son did not find a Mother among the inhabitants of a giant star or entrust His Kingdom to mythical heroes, but to ordinary people. The smallest of stars in space became the cradle of eternal life. One day your discovery will show what the Earth is, what Man is, and what God's love is. You will not betray your faith, Nicholas, because you have trusted Me."

Was it Our Lady speaking, or were these only his own thoughts? The Blessed Virgin's eyes were still fixed on this face. The wounded cheek seemed to pulsate with fresh blood. "If He permitted His Mother's image to be slashed by madmen," he thought, "yet did not annihilate us all in an outburst of divine anger, then He must love us very, very much."

Watzenrode rose, made the sign of the cross, and left the chapel with his customary vigorous strides.

His entourage followed.

Copernicus was the last to leave.

"Yes," he thought, "the discovery I've been allowed to make will indeed produce a momentous change, but it won't be the shock that I anticipated. The world lives at two separate paces: one hasty, feverish, and perceptible; the other slow, hidden, and revealing the Will of the Creator only from the perspective of ages. When everything seems to be disappearing and crumbling, the foundations of an eternal structure are in fact being laid."

CHAPTER 4

BISHOP HOZJUSZ

Two men walked along a path outside the low, unfortified wall that encircled the brick church and the wooden buildings of the monastery. One wore the white cassock of the Missionary Society of St. Paul the Apostle; the other wore a small hat and an Italian-style dark burgundy coat. Both were about the same age, slightly over thirty, and they'd been friends for years.

A continuous wave of visitors rolled up the slope from the town below, traveling in carts and on horseback and on foot. Religious songs resounded through a cloud of fine white dust that enveloped everyone and everything on the road. The forest surrounding the hilltop had been felled some time ago, turning the flat peak into a vast square now packed with countless sheds, huts, and carts with basketwork sides. Thousands of pilgrims were camped there and the place fairly vibrated with noise. Columns of smoke rose into the clear sky as they cooked their meals over open fires. Vendors of devotional articles – rosaries, scapulars, carved figurines – waded through the crowd. Pilgrims wearing hats adorned with shells and robes girded by lengths of rope peddled holy relics and vials of dun-colored earth brought from the Holy Land. Others stood beside their carts hawking beer or sausage or strings of bagels. A Scottish merchant sold brightly colored fabrics from an odd-looking cart with huge wheels. Armenians wearing long gaberdines, gesticulating wildly, offered silks and oriental scents. Minstrels strolled among the tents. The arriving tide of visitors emptied into the square and swelled the sea of human faces.

The two men were too engrossed in conversation to pay attention to the throng. Stanisław Oporowski had been elected provincial of the Order some years ago. An excellent preacher, he not only wrote his sermons but published them as well. Around the time Oporowski had become provincial, the King appointed Stanisław Hozjusz his secretary. A disciple of Bishop Tomicki, Hozjusz had gone to Italy for several years after studying at Cracow Academy and had continued his education in Bologna and Padua, returning with the degree of doctor of law from both. But he had not studied law alone: a very bright and gifted young man, he was interested in everything around him. Under the influence of Bishop Krzycki, he began to write poetry and polemical verse. The learned humanist did not lose his faith as others had; his religious feelings burned strongly and he was ready to struggle against all those who counterposed the knowledge of the ancient philosophers to Christianity, or who put the unity of the Church in jeopardy by proclaiming innovative ideas and a "fifth Gospel". The Dominicans tried to persuade him to join them but the preaching Order did not attract Hozjusz, and he remained a layman.

His religious ardor went hand in hand with a hot temper. Many Cracovians remembered a vitriolic poem he'd written when the news broke that the King had consented to the secularization of the Teutonic Order and the severing of the former warrior monks' ties with the Church. Hozjusz had become interested in the problem of Prussia during his work in the royal chancellery and had acquired such expert knowledge, thanks to his natural thoroughness, that he could pass for a Prussian. By gaining an insight into the problems of the area he had found out what the Order was really like. He discovered all the dangers posed by the knights who wore the Sign of the Cross and had risen from several defeats to recover their former strength. As long as they constituted an Order they had to recognize the supremacy of the Pope and could be summoned before a Church tribunal, but the moment the Grand Master had become a lay prince, and a heretic at that, he was bound by tribunals no longer.

The King displayed a harmful weakness toward Albrecht. Hozjusz knew the Hohenzollern and even liked him as a person. Nonetheless, he was convinced that his betrayal of faith demanded condemnation. In criticizing the erstwhile monks Hozjusz even received the Queen's support. She hated Hozjusz and he did not like the stunningly beautiful but power-hungry Bona either, yet their views on the concession made by the King were identical. Bona was disturbed by the violent objection of the Pope, who was outraged at the Polish king for having agreed to the establishment of a heretic state in Europe. Instead of bowing to Albrecht's pleas, the King should have expelled those who had not carried out their assigned duties, and recovered the lands leased to them centuries ago.

"Shouldn't a king who consents to such a shameless act be called a madman?" Hozjusz had asked in his poem. The verse was circulated unsigned, but everybody knew who'd written it just the same. And yet Zygmunt did not punish the young poet. Perhaps he felt that Hozjusz was right and had only made the concession to his treacherous nephew because of the advancing dullness which with old age had come to the last of Jagiełło's grandchildren. Not only did he not punish Hozjusz, he even took him into his service some years later.

"It's appalling what you've been telling me about England," said Oporowski. "So heresy has sunk its roots there as well?"

"The King of England takes pride in only having rejected the supremacy of the Holy Father," Hozjusz replied, "while staying faithful to the Church. But this supremacy is the keystone – without it the whole structure must collapse. As I told you, Cardinal Pole is a friend of mine. He wrote that Henry condemned to death everyone who opposed the severing of the ties with Rome. Bishop Rochester was executed, as was the wise chancellor, Thomas More. Many monks shared their fate: Carthusians, Franciscans, Benedictines. Pole was out of Henry's reach as he's been in Rome for some time now, so the King ordered him condemned to death in absentia. As if that were not enough, he had the Cardinal's mother, the Duchess of Salisbury and tutoress of Princess Mary, imprisoned and executed. So they beheaded a woman so famous for her virtue and saintly life!" By now Hozjusz had become agitated. He continued passionately: "One crime begets another. England may go the way of Germany. We aren't safe either. Through the Prussian duchy the German faith is seeping into Poland and gaining followers. Unless we put a halt to it now, it will infect all our magnates. They're already whispering their ideas to the young king. They want to impose the new German ideas by force. We have to fight this!"

Oporowski looked at him carefully.

"Don't get excited."

Hozjusz cooled down at once.

"That's the way I am... But you must agree that it's hard to keep calm when you see what's going on in this world. Look around," he said, and with a sudden sweeping gesture indicated the crowd at the foot of the monastery. "Thousands come to pray and pay homage to the Mother of God and ask Her intercession. Over there, in England, things used to be the same. I know the English. They're devout and pious. And yet it was enough for one licentious king to damage the unity of the Church and cause the piety of the masses to suffer a terrible setback. Pole told me that the shrines where Our Lady was revered until so recently now stand deserted."

"It didn't have to happen that way, I suppose," Oporowski said pensively. "I don't know the English as well as you do. Those who are now being beheaded are certainly martyrs and saints. Still, their example hasn't inspired others. Isn't that strange..."

"Not to me, Stanisław. There're saints prepared to die a martyr's death. But how many bishops and priests are there who accept the heretics' teachings just to preserve their comfort and wealth? Albrecht's uncle, the Archbishop of Mainz, allows the towns he governs to change religion if they pay him. Priests are getting married and Holy Orders are being dissolved. Things don't look much better here in Poland. Evil has taken root among the clergy. The love of gold... The time prophesied in the book of Apocalypse is at hand!"

"Not for the first time, my friend. Nor the last."

"You think not?"

"Didn't the Lord say that depravation would come?"

"He did... But are we to remain silent in the face of that depravation? People are failing all around us. Priests are losing faith. What's in store for us? Only death, like the death of those in England? And the hope that someday, many centuries from now, the blood of the martyrs will bear fruit, producing a new harvest?"

Oporowski nodded.

"The blood of saints," he said, "is a sure cure for evil. But you're right – we have to act. God doesn't tell us to wait for miracles. He tells us to work."

"We have to fight!"

"We have to pray. Not every saint has to spill his blood. She," he indicated the church walls with a jerk of his head, "is the Queen of martyrs, but Her own martyrdom was not the martyrdom of blood. She knows what is needed. We have to listen to what She says and we have to imitate Her. This is the reason I wanted you to come here."

"I thought you were going to persuade me to join your Order."

"I wanted that very much. But I know this is not the right place for you."

"You used to say something different."

"So I did. I prayed and prayed that She might bring you to us. A man sometimes thinks that if he asks for something good, his pleas must be answered. But the Lord knows best what is really good. Mary has given me to understand that She wants to see you elsewhere."

"Doesn't She want me?"

"I didn't say that. She will tell you Herself what She expects from you. So go to Her and pray."

For a while, Hozjusz walked in silence with his head lowered.

"I'll go," he said. "But will She tell me anything? There's so much hot blood in me that I can't control."

"Look into Her eyes. They can speak."

"They may speak to people like you, immersed in endless prayer like a fish in a pond, but I live an ordinary life. True – with God's help I haven't lost my faith. He told me to serve Him from childhood, and I have indeed served Him as best I could."

"You're serving Him well. Like a knight."

"Now you've got to the truth of the matter: I'm too quick to reach for the sword. That's why I took up theology. With the Bishop's consent, I'll be ordained before long."

"Then you'll be needed even more. Those teachers of the new faith are avid debaters. Sometimes they raise extremely important questions. You have to have answers. We haven't given that enough consideration so far. We thought that every word we utter should be accepted meekly and without objection. It was an excellent idea for the Pope to convene a council. Let the bishops who attend reflect on the answers to the questions the world is asking."

"You're talking as if it were possible to argue with those people. In England nobody cares to listen to the arguments of those who've remained faithful to the Church. They're hanged, their bellies cut open and their insides torn out. Satan himself is assisting King Henry!"

"Satan is out to kill souls, not bodies. But Satan does use people to carry out his schemes. Not so much those who rebel, as those who've become bad teachers and a source of depravity. Oh, Satan is always to be found within our own ranks!"

They walked on for a while, then Hozjusz resumed: "You spoke about Satan as if you knew him well. But I'm sure he keeps a safe distance from this holy hill."

Oporowski shook his head.

"You're wrong. He's lurking here, even though he's filled with fear. He infiltrates the crowd, sneaks in among the priests and brethren or demands unnecessary miracles. He persuades people to lie and make a show of superficial piousness. He generates bitterness and despair. Believe me, I feel his presence all the time."

"The Holy Scriptures say that the Blessed Virgin shall crush the head of the serpent."

"But they also say that he will bite the heel of the sons of Mary. Could this mean that he'll manage to separate them? That he'll tear them away from their Mother? I'm telling you: go to Her. Let Her tell you what you should do."

"Is it true," Hozjusz asked, "that the Turks have murdered your brethren in Hungary?"

"Yes. Christianity is being torn apart while pagans draw closer in force. Have you heard that the Turks took Buda? They hold almost all of Hungary now. The Zapolyas agreed to become the Sultan's vassals but that didn't protect our monasteries. Those who escaped death have taken refuge in Poland."

"We need great strength to face both the pagans and the heretics."

"We must be united in faith."

They approached the gate leading to the church. Two streams of humanity met there, one leaving the church, the other entering it. They ground against each other like millstones. Among them were the healthy and the sick, the lame and the limbless, the blind and those covered with sores. People cautiously avoided those wearing sacks on their heads; it was clear they were leprous. Parents carried sick and crying children. Shouting madmen with dribbling mouths were led to the church. Some people wore the garb of the nobility and there were a few rich merchants, but the majority were barefoot and poor, their clothes in tatters.

Oporowski took Hozjusz by the arm and led him into the middle of the crowd going inside. Initially, Hozjusz tried to hold back. They could have gone around the church and entered through the vestry without mixing with the crowd, but the pressure of the Paulite's hand was firm and the royal secretary understood that his friend wanted him to go in with all the others.

Now they proceeded slowly, inch by inch. The crowd was dirty and smelled of sweat. People pushed and shouted. "How could he pray in those conditions?" Hozjusz thought. Being of fragile health, he almost feared the crowd that pressed against him from all directions. Yet he tried not to rebel against Oporowski's idea. Maybe his friend wished to show him that Mary was like the hostess at the wedding in the Gospel to which those who'd been invited did not come, so others were invited off the highways, people without wedding garments. The learned, the noble and the rich, attached to comforts, easy living and honors, did not turn up – so She summoned the poor, the frail, the infirm, the wronged and humiliated. And they ran to Her, pushing and shoving.

At last, the group entered the chapel. Those in front of the picture dropped to their knees, crying: "Oh Blessed Virgin, Our Lady! Oh most beloved Mary! Save me! Help me! Come to my aid!" The pleas were interspersed with sobs. The tumult echoed under the ceiling like thunder.

Hozjusz knelt down too. Slowly, he said the Hail Mary. During his theological studies he'd often thought about the words. Offended by the disrespect shown to the Mother of God by the German reformers, he had studied the Scriptures and the views of various old Christian philosophers in an attempt to discover why this brief prayer should always follow the Lord's prayer.

"Blessed... and blessed is the fruit of Thy womb..." The combination of words led him to a description he especially liked: a woman enveloped in sunlight. He had often reached for the Apocalypse to read: "And there appeared a great wonder in heaven; a woman sunlight, and the moon under her feet, and upon her head a crown of twelve stars..." What did that mean – "enveloped in sunlight?" The Apostle Paul said: "And put ye on Lord Jesus Christ..." The sun is the Lord. Mary wrapped Him with the substance of Her body and He in return enveloped Her with the glory of His majesty. For this reason, she had more Grace than any other saint, even though She had remained human. And when we revere the Virgin Mary, we worship Her Son at the same time. Nothing could separate the two. They were always together.

Hozjusz recalled what Oporowski had told him about Satan lurking at the chapel wall. "She shall crush the head of the lethal serpent." She – a woman. There shall be enmity between Her and Satan. What an extraordinary creature She must be if such a great task was entrusted to Her hand. Didn't St. Bernard write that She was the dispenser of mercy, while St. Epiphanius called Her the Hope of the world?

He was now looking at Our Lady's face, which was mysteriously calm. The shouts, the sobs, and the body odor ceased distracting his thoughts. He no longer noticed the pushing nor the foul-smelling breaths. He only looked at Mary, and She seemed to look back at him.

"But if She is the hope of the world," it suddenly occurred to him, "then why should I tremble over its fate?"

He had come there in a depressed mood. Working in the royal chancellery, he was aware of many problems. He knew about the horrible pincer closing around the kingdom. After their victory at the battle of Mohacs, the Turks continued their advance northward. Vienna had resisted, but almost all of Hungary was now under the Turkish yoke.

Meanwhile Poland, whose frontiers were being approached by the Ottoman tide, was at the same time threatened from another direction. Swept by a new faith, a "Satanical faith", as he called it when angry, the German Reich was imposing its heresy. The danger affected not only Prussia with its mixed population, it also attracted the more affluent gentry to whom tithes and Church courts were a running sore. Confident that they had the support of the young King, the magnates were growing bolder and bolder, trying to force others to accept their faith. In Cracow, fighting had erupted in earnest on several occasions between the gentry, who had gone over to the new religion, and the townspeople, who remained attached to

Catholicism. There had been attacks on priests and monks, especially Franciscans, and even on the papal nuncio.

The unity and strength of the kingdom suffered as a result of these conflicts. Would it be able to confront the threat from without when torn by squabbles within?

The situation was dangerous, very dangerous indeed. The only salvation lay in launching a struggle for the unity of the faith. But what an enormous task that was! Maybe that was the reason why – as Oporowski had put it – Our Lady did not want him here. As the King's secretary, he was at the very center of power. He could talk to the King, the senators, and the bishops. He could persuade, write, fight.

Fight... He was uneasy about the anger that rose up in him at the thought of the enemies of the true faith. However, he also believed that unity could not be restored without a struggle. Hadn't Jesus driven the merchants out of the temple with a scourge? There had always been many people in the kingdom who held a faith different from the one taught by the Church. Yet nobody objected to the practice of the Orthodox rite, or the Jewish, Karaite or Muslim religions. But now the followers of this "Satanical faith" wanted to force everybody to adopt their creed. This was what had happened in the Reich, and Luther himself had proclaimed that only one faith could be practiced in any one country.

If this were to happen, Poland would be torn apart, since the masses would not renounce the true faith. He did not believe that what had happened in England could be repeated in Poland. Born of a burgher family, he knew what people of his kind thought. As long as the old King was alive, no change of religion would take place. But what would happen when he died and his son assumed complete power? In his vulnerability to feminine charms, Zygmunt August was similar to Henry. And what about Bona? She respected the Pope but she cast reason to the winds when it came to matters involving her only son. She was actually bribing magnates with gold and offices to secure their support for him. Even a man as wise as Primate Gamrat had succumbed to her influence.

Perhaps Gamrat's lifestyle caused more harm to the faith than the fact that Hozjusz's friends, the poets Krzycki and Frycz, appeared to be leaning toward the new teachings? They were angered by evil, while Gamrat and Zebrzydowski were defending the faith yet contradicting it by their own behavior. Not long ago Gamrat had summoned Hozjusz and asked him to write a speech which he would deliver to an assembly of priests, and in which he would castigate them for their weaknesses: their secular interests, love of money, and neglect of their pastoral duties. Hozjusz spent a lot of time on the speech, torn by misgivings.

It was then that he recalled the tale from the Gospels of the wealthy young man who came to Jesus and complained that since his earliest years he'd faithfully kept God's commandments, and yet he felt that he lacked something. Jesus looked at the man with love, and then said to him, "Go and sell that what thou hast and give to the poor. Only then come and follow me."

To Hozjusz it seemed that he was like that rich young man. He had been faithful to God since childhood and he was endowed with many talents. Not lacking wealth, he'd mixed with the highest officials in the land and furthered his career. Bishop Tomicki, too, had been lavish toward his favorite student. To be able to study, he'd received the income of a Warmia canon as well as funds from the Cracow and Sandomierz chapters and the parishes of Wilno and Gołąb. Writing the speech for the Archbishop he had realized that, although not a priest, he drew income from Church sources. That he fulfilled many clerical duties, wrote sermons for priests and speeches for bishops, was of no importance. It was still Church money. True, he lived modestly and his major expense was books. He also gave alms to the poor. Yet, Jesus had said, "Sell and give away..."

He decided he would not consider that money his own. From then on every penny would go to Church-related activities. And even if he became a priest, it would remain so in the future. He would donate the money to orphanages, to the schooling of gifted paupers, or to the hungry. Only after he'd made the decision was he able to write the speech for the Archbishop.

Standing in the midst of the crowd, feverishly yelling its pathetic pleas, he now understood how badly this decision had been needed. Jesus cast out the merchants and summoned the poor to His side. And the people in the chapel – poorly clad, foul-smelling, noisy and boorish – were the ones who'd faithfully remained by the side of the Church. They had been wronged and rejected, yet they stubbornly clung to their Holy Icon. They came to the Blessed Virgin with their poverty, their suffering and their faith.

"If the money that I administer," he thought, "which belongs to the Church, can feed at least a few of these people, maybe then my words will have the power to convert."

He seemed to see a glint in the Virgin's eyes.

"You're right when you say that you'll have to fight," a voice inside him said. "You'll fight long, fight stubbornly, fight for the whole of your life! Many times your weary arms will droop and your heart will despair. But don't let those difficulties defeat you. I shall be by your side. Don't be afraid. Cast aside all your doubts and worries. Your sins are more dangerous than the dangers you fear...

"Fight, but do not talk of a 'Satanical faith'. Those people are following the compulsions of their own embittered hearts. Jesus always mourns for the sheep that have lost their shepherd. Your calling is to work, lest those who are to be shepherds deserve the name of Sadducees and Pharisees. Such is your task and your responsibility. You must speak, teach and educate, regardless of whether the time seems right. But beware of words that stir anger and hatred. Persuade and explain, beg and pray, and love them as I love them. You are outraged that they slight Me, offend me with their words, damage My images. Look, here's My other cheek, turned ready to accept the blows from their hands. Let My blood be shed, but let them be saved, let them return to the flock..."

The crowd swirled around him. New arrivals forced those who'd been kneeling too long in front of the Black Madonna to make way for them. People pushed, shoved, trod on one another's feet. Solemn sighs mingled with angry growls.

Keeping his eyes fixed on the face of the Blessed Virgin, he allowed himself to be carried away by the ebbing tide. Once outside the chapel, he felt Oporowski's hand on his shoulder.

"Forgive me," the Paulite said, "for having drawn you into the crowd. If you want to pray in peace before the Icon, I can take you into the chapel in the evening after the gates are closed."

"I understand why you did it," Hozjusz answered. "I'll be glad to come here again, although I don't expect to hear anything more."

"So She spoke to you?"

"Yes, I think it was Her voice. My brain seemed to be numb, and yet I understood. I know what She expects of me, and I'll try to fulfill Her Will. I shall give myself over to Her completely."

"She told you much during such a short time."

"One word from Her is worth many. I feel as if I'd been grasped by the arm and forced –"

"She doesn't force anybody."

"No, yet it's impossible to resist Her words. Tell me, Stanisław, why are the scars on her face so swollen with blood?"

"That's how they were painted by the man who renovated the Icon."

"Perhaps the wounds seemed too fresh to him then. But I think it would be enough if they just bore the outline of scars. Blood awakens a desire for blood. And She doesn't want that. She wants us to fight, yet love at the same time. A most difficult task. Man cannot do it on his own."

"You've understood Her well. Satan also urges people to fight and love. But his fighting is hatred, and his love is self-love." Oporowski asked: "When are you planning to leave?"

"Early tomorrow morning. I have to go back to my studies and finish them quickly. *Periculum in mora.* The dangers are ever closer. But life is just a rush toward death. We mustn't halt, nor slow down... You know, I keep reading that excellent work of St. Augustine's, *The City of God*, and my admiration grows every time I read it. It contains so many similarities to our contemporary world. There were martyrs then too, but the fear of torture didn't stop many people from proclaiming their faith in Jesus. There were also those whose lives brought blasphemy on the word 'Catholic'. And yet both the sufferings and the scandals eventually proves beneficial. St. Augustine was right. Up until the very end, the Church's march forward will be accompanied by persecution and decline, but it won't ever be denied its moments of rejoicing. Now I have to return to my work at the royal chancellery. The announcement of the young king's marriage to Princess Elizabeth of Austria gives us grounds for hope."

"May that hope be fulfilled."

"So help us God. But there's one thing I know: even if nothing were to come of this, She watches over us. And as long as She does, there is no evil in the world that cannot be turned to good."

CHAPTER 5

FATHER MĘCIŃSKI

Could it be they hadn't noticed the sign he'd made with his hand? He was overcome by terror. From the moment he realized he could bear no more pain, the suffering had become indescribable – but what could he do? He tried to cry, shout, plead, but his constricted throat could only utter a hoarse, heaving sound.

Then he felt a jerk that shook his whole body. Over the roar in his ears he heard the squeak of the winch winding the rope. Slowly, agonizingly slowly, he was being lifted from the depths of the dark stinking pit and out onto the sunlit square. Although his eyelids were caked with blood, he saw a bright glare through them.

Hands grabbed him and hauled him out. At last he was no longer hanging upside down. His body was still constrained, but already it was easier to breathe. The buzzing in his ears and the painful pressure in his temples became a little more bearable. It was almost a delight to be laid onto the firm ground. He was alive, and his mind was filled with that one thought.

Someone lifted his head and wiped his face with a damp cloth. When his eyelids finally opened he saw the sky, which seemed to billow like a giant blue sail, then he saw the dark face of the man leaning over him and the smile that revealed a few teeth. The smile seemed to be strangely soothing.

He still felt dizzy but rapidly regained his sense of balance. He looked around. Beyond the shoulders of the man stooping over him he saw black pines and walnut trees. Then he saw people: samurai sitting on benches, their heads hairless except for a short plait at the back. They wore colorful kimonos. Each rested one hand on the long hilt of his sword. Behind them stood clerks dressed in black.

In front of the samurai, the great daimyo himself sat in an ornate armchair. Like them, he had a sword and a short dagger at his belt. He waved a fan, presumably to fend off the foul odor from the pit.

The daimyo gestured to a man in black, who humbly approached and squatted at his master's feet. Father Christopher recognized him as the daimyo's interpreter. The feeling of relief was gone immediately. His joy at having regained his life struggled with the wish to die.

The clerk stared at the ground as he listened to the shogun's words, then he rose and approached the friar.

Father Christopher closed his eyes tight. Oh, if only he could flee into nonexistence, flee from what that man was bringing him. He feared it as much as he feared returning to the pit. He heard the footsteps.

The interpreter stood over him.

"Listen," he said in Portuguese.

The man did not smile, and there was no pity in his expression. He was the one who'd supervised the lowering of the friar into the pit and had pierced his head below the temples with a sharp awl.

"You gave a sign?" he asked. "*Honto ka?*", he added in Japanese. "Is that true?"

"*Hai,*" the friar confirmed weakly. "Yes."

"*So desu.*"

He looked at the Jesuit with a strange expression on his face. Finally he made a gesture and the man attending the friar started to untie the stiff canvas corset wrapped tightly around his body. The blood began to circulate freely again, releasing a fresh wave of pain.

"Get up!" the man in the black kimono ordered.

He tried to obey the command and failed. Two men lifted him to his feet. He would have fallen, but they held him up straight. They had to help him walk. He staggered, step by painful step, until he stood before the daimyo's chair.

The nobleman's sharp black eyes looked at him over the fan. He asked a question which the interpreter translated hastily: "So you're prepared to renounce your faith?"

The friar nodded.

"I will repeat what I told you before," the daimyo went on. "It is the wish of the grand shogun, Lord Ieyasu, that no one in our land profess your barbaric faith. We do not want it, nor your teachings. In any case, you can't even agree among yourselves. The people who came on Dutch ships claim your teachings are lies. In turn, you call them liars. Here in Japan we have many faiths and many gods. Everybody can worship whoever he wishes, as long as he respects the universal truths. But you want to force everybody to accept your faith. While you are weak, you plead with us and you try to persuade us that your beliefs are similar to ours. But once you begin to feel strong, you incite your followers to rebel and even call on your warships to assist you. We don't want that. We told you all to go away. But you – you stayed on. Secretly you kept up the resistance of your people. You were the leader of your priests, that's why you have been condemned to death. But we are not heartless. If, in front of all these people, you renounce your faith and say *korobu*, and if you tread on the picture of your deity, your life will be spared and you will regain your freedom. If you refuse – you'll go back to the pit. Now choose. *Ima, isogi!*"

Father Christopher trembled. The daimyo's suggestion filled him with horror, but the thought of returning to the pit was no less terrifying. His body was in agony. He had been so proud that when the other missionaries were driven out of the country he had remained, but all of the others who stayed with him had been caught by the police. Some were put to death, others renounced their faith. While searching for the Jesuits, the police caught and imprisoned a huge number of Christian peasants. They, too, had had to renounce the faith or perish in pits filled with excrement, or by being scalded to death. He had stayed in hiding longest, but in the end he'd been caught like the rest. At first he'd imagined he would die a martyr's death, to the glory of the Society. God, however, had not come to his assistance. After several hours of the torture in the pit he knew he could not bear the pain...

"You stand here," said the interpreter.

Father Christopher was led into the middle of the crowd of people rounded up from the town and adjacent villages. The vast majority were undoubtedly Christians.

Somebody laid a board on the ground – a *fumi-e* – with a picture of Our Lady nailed to it. He could see Mary's face under the mud.

"Put your foot on this face," the interpreter ordered. "And say aloud, as loud as you can, so everyone hears you, *korobu.*"

The sun was shining, but to Father Christopher it seemed shrouded in a red mist. The surrounding hills rose and fell like waves that seemed about to crash down on him. Never before had he wished to die as much as he did now. Everything had failed him and he, too, had failed the people he had sailed halfway around the world to save. Was it possible that God had failed him? He used to feel so sure of himself... Now he knew he was a miserable wretch that could not achieve anything on his own. The burden of guilt weighed heavily on him, a guilt he had not felt before.

He looked at Mary's face with despair, at eyes which seemed to be fixed on him. "Let me die, Lord," he prayed. "Let me die because I can do nothing else."

The interpreter nudged him.

Father Christopher placed a trembling foot on the *fumi-e*. In reality he held it just above the picture, but to the watching crowd the meaning of his gesture was obvious. His moves were being followed by hundreds of pairs of eyes.

"*Korobu,*" he said, in a croaking voice not his own.

No bolt of lightning came down from the sky to smite him.

He came to the place every time he set off to carry out a task assigned to him. The picture of the Madonna della Strada was at the far end of the chapel, left of the main altar. Like the whole del Gesu church, completed only recently, the chapel of Our Lady della Strada was full of marble and bronze ornaments, gilding and stucco work. At that time of day the church was usually empty and the young novice could pray in silence. It was moving to think that the venerable founder of their Society, Ignatius, had often said Mass in front of the same picture, and that Francis Xavier had prayed there before setting out to wander overseas. The Męcińskis were ordinary gentry, but their wealth almost made them magnates. His parents had died and his elder sister Zofia had married, leaving the two brothers, Stanisław and Wojciech, to carry on the family tradition. After graduating from the Cracow Academy, both went out into the world in a different direction. Wojciech had traveled around Western Europe before going to Rome.

At the Academy he had chosen medicine as his field of study. He wasn't sure why; he had always thought of himself as a knight and defender of the faith. He'd been barely five years old when his mother died but her teachings, continued by his sister, were kept firmly in his memory. His father had once succumbed to the temptation of the Calvinist faith, which caused a great deal of suffering to his mother, an ardent worshipper of Our Lady. Through prayer, fasting and pilgrimages, she finally secured his return to the Church. Return he did, only to die shortly afterwards.

Lady Felicjana was deeply convinced that all the misfortunes that had beset the country recently were caused by the religious divisions that had rent Poland for nearly a century. It mattered little that since the internecine bloodshed at Guzów the gentry had been returning en masse to Catholicism. The weakness remained, and all the country's neighbors were eager to take advantage of it. And the gravest threat of all was now approaching: a Turkish invasion.

His mother's teaching had nurtured a desire to give his life for the faith, to redeem with his blood the rejection of the faith by his father and others. This feeling gripped a whole generation of young people, and grew even stronger in Męciński when, during his travels across Europe, he saw that the religious divisions were degenerating into morbid hatred. He realized how strongly the Polish Commonwealth was hated for having overcome its internal religious conflicts.

It was possible that he'd become a doctor because his health was never very good. He knew with regret that he could not bear the hardships of military life, yet the idea of making a gift of blood as penance gave him no rest. In Rome he learned about the crushing defeat suffered by the Polish forces at the hands of the Turks and Tartars at Cecora, a defeat that left Poland defenseless in the face of the advancing enemy. The thought of those who'd fallen in that battle filled him with horror – but also with envy. They had not emerged victorious, but at least they had sacrificed their own blood.

Opaliński took Męciński to the Jesuits of Rome. There were plenty of

Poles there, fascinated by the example set by Stanisław Kostka. Wojciech discovered that there, too, everybody wanted to repay God in blood for the mistakes and heresy that had been committed.

Ignatius Loyola had shown great understanding of the mood of the period when he set up the Society of Jesus! New strength was awakened in the Church, threatened from both without and within. It was necessary to harness the zeal and mold it into a force that would consolidate the Church on all fronts. For years the Society had been sending dozens of its fathers and brethren to Britain. At the same time, many missionaries followed in the footsteps of Francis Xavier, setting off for distant pagan lands – India, China, America... Recently there had been a surge of interest in the country farthest to the east – mysterious Japan, which Francis had once described in such glowing terms. This was indeed a land worth conquering for Jesus.

Męciński was swept by the prevailing mood and joined the order. Just then news came of the victorious defense of Chocim, to which the first Jesuit saint, Stanisław, was said to have contributed. "Even if my health is too fragile for battle," Wojciech thought, "I can still offer up my blood anyway..." He was admitted as a novice, his mind occupied by thoughts of missionary work. His medical skills could prove very useful there. At the boarding school he heard that Japan was a magnificent country, but the missionaries there faced a greater threat of death than in other lands. He decided he would go to Japan.

Each time he had knelt down in the chapel of Our Lady della Strada, Męciński repeated his plea: "Help me, Blessed Virgin, that I may go to the missions and give my life for the faith."

That day he prayed more ardently than ever.

He finished, rose from his knees, took his basket and left the church. He walked down the stairs and turned left.

In the street called Botteghe Oscure stood a tiny church dedicated to St. Stanisław. Next to it was the Hospitium Nationis Poloniae set up almost half a century ago by Cardinal Hozjusz. Composed of several small houses, it offered shelter to those Polish pilgrims coming to Rome who could not afford to stop at an inn. In the poorest of these lived two women who had come to the Holy City for a visit and stayed for good. Bogumiła of Stradom had already been in Rome twenty years. As long as she'd had the strength, she had served the pilgrims coming to the shelter; cooking their meals, doing their laundry, and nursing them in illness. She regarded this as penance for a misspent youth. But she was old now and her strength had failed her. Approching the end of her days, she was cared for by her distant cousin, Ludwina of Kęty. Ludwina had come to Rome only two years ago, but wished to spend the rest of her life helping the pilgrims.

The women were very poor, their only income being donations left by the pilgrims, who were none too rich themselves. The young Polish Jesuit novices had agreed to help the women by giving them part of the provisions they received. Męciński brought them a basket of food every few days.

He stopped in front of their tiny room and knocked on the door. Ludwina appeared. She was not old, but she looked frail. The hard work and fasting had changed the lively townswoman from the suburbs of Cracow into a pale, thin penitent. Yet there was a smile on her face.

"Welcome, brother, welcome," she said. "So you've come again to bring us assistance. May Our Lord Jesus Christ and His Mother reward you with what you desire the most. And the same to your friends." Then, in a quieter voice, she added: "Sister Bogumiła is getting weaker and weaker. I'm afraid she'll be leaving this world before long. Go and see her, please. She said she'd like to see you very much."

He had to stoop to cross the threshold. The small windows let in little of the golden Roman sunshine and the room was gloomy. An old woman lay on a low bed in a corner. Her breathing was labored. The unbearable odor of disease irritated his nostrils. A small dog lay at the foot of the bed. The woman had evidently heard Męciński come in, for she turned her head in his direction and opened her eyes.

"Ah, it's you, Wojtek... How glad I am to see you. Have you brought us food again?"

"Of course."

"You lads are good. And have you prayed today, as you always do, before the Blessed Virgin?"

"I have."

"And you keep praying for the same thing?"

"Yes, that's right."

She lay on her back, gasping for breath. Then she said: "You really want it so much?"

"If I don't make a sacrifice of blood, I'll feel unworthy of those who fell in the struggle against the pagans."

"Unworthy?" she began, but broke off. "I wanted to ask God to let me give my old life for you, so you could set off into the world spreading the Word of the Lord... loving people..." Again she gasped. "Will you go?"

"So I've been promised. But –"

"Something's changed?"

"Unfortunately."

"Tell me about it."

"My brother Stanisław is dead. The news reached me yesterday. I've received a great many letters."

"People want to express their sympathy."

"Yes. But at the same time the whole family is demanding I leave the novitiate and return to Poland. They tell me I'm now the last of the line and I mustn't allow our name to disappear."

"And what do you say to that?"

"I won't leave the Order. I want to go to the missions and sacrifice my life for the faith."

"Others put less effort into praying for their lives than you do in demanding death... It won't be easy for you to refuse your relatives' requests."

"But I will!"

"You will if you entrust yourself to God. If you're ready to do what He wants you to. What do your superiors say?"

"I took the letters to the Father General himself. He told me to go to Poland and tell my relatives openly about my decision. I must also take care of the estate I've inherited."

"Is there much?"

"Very much."

"What are you going to do with it?"

"Give it all to the Order and its house in Cracow."

"Your relatives will oppose that in every way they can. You'll need a lot of strength. The most difficult thing of all is to fight those you love."

"I won't give in."

"Pray to the Lord, beseech Him, and trust yourself. It's a great gift of grace to be able to give your blood to God. But you have to earn that gift.

You have to renounce your own self. Then, maybe, in the end..."

"I'll pray."

"Yes, pray. When you're in Poland, go and see Her at Jasna Góra. I'll also help you as best I can. I wanted to save you, but now I see I have to join you in your prayers."

*   *   *

The sun scorched the valley but there on the high mountain ridge the air was fresh and clear, full of the scent of the thickly wooded slopes. Rivers at the bottoms of the deep ravines flowed south, or west toward the sea just a short distance away. The pines, chestnuts, and oaks were identical to those found along the banks of the Wieprz – back in Poland, and there were carobs, figs and olives. Cork oaks, their trunks stripped of bark, shone amid the surrounding verdure like red and gold columns.

Magnificent buildings rose out of that green ocean, including a boarding school and a university run by the Order. The university had been built in the mountains so that students from the north would not feel uncomfortable in the hot climate on the seacoast. Evora was a great forge of Jesuit missions. Expeditions set out from there for all the corners of the pagan world.

Recently, however, the mission of the Jesuits had been seriously jeopardized. Linked to Spain by a union, Portugal had found itself in the shadow of the Castilian-Aragonese monarchy. The Spanish fleet assisted Dominicans and Franciscans rather then Jesuits, while the Portuguese navy was in disarray after its recent series of defeats. On all seas it fell prey to the ruthless and belligerent English and Dutch. Not only did they attack Portuguese trading posts and sink or seize Portuguese ships, they also bought the favors of pagan rulers and portrayed the Papist missionaries as people who used religious teachings to open the door to Portuguese invasions. In addition, they undermined those teachings as well, provoking religious disputes. The first reports of local rulers turning their backs on the Jesuit missionaries and replacing friendliness with enmity had come from distant Nippon, the land to which Francis Xavier had drawn particular attention eighty years ago.

Francis thought highly of Japan from the very beginning. When he landed at Kagoshima, he found that the Japanese were more inclined to listen to Christian teachings than other Oriental peoples. "This," he wrote to Europe, "is the best nation of all those discovered so far. I don't believe any nation will be found that might surpass the Japanese." But the first persecutions, incited by Shinto priests, occurred even before Francis' death. Undeterred, he penetrated deeper into the newly discovered land searching for the town of Yamaguchi, the seat of the Grand Duke who was said to be willing to hear about the Christian faith.

Reaching Yamaguchi, he planted the first seeds of faith and traveled on to Miako, the capital of the kingdom. Discovering that the King was weaker and less important than the local dukes, he returned to Yamaguchi. Numerous conversions took place there, but the local priests began to raise objections. This opposition was overcome by the missionaries thanks to their skills in debate and the fact that they pointed to the immoral conduct of the bonzes, the Buddhist monks.

But Dutch traders and pirates had appeared on the seas around Japan; the Jesuits' hopes that Catholicism would conquer Nippon began to fade. The friendliness of the Japanese gave way to persecutions. More and more reports reached Europe of missionaries being hunted down and tortured.

The news of martyrdom only reinforced the enthusiasm prevalent in the Jesuit college at Evora. The members of the Society, who wore black cassocks and maintained a spirit of knightly valor, scorned all fear of having to shed one's blood. The more reports of martyrdom there were, the more eager the Evora students were to be involved in it.

Wojciech Męciński was one of the most zealous of all. He had successfully resisted the temptations encountered during his trip to Poland, withstanding his relatives' pleas and pressures, the wedding plans laid for him, even the threats. Everything he'd inherited he gave to the Jesuit college of St. Peter in Cracow. Once that was arranged, he begged the General, Father Vitelleschi, to consent to his return to Rome. He still dreamed of his mission to Japan, where the opportunity of dying a martyr's death was greatest.

In Rome he'd found that both Ludwina and Bogumiła had died, one shortly after the other. But at once came hope that his dreams would be fulfilled: Father Vieira, who was in charge of the Japanese mission, was looking for candidates for the dangerous trip to the East.

Męciński approached Father Vitelleschi with a request for permission to take part in the mission, but was turned down. For some time the General had been observing the young Pole, who had made lavish donations to the Order and was so eager to die a martyr's death. The experienced educator was not sure whether Męcinski's desire was rooted in faith; human pride was a strong force, one that could also lead a man to martyrdom. A missionary's aim was to work, not to die. But when he was informed that the stubborn Pole spent several hours each day kneeling in the chapel of Our Lady della Strada, he gave his consent.

And so Wojciech Męciński went to Evora. Within a year he completed his theological studies, learned Portuguese, and was ordained. He wrote to the General, thanking him for his consent and assuring him that he would not trade his Japanese mission for all the treasures in the world. Soon afterwards a letter from Father Vieira summoned him to Lisbon. The decisive moment had arrived.

He had already packed and had said goodbye to his friends when another letter arrived, this one from Rome, from the General. Vitelleschi ordered him to return to Poland at once. News had reached Rome that Męciński's relatives were contesting his donation and claiming that he was dead, but that his death had been concealed by the Jesuits.

Męciński was stunned. Vieira was to set sail in a week's time – he would sail without him. Japan suddenly disappeared from the horizon. All his prayers and pleas had been in vain. Instead of going to those distant islands to be martyred, he was to travel across a war-torn Europe and again face the family whose pressures he'd resisted only with great difficulty. A great cause awaited him in Japan – in Poland he would be occupied only by petty, irritating matters. There was Jesus – here were his greedy relatives.

He could not sleep at night. Inwardly, he rebelled. All the mocking words of blind obedience imposed on the Order by Ignatius, words he'd heard so many times, rang in his brain. In the end he knelt down, buried his face in his hands, and stubbornly, endlessly, recited the Angelus.

* * *

The chamber of the Piotrków tribunal was packed with people. Great interest had been aroused by the suit against the Jesuits, who were charged with having hoaxed a minor into donating enormous wealth and then concealing the donor's death. The crowd included supporters of the Order and its numerous enemies, among them the heretics who expected the Order to come out of the suit discredited and were clearly enjoying the prospect. Formally, the plaintiff was Seweryn Kurdwanowski, Zofia Męcińska's husband, but he had the support of the whole family including various cousins.

That day the court was addressed by one of the Tribunal's advocates, supporting the plaintiff. He was a nobleman of small build and wore an old classic Polish robe called *kontusz*. He had already been speaking for an hour and it was evident that he'd continue for some time. With one hand stuck under his sash and the fingers of the other making expansive gestures, he paced the floor along a barrier separating the court from the public and set out his case in a monotonous drone.

"*Tandem*, I am saying: the reverend fathers dispatched young Wojciech out into the world, to some overseas land, where he died. However, having seized the Męciński family estate, they now insist that he said Wojciech is alive and upholds the bequest he had made *iure caduce...*"

The people in the courtroom kept turning their heads in the direction of the bench where, next to his advocate, the prior of the Piotrków Jesuit house sat with another clergyman.

The speaker broke off, wheezed, and wiped his forehead with a big, brightly colored handkerchief produced from his sleeve. He gestured to his assistant, received a mug of beer from him, then, leaning backwards, slowly drained it and wiped his flaxen moustache with the back of his hand. The spectators in the courtroom, who used such interruptions to whisper and make other noises, became quiet again.

The advocate cleared his throat to indicate he was about to resume his speech, when suddenly someone exclaimed in awe: "God almighty, it can't be! Away with you!"

All heads turned in the direction of the voice. A great commotion began at once, as people leaped to their feet.

Along a path through the crowd walked a young friar, making his way toward the bench occupied by the Jesuit superior. Those who remembered Wojciech Męciński recognized him at once, despite the fact that he'd matured somewhat and his face was drawn.

Zofia Kurdwanowska cried: "Holy Mother of God! That's Wojtek!"

The man who'd been pronounced dead walked over and sat down beside the prior. The crowd stood shouting, divided into those who were shocked and those who found the appearance of the alleged deceased rather amusing. The tumult became so great that the walls of the courtroom seemed to shake. At the bar, the advocate stood transfixed, his mouth gaping wide, not knowing what to say.

Kurdwanowski jumped to his feet and shouted angrily to the Jesuit prior: "What kind of tricks are you trying to play here, Reverend Fathers!"

"There's no trick," the clergyman answered calmly. "The man who made the donation has come to reaffirm his decision –"

"Are you telling me, Father," Kurdwanowski interrupted, "that this man here is Wojciech Męciński, of the house of Poraj, my wife's brother?"

"That, sir, you can see with your own eyes. Your wife has already recognized him, as have many others."

"What does it matter that he looks similar? Maybe you've substituted someone else?"

"Are you suggesting fraud on our part, sir?"

The courtroom drowned in uproar. Everyone jumped up again, shouting and stamping their feet. Some men reached for their swords. The judge rang his bell in vain – the tumult would not subside. Only when the usher, at the judge's orders, pounded his staff on the floor and loudly proclaimed that whoever did not quiet down would pay a large fine in addition to being expelled from the courtroom, did the noise slowly begin to abate.

The judge then asked Męciński to approach the bench.

"Who are you, sir?" he inquired.

"My name is Wojciech Męciński. I'm an unworthy member of the Society of Jesus."

"Are you ordained?"

"Yes, I am."

"Did you make the donation we are examining here, Father?"

"I did."

"Why have there been reports of your death?"

"I don't know. Perhaps those who have been publicizing my death could explain that."

Kurdwanowski spoke up: "More than a year ago my wife received a letter from her brother, telling her he had been chosen to go on a mission to a remote and savage country and would never return, as the missionaries sent there were being killed one after another. If my brother-in-law went there to die, how is it possible that he is here now?"

"How do you account for that, Father?" the judge asked Męciński.

"Very simply. I did indeed write that letter, when I was leaving Rome for Portugal. From there I was to travel to Nippon, and I would have gone had not my superiors ordered me to Poland instead, to reaffirm my donation. Not that it was easy for me to get here."

"Have you any proof, Father, that you are who you claim to be?"

"I have been recognized, haven't I? But if you still have doubts, sir, please continue your questions."

The judge stopped to think.

"Tell me, Father, who were your parents?"

"My father was Jan Wojciech Męciński and my mother was Felicjana, maiden name Głoskowska, of the house of Jastrzębiec. Both are dead."

"Have you any brothers or sisters?"

"Yes, one brother, Stanisław, and a sister, Zofia, who is present here, Stanisław is dead. At my request, his body was buried in our congregation's church in Lublin."

"And you, where and when were you born?"

"At Osmolice, in the year of Our Lord 1598, the same year that His Majesty the King went to Sweden and was imprisoned there."

"And when did you make your donation?"

"In 1625, the year of the Swedish invasion of Livonia."

"That would indicate you were of age at the time."

"That's correct."

"In that case," said the judge, turning to Kurdwanowski, "on what do you base the charge that Father Męciński had no right to dispose of his estate?"

The plaintiff seemed confused. "I heard," he attempted to explain, "that my brother-in-law had given away his estate four years earlier, before actually coming of age..."

The suit was dismissed. Before the court, Męciński reaffirmed his desire to donate his whole estate to the Cracow Jesuits.

When the judge had left the chamber, some of Męciński's cousins came over to him. With tears in her eyes, Zofia pushed her way throught the crowd.

"Dear Wojtek.. Oh, my God... I'm so glad to see you again, and so sad about all this confusion. I'm ashamed of myself. But I was sure you were dead! Everybody said so... So did Seweryn... Please don't blame him."

"I'm not blaming anyone."

"I recognized you at once but you look so haggard."

"My journey across the German lands was arduous, and dangerous, too. They're none too friendly toward priests and Jesuits there. When they learn you're a Pole they're even more distrustful. And I contracted an eye ailment."

"Poor boy. Is it serious?"

"Well... I'm a doctor and I know what it means. I might lose my sight."

"That's terrible."

"The worst of it is that I wouldn't be able to return to my work. And the Father General promised me that when I settled all my affairs in Poland I'd be allowed to sail to Japan."

"So you're still set on going? It's certain death!"

"It's always been my deepest desire to give my life for Jesus."

Zofia looked at her brother through tears.

"What are you going to do now?"

"I've decided to go to Our Lady of Jasna Góra, to beg Her to save my sight."

Zofia was quiet for a while, then she said: "Yes, go. Mother always told us that when we faced hardship we should look to the Blessed Virgin for help. She will always help you to do the right thing, not what might just seem right. Put yourself in Her care, Wojtek. Let Her decide..."

Kurdwanowski approached and, without a word, squeezed Męciński's hand. The Jesuit returned the pressure with heartfelt friendship. He wanted to forget that because of this man he might be denied the fulfillment of his greatest wish.

* * *

Now he was on his knees in front of the Icon, gazing at the scarred face. For an hour he'd repeated: "Oh Mother, spare my sight. I want so much to devote myself to Jesus! If I go blind..."

Mary's eyes looked at him softly, kindly. The scars on Her cheek no longer bled. The artist who had renovated the Icon had painted out the traces of blood, and only the scars were visible.

He kept repeating his prayer: "Please, save my eyes. Let me return to Portugal and then sail to Nippon. I want to give my life for the true faith."

"Give your life!" – he suddenly thought he saw this question in Mary's eyes. "For whom? Jesus? Or for your nobleman's pride, your ambition to prove that you are not inferior to those who fell in the field of battle? You have remained a knight, knowing only one choice: to triumph or die. Do you recall what My Son told Jacob and John, the sons of thunder: Can ye drink of the cup that I drink of? And they assured Him that they could. But they knew not what they said. You too are giving assurances, yet you do not know either...

"For He appraised the surge of their emotions. Rash men seize the Kingdom, try to force their will on God Himself. You shall drink from the cup which you desire so greatly, but first your will must be united with the Will of Christ. He Himself came to Earth to give His Blood. Not because of a blind sense of duty, but because of His love of man. You shall not lose your sight, but you must love the way He loved."

Męciński trembled.

The prayer froze on his lips.

He felt a gust of hot wind from the candles burning on the altar. It covered his face like an invisible hand and rested for an instant on his eyes.

The prior, Father Gruszkowicz, shook Męciński's hand cordially. "It's a great joy for us to know that the Blessed Virgin has once again demonstrated Her might and Her mercy," he said. "So there has been a miracle?"

"I don't know... For two days I've felt no pain in my head. But that sometimes happened in the past, too. Our Lady gave me something more important. She assured me that whether I recover or not, I'll be able to go on my mission."

"When do you leave for Rome, Father?"

"Any day now. And then, with the help of God, I'll be going far away."

"We shall pray for you, that you will be allowed to illuminate many pagan souls with the light of the faith. We'd like to give you a small present... a picture of Our Lady copied from the Holy Icon by one of the friars. Please take it with you. Let it tell those people about the beauty of our Queen."

"I thank you from the bottom of my heart. It's a magnificent gift. I'll repay it with prayer as best I can."

"Is it true, Father," asked the prior, "that in Japan missionaries are persecuted and slain?"

"That information has reached us."

"So you too are set for martyrdom?"

He did not answer at once. "I will accept the Lord's Will," he said finally.

***

The first journey out of Lisbon ended pathetically. Caught by gale-force winds and buffeted by mountainous waves, the ship tossed about for weeks, ending up somewhere off the Brazilian coast. Then a fresh storm drove it back to Lisbon. During the dreadful return trip, Męciński treated and looked after his fellow travelers until he fell sick himself. He was so weak when they sailed into port that he had to be carried off the ship.

"And so your journeys are over, Father," someone said sympathetically. He knew that his body would not be able to cope with another voyage and he accepted the verdict calmly. He'd been threatened with blindness, yet he could see, and he believed that She would cure him again. But he had to accept God's Will with full confidence. That, too, ·was martyrdom, though not the martyrdom of valiance.

His illness lasted almost three years. When he recovered he was allowed to sail again, but the trip was again ill-fated. The ship wandered about the stormy sea for many weeks. All the missionaries fell sick, and when their superior died, Męciński assumed his duties. Barely able to stand up, he tended his companions and won their confidence. They experienced every possible misfortune, including a fire on board and running aground, but eventually they put in at Goa.

He spent several months there, took charge of the local hospital, learned about exotic diseases, and at the same time taught religion. He catechized, baptized and reinforced the faith. From Goa he was dispatched south, to Cochin. He accepted his assignment without complaint, but his thoughts dwelt constantly on Japan. While in Goa, he had learned that

Father Vieira, whom he was to have accompanied to Nippon years ago, had died a martyr after reaching his destination. He also heard about the horrible renunciation of the faith by Father Christopher.

Both pieces of news came as a shock to Męciński. He still dreamed of giving his life, but now he did so differently. He was not consumed by the relentless pursuit of death, but devoted himself to selfless work in accordance with Christ's Will. The Virgin Mary had been right: earlier, he'd wanted to make a noble gesture; all he thought of was God and himself. Now he realized that if his sacrifice were to be accepted it had to be offered to those he wished to save, whom he had begun to love for that reason. If he envied Father Vieira, it was only because it had taken him less time to realize that. If he wished to redeem Father Christopher's weakness, it was because he felt great compassion for him.

From Goa he was allowed to go farther east, to Malacca. The place was torn by a war between the Portuguese and the Dutch, so he sailed on toward Macao. He thought he could already see the land he yearned for on the horizon, when the ship he was sailing on was attacked by the Dutch, who took him prisoner. He was taken to Formosa, where he would have rotted to death except for his medical skills, which allowed him to survive six months' imprisonment and help his fellow prisoners.

Finally, he managed to escape and reach Macao at last. From there he could seriously think of sailing to Japan, but he fell ill again and was bedridden for many months. Meanwhile, he learned that Father Mastrilli, who'd reached Japan determined to redeem Father Christopher's betrayal, had been caught, had heroically resisted the torture of the pit, and in the end had been beheaded.

He lay in bed and tried to overcome his grief. Every day as soon as he awoke he said acts of trust and acts of joy. This is what God wants, he kept telling himself. I do not deserve the grace of shedding my blood. His Will will be done, His Will will be done...

As last he regained his health, but as soon as he began to seek an opportunity to go to Japan he was summoned by the Order's supervisor for the Far East. Father Diza, who flatly declared he did not wish Męciński to go. He had another task for him: he was to take up a quiet catechization post in Cambodia.

This did not drive him to despair either. For many hours he knelt in front of the picture of the Black Madonna of Jasna Góra, suppressing the rebellion within himself. He reasoned that the Lord was still eradicating his pride. In the morning, after struggling with himself all night, he reported humbly to receive his orders. He sailed to take up the work assigned to him.

He spent three very long years there, healing, baptizing, and teaching people the truths of the faith. He worked long hours every day. At night he had visions of Japan, which he thought was summoning him. All hope that he might some day go there had already vanished. He was now forty-three, which, together with his recurrent sicknesses, made him virtually incapable of withstanding the inhuman hardships of missionary work in that land of persecution. He told himself that whatever God decided, he would obey. The inner calm he forced on himself slowly spun an invisible cobweb around his heart.

When he had already resigned himself to the fact that he would never see Japan, everything suddenly changed. Father Rubino, a good friend of Męciński's, became the new supervisor for the Far East and he decided to go to Japan himself at the head of a group of Jesuits in order to atone for Father Christopher's deed. Męciński wrote to Father Rubino, asking timidly to be taken along. The reply came unexpectedly quickly – yes!

In the early spring of 1642, the eight missionaries selected for the expiatory expedition met in Manila. Before they set sail for Japan, Father Rubino addressed them.

The expedition had aroused many objections in Jesuit houses in the East, he said. The persecution in Japan had become extremely brutal. Under orders from the ruler of the country, Shogun Hidetada, the police were patrolling the beaches to see that no missionary has landed. The populace had been ordered to report the sighting of any stranger and those who failed to do so faced cruel punishment. Christianity was to be completely eradicated, eliminated without a trace. There was no priest left in Japan still engaged in pastoral work; only a handful of clergymen, including Father Christopher, had been spared in return for renouncing their faith. They lived as free men and were even engaged in various scientific projects.

Given how things stand, people were telling him, you are only going there to find death. That is just tempting the Lord. A missionary can dream of a martyr's death, but only when it befalls him as a result of his missionary work. You are sailing to a country in which Christianity has ceased to exist. You will not achieve anything there. As soon as you land, you'll be betrayed, imprisoned and martyred. Even the Lord did not turn Himself in to the Jews, but hid from His pursuers. Our Father Ignatius demanded prudence from us. Your death will not further any cause, only incense the persecutors...

"I concede that I myself am not sure who's right," Father Rubino went on, "those who want to stop us or me, organizing this expedition. I prayed for a long time before I made my decision. Here's what I think: the Lord has dispatched us to teach His Truth all over the world. But He acts through us, and when we're not able to do what He demands, He takes matters into His own hands. By giving Him our lives, we're calling on Him to do just that... Maybe I'm wrong. The Lord will judge me. I've made up my mind – I'm going. If I succeed in baptizing just one child and keeping up the spirits of just one man who's doubted before I die, I'll be happy to sacrifice my life. You'll do what you choose to do. I won't force anybody to accept my decision. If you wish to return to your previous tasks, feel free to do so."

They stood silent and shocked. It was true that after the dreadful slaughter of the missionaries sent to England, the opinion was gaining ground in Jesuit homes that expeditions such as this were only a waste of human resources. Missionary work in the Orient often carried the danger of death, but at the same time it resulted in thousands of conversions. In Japan there was nothing to gain now. But could they deny assistance to those who'd accepted the new faith as a result of Father Francis' mission?

A minute later, one by one, they had all said they wished to go. Father Rubino said a prayer of thanksgiving, then announced that the expedition would be divided into two groups. Męciński was to go with the first group, which was to be headed by the supervisor and was to leave as soon as possible.

When he returned to his cell, Męciński took a piece of paper, sharpened a quill, and wrote a letter to his sister. He told her that after so many years, the long awaited moment had come. "When this letter reaches you," he wrote, "I will no longer be alive." He was praying to Jesus and Our Lady to give him the strength to demonstrate his courage when the moment of truth came. He asked Zofia to pray for him and assured her that if the Lord chose to reward him he would have her, her husband, her children and grandchildren before his eyes when he died. From Heaven it was possible to do things we were unable to do in our lives, he concluded.

One evening, after a month at sea, four missionaries set foot on the shores of Japan. As they had agreed beforehand, they split up at once. Each one set off in a different direction, seeking to establish contact with the faithful.

They had been following his tracks for days and by now he was certain he would not be able to escape his pursuers. He knew that from the way the locals behaved: they were more and more intimidated and fraught with fear of the questioning, interrogation, and torture. The hunters were tough and ruthless. Not only were they pursuing him, they were also determined to erase all traces of his existence.

It was only his eighth day on the island. What had he done during that time? He had found Christians, but he had also discovered that they were mortally afraid. None of them dared receive him in his home. They told him that the police already knew about the missionaries' landing and were looking for them everywhere. He had been hiding out in the daytime and only dared to meet people at night. They brought children to be baptized and begged him to hear their confessions.

Only here had he realized what fear meant. Over the years he had dreamed of martyrdom and thought that this desire was stronger than all fear. But now he felt that fear. It came to him like the flutter of invisible wings when he was alone, and he saw it in the eyes of the people coming to meet him. He overcame it by reminding himself that it was the Will of Jesus Christ that had finally brought him to the islands of Japan. Now, after thirteen years, he thought, there was one thing he could be sure of: it was not his will that had triumphed – it was the Will of Jesus.

That night he took shelter in a lone bamboo hut at the edge of a field. At dusk, several people from the neighboring village sneaked through the trees to the hut. Using his last drops of wine, he said Mass and shared out the Host. He now had no more wine or communion wafers left. They sat on their heels in a circle to eat some dried fish and rice pancakes. He saw black, terrified eyes staring at him.

"What shall we do when they come asking about you, padre? What shall we do when they ask us to renounce the faith? What are we to do? What shall we do?"

"Oh Lord," he thought, "let me comfort them and keep up their spirits. I feel for them so much. I love them so dearly. What can I do to save them and their faith?"

"Are we all going to die, the women and children too?" they kept asking him. "Do we all have to die?"

Instinctively, he shook his head.

"No," he thought, "you will not die, although you'll be left to yourselves when I and my fellow Jesuits perish. It seems that everything will be lost when our strength fails us, but it is then, as Father Rubino said, that He Himself takes matters into His own hands, and those hands are more powerful than ours. You'll therefore wait and help will come, although it may not be what we now imagine it to be. Nobody is lost until he himself wishes to be."

"Keep in your hearts what you have received," he said. "It will be hard, very hard. Maybe your children will forget the name of the true God, yet God will stay with you. He will guard you until the day one of our priests comes to these shores again. Maybe this will be in fifty years' time, or even in a hundred..."

They looked at him with concern, but at the same time were relieved that he was not ordering them to die at the hands of the torturers. The idea, he thought, was not that they all die, but rather that he should die for them and they should live.

The sun was beginning to come up. One by one, the faithful knelt down before Męciński and he made the sign of the cross on their forehead. A young woman who had brought him food was the last to leave the hut.

"Please stay one more minute, Sakiko." He reached under his shirt and took out the picture he'd received long ago at Jasna Góra. "Look, this is the Mother of Christ..." He always carried it with him and prayed before it every day. He had a strange feeling that the Icon was a shield, a buckler, like the plate protecting a knight's heart. As long as he had it, he was immune to danger.

But now he knew that the time of fulfillment had come. The Virgin had not only healed his eyes, She had made his dreams come true. Having first purified them, She had made them worthy of the One to whom they were dedicated.

"How beautiful!" Sakiko whispered.

"I want to give this picture to you. Take it and pray before it. Hide it well and never lose it. The day will come when you will be able to show it openly, or, if not you, your children."

She left, clutching the icon to her bosom. He was alone then. The morning wind rustled the leaves above the hut. Dawn came. The red disc of the sun slowly emerged from behind the darkly wooded hills.

He no longer had his shield. All he had left was ordinary human fear, but at the same time he felt peace and joy, like the bottom of the sea, that is unmoved by the storm raging on its surface. He lay prostrate on the ground and prayed for the Japanese Christians whom he was leaving in God's care, for the enormous world that was torn, aching, longing for unity yet moving farther away from it all the time, and for the distant land of his fathers...

* * *

The prior, Father Augustyn Kordecki, came down to receive his visitor. The young nobleman bowed and then pressed his lips to the hand of the man all Poland revered.

"My name is Albert Męciński, of Kurozwęki," he said.

"I am pleased to meet you. What brings you here, sir?"

"I've come to ask you to accept a gift. In these dangerous times everybody wants to pay tribute to our Queen, who so recently saved this land and reversed our ill fortune. I too have taken the liberty..." He produced a parchment hidden under his sash. "Here's the deed to the Minorowskie manor which, with your permission, Reverend Father, my family and I wish to donate to the monastery that it may serve the Blessed Virgin."

"I thank you with all my heart on Her behalf. The Mother of God greatly values noble hearts and knows how to show Her gratitude. Did you say your name was Męciński? Many years ago, there was a man by that name here, a priest of the Order of St. Ignatius. He was about to set out for some foreign land to convert the pagans... There are still some people here who talked to him then, and who still remember him. Was he perhaps a relative of yours, sir?"

"Indeed, he was a cousin of mine. His name was Wojciech."

"And what happened to him?"

"He died as he wished: a martyr in Japan. He and several fellow missionaries underwent terrible tortures in Nagasaki. In order to force him to renounce the faith, they hung him upside down in a pit full of stinking filth. He hung there for seven days before he died, but he never renounced the faith! Most important of all, another Jesuit, his superior, who had earlier renounced God out of fear of torture, returned to the faith when he witnessed this martyrdom and, despite his advanced years, he withstood torture with dignity."

"The blood of a martyr is never shed in vain," Father Kordecki said. "The Blessed Virgin, our Queen, is the Mother of all martyrs. She sanctifies their sacrifice and makes it worthy of Her Son. We should be very happy that She has chosen this place as Her residence. If only we can be faithful to Her! For if we remain faithful and turn to Her, even at a late hour, like the poor man who only accepted martyrdom when he witnessed the example of our countryman, then believe me, sir, She will raise us up to the heights and make us shine like a beacon to the world, for the good of our faith."

CHAPTER 6

KING JAN III SOBIESKI

"I'm telling you, Jan, My love," she said, "that what you're planning to do on that expedition with your army is a great folly. The army should be commanded by Jabłonowski. You could go there as well, only later when the Turks are beaten back from Vienna, so the Emperor understands to whom he owes his salvation. It's me who's telling you this" – and here she pointed her finger – "and you know you've never gone wrong when you listened to my advice."

The King sighed quietly. He had already been sure that his beautiful, temperamental wife understood his arguments, and now she was starting it all over again. He decided to keep silent, but she wouldn't let him.

"Why don't you answer? Say something."

"What can I say, my dear? I've explained it all so many times already."

"You mean Jabłonowski isn't capable of achieving victory?"

"He's a hetman and an excellent commander, but out there he would only be leading our armies. The Emperor would be the commander-in-chief, and he doesn't seem to know much about the art of war."

"So tell them to make Jabłonowski an overall commander."

"I can't, Marysieńka. The Germans would never accept that. Besides, we've signed a treaty, and the ruler who's with his army is to take command."

"You always sign something without asking me first and then we have nothing but trouble. You shouldn't go, you're not well..."

"You know that I've fully recovered since we've started getting ready for war."

"Recovered! You're itching for battle and that's what's making you feel better. But what will it be like when the armies march off? This war against the Turks may not go that simply."

"No, it won't be simple. We'll be facing a mighty enemy. But I trust that Jesus Christ and the Blessed Virgin will give me strength and watch over me."

Marysieńka shrugged.

"Ever since you met that monk, you've lost all sense of proportion," she observed. "I'm a God-fearing woman myself, but I hate taking things to extremes. The Turks have Leopold scared to death, so he's begging us for assistance. I agree that we have to help him, but he should show his gratitude."

"There'll be time for that after we've won, my dear."

"If you don't take care of it beforehand, you'll forget about everything. I know you too well, Jan. You're not one for foresight. You're forgetting we have children and have to think about their future, and then there's my father, a poor old man who's been deprived of everything, and my poor brother... Since you don't think about them, I have to."

"I didn't say I wouldn't attend to those matters."

"It would be best if you raised the question when your army is winning. That's what kings do. But then, you think you have to fight the battle yourself!"

"True, I admit that. I've spent more of my life as a soldier than as a king. In this time of need, my sword will be of greater help than royal wisdom."

"And what if you get sick or, God forbid, die?"

"I wouldn't hestitate to give my life in this cause."

"There you are. That's precisely what I expected. You'll perish – and what about us? We'll be left with no security. You're only thinking about yourself."

He sighed again.

"You don't understand, or you don't want to. I'm not going there to get killed, I'm only telling you that if I did... My mother..."

She flayed her arms in angry protest.

"She's been dead a long time and you know how she treated you! We haven't talked about her for years. I'm sure you're only mentioning her now to irritate me."

Recently he had been recalling his mother often, despite the fact that more than twenty years had passed since her death. They had parted in anger. He hadn't seen her during the last year of her life, and had not returned home in time to see her before she died. Mother... She seemed harsh and strict, but he loved her greatly as a boy and knew that although she seldom smiled, her stern face concealed the warmth of love.

His father had been deeply immersed in public affairs and had little time to spend with his sons, Marek and Jan. Until the boys left the family home to study at the Nowodworski college in Cracow, they'd been brought up chiefly by lady Teofila. They lived at Żółkiew, on their great-grandfather's ancient estate. Everything in the house bore witness to him and his exploits. His granddaughter had not allowed anyone to touch anything, leaving all his effects as they were when he set off on the expedition across the Dniester. In his bedroom, a lamp always burned in front of an Icon of Our lady of Częstochowa, hanging above a spartan soldier's bunk. Below the painting was a baton presented to him by the Pope, and a slashed coat stained with blood, brought from the battlefield at Cecora. In the local church there were black marble statues on the tombs of his great-grandfather and his grandfather Jan, for whom he'd been named, and who'd also died of wounds received at Cecora. Next to them was the tomb of Stanisław Daniłłowicz, Teofila's brother, cruelly murdered by the Tartars.

When she took her sons to the tombs, their mother had explained to them: "They were killed defending the faith. That is the death of a true knight. You have to be worthy of your ancestors, you have to guard the faith and shield it from pagan attacks, even if it costs your lives. Always remember the words: *Dulce et decorum est pro patria mori*. These words must lead you through life. I will curse either of you who betrays them."

Later, when she learned about the shameful defeat at Puławce, she said again and again: "I wouldn't consider either of you a son of mine if you fled from the battlefield the way they did."

The Sobieski brothers' studies at the Cracow Academy passed quickly. Both were members of the sodality of the Immaculate Conception of the Blessed Virgin; they wore Carmelite scapulars and took Holy Communion once a month. Every day they said the litany of the Blessed Virgin. On Our Lady's feast days they took part in processions to seven Cracow churches, wearing white sacks and practicing self-flagellation as they went. Marek, the elder brother, was chancellor of the sodality; Jan was only twelve when he delivered a great speech in praise of the Blessed Virgin. At that time, their great hero was Władysław III of Varna and the idea of sacrificing their lives for the faith kept returning to them. Marek's desire, cherished from his youngest years, was fulfilled. On the eve of his terrible death he wrote to his mother from the camp near Batoh: "I humbly beg of you to remember me, my lady..."

Teofila Sobieska did not shed a single tear for her beloved son. However, she did develop a dislike and contempt for her younger son, who had not joined the army and had not accompanied his brother because of a wound acquired in a duel over a girl. This contempt grew even stronger when she discovered he was having an affair with Zamoyski's wife. Soon afterwards relations between Jan and his mother were completely severed, as Marysieńka took offense and incited her infatuated lover to rebel against the interference. As a result, Teofila transferred all her maternal feelings to her daughter Katarzyna. She died a little later, her death possibly accelerated by sorrow over her son's behavior, which flew in the face of family tradition.

During all the intervening years Jan had rarely thought about his mother, but recently his memories of her had returned with unusual force. She had appeared in his dreams several times, and she was as kind as he remembered she could sometimes be. These reawakened memories became a burden. He realized with pain that he'd never received her forgiveness nor her blessing. The court theologian, Father Stanisław Papczyński assured him: "She did not die in anger. Her dying words were to ask the Mother of God to watch over you, Your Majesty. And so the

Immaculate Virgin is keeping watch, and waiting..." Sobieski felt that Papczyński had some strange communion with the world of the dead.

The carriage rocked gently, accompanied by the snorting of the horses, the pounding of hooves, and soldiers' voices. A dry spell had persisted for many weeks and the horses kicked up clouds of dust which enveloped the party like a smokescreen. In spite of that the carriage door had to remain open: the summer was very hot and uncommonly airless. Epidemics raged in the towns and it was said that Kara Mustafa was a great wizard, sending poisoned air to stop the Poles coming to the relief of Vienna. These rumors only increased people's determination. The country was taking to arms and readying itself for battle with a zeal unknown for many years. From time to time the King's party came across armed detachments of noblemen on their way to rallying points, others marched along the road to join regiments on foot. They were just passing one such group. The prospective soldiers, young lads all of them, wearing various kinds of clothes, halted. Some were from the countryside, others were apprentices from towns. When they realized that the King was in the carriage, they took off their caps and cheered. Sobieski leaned out of the carriage and waved to them.

"The whole country is on the march," he observed.

"The people are really aroused," Marysieńka conceded. "I've never seen so much enthusiasm."

"And they tried to stop me," he said, clenching his fist at the memory. "I remember them saying: 'Why should we care that the Turks rob the Germans?' These fools. Once they robbed them, they would have come after us. And then we'd have had to face them on our own. Fools! Or maybe they aren't fools at all? Their words were paid for in gold."

"That isn't what the Eagle wanted," she replied. As always, she defended Louis. "It's de Vitry and Morsztyn that are to blame. They deserved their punishment. Especially that Morsztyn, he had it coming to him for his lies."

Sobieski did not answer. He knew full well what to think about that matter. The recently exposed plot had opened his eyes to many things. He wanted to forget about what had hurt him so much, suppress his suspicions and his knowledge that he had been betrayed. "I'm going to Our Lady," he thought, "and I don't want to go there feeling resentment toward anybody.

After all, wasn't I like them when I opposed King Michał Korybut Wiśniowiecki? I forgive them, that I may be forgiven too."

Since the plans to assassinate him were uncovered, he had thought increasingly about death. The prospect of waging war against the Turks, not by himself and not on his own ravaged land, but with others and with the Pope's blessing, evoked his enthusiasm. But it did not reduce his ability to weigh matters soberly. He did not take the war lightly; the Turks were an awesome force. The faithful Armenians had informed him in detail about the forces commanded by the Grand Vizier. Their French-trained artillery was perhaps the most formidable in the world; the janissary regiments were famous for their daring. The Hungarians supported the Turks, and although Sobieski knew that Thokoli had been forced into the alliance, he also understood that for the Hungarians freedom was more important than the fact that Austrian papists faced disaster.

He was already aware that the army he would lead to Austria, would fall short of the troop strength he had promised. Lithuania was dragging her feet and – he was now almost sure – would fail him once again. The recruitment of Cossacks which he had ordered, and to which he had committed his own funds, did not seem to be moving forward. His vassal in Brandenburg kept making excuses, then empty promises. Meanwhile, in Austria, the Emperor's forces were outnumbered and battle weary. The Emperor sent desperate pleas to Sobieski to come to his aid, yet at the same time he distrusted him. Who could rush to his rescue and in what strength from a Europe divided and preoccupied with its own problems? In terms of Poland's potential the army marching south was large, but in comparison with the Turks it was nothing. He had faced overwhelming odds many times before, but this time the disparity seemed outrageous. This battle would decide everything. Was it victory or death that awaited him? Had not Władysław of Varna gone to meet his advancing enemy in a similar situation?

Aware of the dangers he faced, he decided to visit Częstochowa on the way to Cracow, where he had ordered his forces to converge. Life had taken different turns, but the cult of the Virgin Mary he had developed in his younger years remained strong. The magnificent lamp he had donated to the shrine at Jasna Góra as a token of thanksgiving for his wife's recovery from serious illness, burned with an eternal flame. It was his habit to express gratitude with generosity. Their son Aleksander, who also had survived a sickness, had been given into the service of Mary. Jan funded churches and chapels, gave generously to monasteries, and paid for masses. "God has given me so much," he boasted sometimes, "that I want Him to know I'm not one for ingratitude!"

But the court theologian, a White Friar from Nowy Jeruzalem, demolished this reasoning.

"There's no great merit in giving away wealth, Your Highness," he said. "Your predecessors understood that. They gave themselves, not precious offerings, to the Mother of God. They recognized Her as Queen. Don't be offended by this, but there has never been a queen named Mary on the Polish throne, as only the Virgin has the right to that crown. I know you love your wife, and that love explains many things... Still, it would be good if you both went to Our Lady and put yourselves in Her service."

He wondered whether Marysieńka understood the meaning of their visit. He had tried to explain it to her, cautiously, not mentioning that the idea had orginally been Papczyński's. She did not like the priest. Since the discovery of Morsztyn's letters, in which the frivolous poet had fantasized about King Jabłonowski with Marysieńka as his royal spouse, the intimacy between the royal couple had lessened. Although Sobieski firmly rejected even the slightest suspicion of his wife's guilt, a chill had crept in. Their respective illnesses had earlier moved them apart. He was increasingly weak and contemptuous of his swollen body, she bloomed as if the passage of time had no effect on her. Once, he had loved her for everything she was and everything she did, now he was beginning to realize what love really meant.

Marysieńka was a religious woman, had her private confessor, took care of the nuns of the Holy Sacrament, whom she had brought to Poland, and visited the Sisters of Charity and the Nuns of the Order of Visitation. She certainly did not remember the vows she had made in the church of the Marmelites, sinful as they were, even though born out of faith. Those days were past and better forgotten. Sobieski remembered and felt that the Lord had taken them at their word and united them – forever.

The pounding hooves of their escorts' horses resounded sharply as they left the dirt track and galloped along a road paved with rough stones. The dust had settled and the green hills could be seen clearly in the distance. Suddenly a shout was heard and the whole retinue stopped. A white-robed friar appeared by the door of the royal carriage.

"Your Highness," he said. "You can see Jasna Góra from here!"

That morning Sobieski had told Papczyński to halt the party when the tower of the monastery appeared on the horizon. He gestured to a servant in the dickey-box, who jumped to the ground and opened the door and placed a step under it. Sobieski climbed down and stood on the edge of the road, his hand shielding his eyes from the bright July sun. A thin vertical line could be seen far beyond the hills.

"We'll be there in a few hours," he said.

Marysieńka and the children also got out of the carriages. A French nanny held little Jan in her arms. The boy saw his father and reached out for him. He was a pale child, had barely begun to walk and did not speak yet. The doctors fussed around him anxiously. Would he grow up like Konstanty and Aleksander? Sobieski felt a special attachment to his youngest son, as he did to his only daughter, Teresa.

"*Ave Maria gratia plena...*", Father Stanisław intoned.

With their eyes fixed on the church steeple they recited a section of the rosary, then again took their seats in the carriages. Marysieńka rode in another coach with her sons, Sobieski took Teresa and Father Stanisław into his.

The road wound among the hills and the steeple frequently disappeared from view, only to appear again much larger. They passed fields of ripe grain, meadows, and woods. When they passed through a village, blond peasant children ran out of thatched cottages and greeted the travelers, waving their hands. Teresa leaned out of the window and returned the greeting with her handkerchief. Her mother would never have consented to such an exchange of familiarity with commoners, but when she was with her father she could do anything she pleased.

Papczyński sat pensively. Suddenly, he interrupted his thoughts and said: "These people have been wronged, yet they reach out to you in love."

Sobieski turned to him.

"You never stop talking about them, Father."

"I never stop thinking about them either, Your Highness. I'm one of them."

"Tell me something about yourself, I know so little. I hear you come from the mountains?"

"Yes, I was born in the foothills near Nowy Sącz, during a thunderstorm. My mother had to cross the Dunajec, and in that kind of weather our mountain rivers become fast and dangerous. Before she stepped into the boat, she offered the child she was to bear to the Blessed Virgin. I was born several hours later, during the night, and I've belonged to Our Lady from the very first moment of my life."

"Did you know, Father, that I was born during a storm too? Under cover of rainfall the Tartars got up close to Olesko and tried to take the castle, but our men defended it bravely. And my mother, too, made a pledge."

Papczyński smiled.

"So you also have your duties... I have to tell you that I was given the same name as Your Highness."

"Really? You're Jan too? The Baptist?"

"Yes. But that's where the similarities end. I was born in a peasant cottage, in poverty. I herded cows and gathered brushwood for the fire."

"Yet you went on to gain great knowledge."

"My parents wanted me to study, and good people helped me, but learning didn't come easy and the Jesuits thought I was a dunce. Our Lady helped me a lot, which is why She now demands a lot of me... Then I entered the Piarist novitiate at Podoliniec, where I received the name Stanisław of Jesus and Mary. I thought I'd spend the rest of my days working in that worthiest of orders. But as you remember, I had to leave the congregation. The church authorities relieved me of my vows, despite my pleas."

"The Piarists accused you unjustly. They persecuted you."

"May God forgive them and may their deeds be forgotten. I bear no grudge against anyone, and I revere the congregation with all my heart. Evidently this was the way it had to be, this is what She wanted."

"And so you started your own Order."

"If I succeed in setting up the institute, I'll owe it to the gracious assistance of the reverend bishops Gembicki, Oborski and Wierzbowski. Your Majesty's nephew, the Warmia priest, has also shown me great kindness. And thanks to you, Your Majesty, we came into possession of the Korabiew forests."

"May your Order last forever. The first Order to originate in Poland, and one praising the glory of the Immaculate Virgin. I was a member of a

Cracow sodality and now I serve in the literary fraternity at St. John in Warsaw, and I've heard that certain theologians contest this idea and claim the Church has never talked of Mary in these terms."

"It hasn't," said Papczyński, taking up the subject with passion, "but that doesn't mean it's opposed to it. People have always believed in the Immaculate Conception. The Church allows prayers to the Virgin, and the observance of Her feast. The flower blossoms in its time and the time just doesn't seem to have arrived for this truth to ripen and be confirmed by the Church. But those who love the Blessed Virgin are confident: that day will come. And who knows, maybe the teachings will be proclaimed by a child, like the one who waved to us? When adults' hearts turn to stone, it's the children who start calling out –"

He stopped abruptly, as if he had said too much.

Sobieski cast a careful sideways glance at the man who'd been his confessor and advisor for several years. From what Papczyński occasionally let slip, and from what others said, he knew that the life of the Marians' founder had been one long tale of martyrdom. Misunderstood, falsely accused and suspected, a victim of prejudice and betrayal, he had built the structure and principles of the new congregation through great pain and effort. He did not want to remember the wrongs he'd suffered, replacing hostility with love. If he appeared harsh at times, underneath that harshness was a heart full of charity. He dedicated the majority of his prayers to those facing the awesome trial of the day of judgment, especially the souls of soldiers. He did this despite the fact that these men were often a greater burden to the peasants than the enemy, demanding shelter, food and fodder for their horses. Again, the King had the impression that the world of the dead was strangely close to Papczyński. Sometimes it looked as though he was closer to the dead than to the living.

They rode on in silence. The priest clasped his hands together and was praying. Teresa, wearied by the journey, fell asleep with her head on her father's shoulder. Her golden hair broke loose and covered her round face. Of all his children, she alone appeared to glow with health.

They were approaching their destination. The trip to Częstochowa had been a long one, in many ways.

At Papczyński's insistence, some days ago they had visited Studzianna. There, in the church of the Oratorian friars, more often called the

Philipians, was a highly revered picture of the Holy Mother. Kochowski, an old comrade from the battles fought under Hetman Czarniecki, and now a court writer and poet, claimed that this picture of Our Lady of Studzianna was the most famous in the country; more famous than those revered at Sokal, Leżajsk, Troki, Bochnia, Chełm, Żyrowice, Skępe, Pajęczna, Jarosław, Tuchów, Myślenice, Podkamien, Klewań, Piotrkowice or Gidle, or the one in the church at Piasek in Cracow.

Not everybody agreed. Most people praised the Icon they happened to esteem most. And there was still Our Lady of Grace at the Jesuit church, the patron of Warsaw, and the Dominicans' Queen of the Holy Rosary. Sobieski remembered how Pac worshipped his local Virgin Mary of Ostra Brama. But Pac was an enemy prepared to take up arms to prevent Sobieski's election to the throne, someone who had stood against him many times. Was there any reason why one Icon should be of greater worth than another? Pictures were only reminders that Our Lady was there, listening to us, waiting for us, loving us, and wanting to help us. Some might appear more beautiful than others, but they were all the work of human hands. It was not the picture that was revered, but Our Lady Herself, a living Person more beautiful than any painting.

"Go to Częstochowa, Your Majesty," Papczyński had told him. "Not that you're nearer Our Lady there than in any other church. You can find Her just as easily in Goźlin, even though Broliński, the parish priest, rejects the idea of the Immaculate Conception. But at Jasna Góra She showed Her grace to the whole nation. Many kings have worshipped her there. You should go and make your vow."

"I'll give myself to Her", he thought. "Let Her grant us salvation and victory. Not for myself, but for my kingdom."

Military glory had always mattered a great deal to Sobieski. He loved talking about his victories and hearing others praise them. It wasn't enough for him to win a battle, when he talked about his triumphs he was given to exaggeration.

"Oh my dear Jan," Jabłonowski used to say. "You're a great knight, but when you talk of your exploits you outdo Potocki the poet."

Marysieńka mocked him too: "You're boasting again, my love, as if you didn't really do the things you say."

He promised that he would stop talking that way, but when friends encouraged him to recount his tales his determination began to falter after a few glasses of wine. His recollections became more vivid and his friends urged him on: "Tell us again how you knocked that Turk off his horse..."

Seeing Marysieńka's mocking eyes the following morning, he would beg her humbly: "Don't yell at me, please. I only yielded to temptation a little." On this matter alone she forgave easily.

The years had passed and his health had deteriorated. He'd felt differently going into battle at Chocim; ten years had made a more cautious man of him. At Radziejowice he pored over maps for hours until his battle plan was prepared down to the finest detail. He didn't want to leave anything to improvisation. At Chocim he had been fearless. While setting out for Vienna he only pretended to be brave. The bold plan was the product of considered judgment and experience, and also of the awareness that he was no longer the man he had once been.

She has to help, he repeated to himself.

At last they reached Częstochowa, a small town stretching along a narrow winding river. Beyond the houses were open fields and orchards covering the long slope of the hill, its summit encircled by trees, and the monastery with its tall spire suspended above them. A wide road led from the town to the monastery.

In the marketplace their way was blocked by a crowd eager to greet the King. At the head of the welcoming party stood the mayor of Częstochowa, surrounded by councilors; behind them were women, children, and representatives of the town's guilds and societies with their colorful standards and ceremonial dress. Loud cheers greeted the royal carriage. Mortars were fired, presumably borrowed from the monastery for the occasion. Children surrounded the carriages and showered the Queen and the Princess with flowers. The mayor's wife and the wives of the aldermen held up bread and salt on a tray covered with an embroidered towel. As Sobieski stepped from the carriage, the mayor began his speech.

"Oh great and magnificent King, conqueror of pagans, vanquisher of traitors..." he began to stutter and clear his throat, unable to continue.

Without waiting for the man to finish, Sobieski patted the mayor's shoulder and offered his hand to his wife. Before she took it she wiped hers carefully on her apron, blushing a bright crimson. Mindful of Marysieńka, he resisted the temptation to kiss the woman's young, burning cheeks.

Instead he stroked the children's heads. The crowd continued cheering, but the King ordered the retinue forward out of the marketplace.

Halfway up the hill stood the church of St. James, surrounded by the hospice and the cemetery. Sobieski ordered the carriage to stop, deciding to continue the rest of the way on foot to show that his visit was in fact a pilgrimage. Propping himself on a stick, he started toward the summit. On one side walked Father Stanisław, on the other his trusted servant Matczyński, the royal Master of the Horse. His sons and Teresa walked behind. Only Marysieńka and their youngest son stayed in the carriage, which followed slowly. They had barely covered half the distance when he felt tired. His face was red, sweat streamed down his forehead, and he panted heavily. Papczyński and Matczyński took his arms. The carriage drove up and Marysienka leaned out the window and begged him to get in, but Sobieski insisted he would walk. He could ride a horse without tiring too much, yet his swollen legs could barely support his overweight body. He dragged himself on but found the going more difficult with every step. A piercing pain shot through his abdomen, his hips stiffened, and he gasped for breath. Blood throbbed in his temples. He was terribly weak.

"Marysieńka is right," he thought suddenly. "I won't make it." He did not regret his life so much. People had failed him, Marysieńka did not really love him or need him, only Teresa and little Jan genuinely felt for him. "I don't care if I die," he thought, "but first I want Her to allow me to win. Let it be Her victory." He wanted to reach the chapel at all costs, to tell the Blessed Virgin that he wanted Her to reap all the glory of his triumph – if She granted it. As for himself, he was ready to give his life.

Although he gathered all his strength, he finally had to get into the carriage. Marysieńka told him quietly: "Now do you see that I'm right? You shouldn't go."

He didn't answer.

He would have given everything if the woman he loved so much understood his feelings, but their thoughts were far apart. Their marriage had meant the end of a fiery love affair and for a long time he had thought this was because of troubled times, that the return of peace would bring passion back. He was wrong. When the passion burned itself out, he wanted to preserve at least friendship and understanding, but that did not happen either. Marysieńka burst with energy, setting in motion dozens of campaigns and plots, recruiting people for her activities and then forcing her husband to pay the obligations she incurred. He often had to refuse someone a position when it turned out that the Queen had earlier promised the post to someone else. If only he could trust his wife's protégés! But they were generally mediocrities, who treated the favor merely as a reward for their services to the Queen. Frequently he didn't even know what kind of service that had been, or if it hadn't perhaps involved some activity that prejudiced the interests of the realm.

But for all that, he would never stop loving her. After his election a few people suggested that he get his marriage annulled – it had been condemned by the majority of the gentry – and marry Eleonora, the widow of King Michał. How outraged he'd been! He made it clear that he would sooner refuse the crown than renounce Marysieńka.

She was not a bad woman. Sometimes, unexpectedly, she revealed a hidden side of her soul, and he would notice tenderness in her gestures or the looks she gave him. This happened most often when he was in bed with an ailment, tormented by pain. But it lasted only briefly. The next minute she seemed ashamed of her moment of weakness and became firm and demanding again. One day she told him with disarming frankness: "I wasn't brought up to be good, but to be wise."

The carriage jolted along the rutted road, swaying wildly, transmitting each bump to his aching kidneys. Finally it pulled up at the monastery gate. They were met by Paulite friars and guardsmen wearing navy-blue braided jackets. There also were religious fraternities from Częstochowa, St. Roch's, and St. Barbara's churches, and there were costumed peasants from the surrounding villages: Grabówek, Lisiniec, Szarlejek, Kawodrza, Gnaszyn, Łojki, Konopiska, and Blachownia. The provincial, the prior and the Monastic Council greeted the visitors. Children brought flowers, there was singing, cheering and speeches, then the royal couple was ceremoniously led inside. Bells rang, and an orchestra played, cannon fired one round after another.

The guests were taken to the refectory, where a meal was set. Marysieńka looked at the walls decorated with stucco molding and paintings, then leaned toward Prior Grębiński and asked: "Is this where King Michał's wedding feast was held?"

"Yes, Your Majesty, a truly magnificent ceremony, a feast for the eyes."

She gazed at four cupids on the ceiling, twining a wedding garland with a chain.

"Eleonora didn't reign long," she said.

"Sadly," he said, taking her words to be an expression of sympathy. "She was a good and pious lady, it was a pleasure to see how much she prayed. She came here even after her husband died... While she was still in Poland."

"She dreamed of – " Marysieńka did not finish. "She won't be coming back now. The wife of the Duke of Lorraine won't come here, neither will her children nor grandchildren."

Sobieski asked the order's provincial, Fr. Czechowicz, about the monastery's defenses.

"We're going to war against a powerful enemy," he said. "I worry that when I'm with my army in Austria, the Vizier could send the Tartars on a raid across the mountains to start a diversionary action. I'll be leaving soldiers to guard the Carpathian passes, Cracow is well garrisoned, but it would be up to the monastery to defend itself."

"There's no need to worry about us," Czechowicz assured the sovereign. The friar was an old man with a reputation of being an excellent theologian and preacher, and he'd already served several terms as the Order's provincial. "In the event of danger, we would put up no less resistance than we offered the Swedes twenty-eight years ago. After we beat them off, King Jan Kazimierz ordered the fortifications reinforced and he even took part in the work. The walls are strong, we have enough cannon, and a hundred well-trained soldiers. The granaries and arsenal are fully stocked due to Your Majesty's assistance, which we repay as best we can with prayers."

"I'm always grateful for prayer, Father Provincial. We'll go into battle with Our Lady's name on our lips, but it's also our duty to safeguard Her shrine. I wanted to make certain about that. Should I fail to return –"

The friar's hands fluttered about in vehement protest.

"Don't even say that. Our Lady will watch over you. We've made a replica of the picture as you asked, so you can have it by your side."

"I'm deeply grateful. Father Papczyński will say Mass in front of it every day during the campaign. What have you prepared for us today, Father?"

"Nothing, I don't think. It's late, and all of you must be weary after the journey. Tomorrow we'll have a solemn Mass in the chapel for your victory and safe return. After Mass we'll bless the replica of the icon. Also the Monastic Council would like to give you something we found in our treasury."

"What, Father?"

"The sword your great-grand father offered to Our Lady before going on his last campaign."

"Really? I didn't know about this."

"He swore everyone to secrecy. He evidently had some apprehension of what was going to happen, but didn't want to dispirit his men. Father Stanisław, who was the prior then, recorded in the book of gifts that your great-grandfather gave him the sword he had received from King Stefan, asking the Virgin to accept it and pass it on to luckier hands. The chapter resolves that since you are about to do battle in defense of the faith, you should have it."

He was stunned. His great-grandfather's sabre hung on the wall of his bedroom at Żółkiew. A high price had been paid for that sword, to those who'd found it on the battlefield after the defeat at Cecora. His mother had often put her hand on it and said, "This will belong to the one of you who proves most worthy of it." But in the end, neither had received it. Marek was killed too early, while he, rejected by his mother, hadn't dared reach for it even after her death. Perhaps the sword they were giving him here was a sign from the grave? If so, what kind of a sign? Victory or death?

In the evening he felt a desire to make his confession. Papczyński obtained the keys to one of the empty chapels. The confession was brief; Sobieski mainly confessed to outbursts of anger. Father Stanisław knew his penitent well, and knew that underneath his hot temper lay kindness, with each explosion of rage immediately compensated for by generosity.

When the King finished, the friar prayed silently for a minute, then he said: "You told me that you were coming here to give your life to the Blessed Virgin and to tell Her that you were prepared to accept death if She would save Christendom and the Commonwealth Republic. Those were beautiful words, but incomplete. To give oneself to Our Lady, a man must subjugate his will to Hers. You say you want to win, then die. I know that life has become a heavy burden, but you must remember that She may choose to give you victory, yet spare your life. And what if this victory, which will be a blessing to others, spells suffering and bitterness for you? What if everything that torments your heart remains? Will you accept Her Will just the same, with humility in your heart?"

Sobieski was on his knees, panting heavily. Pain numbed his legs. Papczyński pointed to a bench.

"Sit down, Your Majesty," he said. "You see, She always does things in such a way as to save both the cause and the man. The cause is great and we must beg Her assistance, but we shouldn't be specific about what we offer Her. You want to give your life, the greatest thing you possess. But it is She who will say whether She wants you to live or die. Sometimes it's harder to live, and the harder a thing is the greater its value. You love your wife very much..."

He sighed.

"But everything between us seems to have gone wrong."

"The two of you have been united for eternity. You have assumed responsiblity for her."

"I still love her..."

"Love means more than just looking for the joy of loving. It also means putting up with one another. Only She knows how we can help the one we love."

The royal couple walked from their quarters to the chapel entrance behind a line of friars holding candles. Sobieski wore the tunic called the *zupan*, one made of white Venetian brocade fastened with jeweled golden buttons. Despite the heat, he had an expensive fur-lined cape thrown over his shoulders. Marysieńka wore an azure farthingale gown with French décolletage, and a golden shawl. A pearl clasp held her black curls in place. The children and the royal retinue also wore their finest clothes. The procession moved slowly and majestically, watched by the admiring crowd on the ramparts.

A fanfare signaled the uncovering of the Icon. The King rose from his chair and knelt on the faldstool; Marysieńka did the same. She also had confessed to her chaplain the previous night. The provincial came into the chapel to say Mass as the voice of the choir rose through the blue smoke of incense shrouding the Icon.

Sobieski lowered his head, pounded his chest with his fist and sighed deeply.

"Give us victory, My Lady, grant us Your help and salvation. As for me, do whatever You choose. I'll humbly accept Your Will, whether it's life or death. I know what I've been and what I am. Let me suffer for the grave sin both of us have committed."

He glanced at his wife, saw that she, too, was praying, then he raised his eyes to the Icon. Mary's dark face seemed burdened by the weight of Her crown, and he thought he saw suffering in Her eyes.

Suddenly a thought occured to him: "Any crown is a heavy burden. Instead of honoring Her, we have passed all responsibility on to Her. Seeking honor and glory for ourselves, we've left the toil to Her. But She has accepted it. I don't know why She loves us, yet She does love us, even if we repay Her with ingratitude and disloyalty. Papczyński is right: She does not look for the joy of loving. She puts up with us..."

Give us victory, he prayed, and let it be Your victory alone.

Once, on his way to the battle of Chocim, seeing no other way of persuading Hetman Pac not to pull out with the Lithuanian army, he had offered him supreme command. Later he could never understand why he'd done it. He'd been guided by some unfathomable instinct, alien to his glory-seeking nature. Now it occurred to him that this may have been Her prompting.

The Mass ended. Czechowicz left the altar to bless the replica of the Icon prepared for the King, then he approached Sobieski. Out of the crowd of Paulites stepped a friar carrying a sword in a jewel-studded shagreen sheath resting on a purple cushion.

The provincial announced: "Your Majesty, here is the sword that your great-grandfather placed in our treasury, asking the Blessed Virgin to put it in the hands that would conquer the heathen. We give it to you. Take it, go, and win!"

The friar knelt down and passed the sword to Sobieski. Greatly moved, he took it in silence and gazed at the magnificent Persian weapon which had been waiting for him over sixty years. Slowly, he slid it out of the sheath, then raised it high. The glittering steel shone blue in the candlelight.

"Thank you, Reverend Fathers," he said. "I'll use it against the enemies of the Cross. If the Blessed Virgin permits, it will secure victory.

But detach the pommel. I will take the sword, but not the hilt or sheath. Let the jewels stay at the feet of the Virgin of the Immaculate Conception, the One who gave us triumph and salvation. We mortals should only consider ourselves useless servants."

CHAPTER 7

CASIMIR PULASKI

The bridge was deserted, and the border that ran down the middle of the Liswarta River and separated Poland from Silesia, which had been seized by King Frederick of Prussia, was closed tight. On the pretext of protecting his country from an epidemic that raged in Poland in these closing years of the eighteenth century, Frederick had posted guards at all border crossings and placed outposts beyond the frontier.

Detachments of Prussian troops were camped on both sides of the river. Several soldiers sat under a crude shelter on a low rise near the bridge. They wore tricornered hats and short, powdered cues; with their uniforms buttoned to the neck they looked like wooden figures. They sprang to their feet when someone spotted two riders approaching the bridge from the direction of Częstochowa. The alarm bell sounded and the barrier at the bridge was lowered. A noncommissioned officer confronted the horsemen and demanded sternly: "Who are you?"

The riders wore old clothes, although one of them looked as though he might be a member of the gentry. His ill-fed horse betrayed good breeding, and the young, slightly-built man sat on his mount as if the two were one.

His complexion was dark and he sported a small black moustache. His eyes flashed. Tightly drawn lips showed impatience and readiness for any risk. Instead of answering the question, he produced an official-looking paper and passed it over the barrier without a word.

The Prussian read it carefully, inspected the pair, nodded his head, growled *"Stimmt!"* and signaled to raise the bar. The riders crossed the bridge onto Silesian soil.

"Those soldiers are Poles," the young nobleman's companion said once they were on the other side. "I'm sure we could persuade them to go with us."

"Not now."

The distance from Lisy to Lubliniec was six miles. They rode prudently, alternately prodding the tired horses into a canter then letting them walk. The September sun gently stroked the wall of trees along the road. Autumn was in the air. The scent of heather and mushrooms filled the forest.

They avoided the center of town, reached the palace by a series of side streets. Bypassing the main gate, they entered through the backyard.

"Hey!" the nobleman shouted to a moustached man wearing a long-sleeved vest, who looked like the overseer and stood with his legs astride counting carts as they came from the fields. "Come here!"

The man walked over unhurriedly.

"What do you want, gentlemen?"

"Go to Her Ladyship the Duchess and tell her that I have arrived," he said as if issuing a military command.

"You want to see the Duchess?"

"That's right, and be quick about it. We've got little time."

"And who are you?"

"Just say the squire of Winiary is here, and don't get the whole palace in an uproar. Tell the chambermaid, no one else."

The overseer left, turning around several times to get another look at the strange visitor. He came back running and shouting: "Her Ladyship is waiting for you, sir. Come, I'll show you the way."

The palace was fairly small and far from luxurious. It had been rented by Lubomirski, the lord of Kolbuszowa. After some recent ill-advised political moves he'd decided to withdraw into Prussian territory, since he held the rank of a Prussian general. He had recently been joined by his niece, the Duchess Krasińska. The parlor into which a maid ushered the visitor was cramped, and the gilded furniture was slightly the worse for wear.

A door opened and the Duchess walked quickly into the room. As always, the sight of her captivated Pulaski. Ten years earlier, when Prince Karol, Duke of Courland, and Franciszka Krasińska were married secretly, she was considered the greatest beauty in the country. Modestly dressed to receive her caller, with barely a hint of rouge on her face, which had retained a natural girlish charm, she was still exceedingly beautiful.

"Casimir Pulaski!" she cried. Her hands touched his shoulders. He bowed in a familiar manner. "How wonderful to see you! I've been waiting impatiently ever since you sent word that you'd be coming here."

"I'm at your command, my Lady."

"Ah, at my command," she laughed. "Who would command you now, Casimir? You're the one who gives orders. As an old friend I can only advise you. Please sit down. I haven't seen you for such a long time – you know you've changed? When you were in my husband's entourage you were an unassuming boy, but now you're said to be one of the best commanders that the Confederates have."

"I remain your servant, Your Grace."

"You must tell me about your victories and your plans. We'll have coffee in a minute, later we'll have dinner. But you've got so much to tell me... Will you be going back at once?"

"This evening."

"Did you have any trouble at the border?"

"None at all."

"The officers here are very kind. I told them I wished to see the steward of my estate." Her laughter came in a trill. "They issued the permit even though they've been ordered to ward off this epidemic as if it were the plague itself."

"It's not as bad as they say, but the Prussian king finds it a convenient excuse for closing his borders against us."

A servant brought in the coffee. The Duchess dismissed him and poured her guest a cup.

"Drink your coffee and tell me everything. From the beginning. You were captured?"

"Yes, after the fall of Berdyczów. I wouldn't have surrendered it if it hadn't been for the disobedience of my troops."

"And they freed you after you swore you wouldn't fight again?"

"Yes, but I broke that promise. I had every right to do so."

"Absolutely," she assured him, like a priest granting absolution. "They don't keep theirs either."

"So I joined my father and brothers in Moldavia, with all the others. But the Turks were in no hurry to start a war and we decided to return to Poland and fight. We took Żwaniec and launched attacks from there, then Potocki had sent envoys to my father inviting him for talks. It was a trick. He never returned. They handed him over to the Turks as a traitor."

His words hissed through clenched teeth.

"How horrible," she sighed. "I don't understand Potocki at all, behaving like that when the Commonwealth needs the cooperation of everyone! My uncle" – she called the Bishop of Kamieniec uncle although the relationship was rather distant – "often said that your father and that Carmelite friar were the real driving force among the confederates at Bar."

Pulaski bit his lips angrily at the memory. Two years earlier, his father and the Carmelite friar Marek had been like men possessed by a mystical zeal in their denunciation of Poland's weak king, Stanisław Poniatowski, and his powerful mistress, the Empress of Russia. They had evoked a crusading spirit among the angry gentry that gathered in the old fortress of Bar to protest continuing Russian influence and encroachments. The friar had made gloomy prophecies, likening them to shipwrecked mariners who clung to the boards of a sinking ship, and crying out that the Mother of God would forsake the Polish crown unless they took arms. Old Pulaski, with holy gorgets, scapulars, and rosaries hanging from his robes, was equally loud in denouncing the new Russian-sponsored measures that were weakening the country. Deeply offended by Repnin, Catherine's ambassador in Warsaw, the old man cried out for vengeance, although he never revealed what had happened between him and the arrogant Russian. He sacrificed everything he owned and longed for battle, wanting to recruit God, the Virgin Mary, and all the saints to fight in his cause.

His near-religious ardor infected his sons. During midnight Mass on Christmas Eve, the three young men took a solemn vow that they'd erect a huge statue in honor of Our Lady at Jasna Góra once their war had been won. The statue would be known as Our Lady the Victorious, and it would strike terror in the hearts of all future enemies.

Then their fervor waned.

Franciszek had been the first to fall from grace. Riding out to join the Confederates, he took his mistress with him and hid her among his troops. Dressed like a man, Dorota rode in battle with Franciszek's soldiers, knew how to wield a saber and shoot a pistol. He showed her to his two brothers only after their fierce old father was dead; the old man would never have allowed such madness.

Poor Franciszek. But it had been he who had shielded Casimir with his body when Russian troops under the German general Rönne ambushed them near Włodawa. Franciszek and Dorota had both died in that battle. Casimir had escaped.

The youngest brother, Antoni, had been captured and carried off to Russia some time before that. Rumor had it that he had been exiled to Kazań. With their betrayed father dead in a Turkish prison, Casimir was alone as the confederates' commander. Besieged in the doomed trenches of the Holy Trinity, he managed to break out at night and led his troops to safety across the frozen Dniester River. Once they were safe, he returned to Polish territory across the snowbound Carpathians and kindled a new rebellion in Lithuania.

The war had given him a reputation as one of the best, most active, and inventive confederate leaders. Restless and bursting with ideas, he attacked the enemy wherever he could find them. But the Estates General, the political arm of the insurrection which had taken shelter in the territories of the old Holy Roman Empire, in the town of Prešov, didn't trust Pulaski. They thought him too ambitious and too difficult to control. They preferred older, steadier men, even though the German Emperor himself praised Pulaski's valor.

Loved by his men in battle, Pulaski couldn't win the favor of the strategists. When the French Colonel Dumouriez came to Prešov to be the confederates' military advisor, Pulaski quarreled bitterly with him. Short and skinny, the Frenchman had been awaited like a Messiah, but he acted more like a commander-in-chief than a military adviser. He shouted and swaggered among the exiled Poles, whom he insulted with his unconcealed dislike and contempt. It took an intervention by the Council of War to induce Pulaski to listen to the Frenchman's battle plans which, in the young commander's view, were doomed to disaster. Dumouriez had never been to Poland. His plans were made according to maps, and with no notion of hit-and-run fighting. He had no use for cavalry; according to him, the Poles were to sell their horses and equip infantry regiments which would capture forts and then sit in them, waiting for the enemy. Given a troop of French engineers, Pulaski was ordered to return to Poland, capture the town of Lanckorona and turn it into a fort.

Back with his troops, Pulaski dismissed the Frenchman's strategy as of little practical value for the war in Poland. He was a cavalryman. Fighting meant movement to him. Faced by the regular armies of the Russian Empire, his victories depended on surprise, harassment and ambush. He left his borrowed engineers at Lanckorona and joined forces with another confederate commander, General Walewski, with whom he tried to take the Wawel Castle in Cracow. The attack failed, but Pulaski succeeded in winning over to the confederates' side a regiment of the King's Dragoon Guards that had been stationed in a Cracow suburb. With these dragoons, who could be used as infantry to garrison forts, Pulaski's force rose to a thousand men and he devised a plan to seize a fortress for use as a base. "Jasna Góra is better than Lanckorona," he told Walewski, who promptly agreed.

These were the memories that passed through his mind as he listened to the beautiful Franciszka. She, knowing about the destruction of his family, took his mood for personal sadness.

"So now you're all alone?" Franciszka asked.

"Yes."

"Poor boy. And you haven't found love yet?" She touched Pulaski's hand.

"My loves are my horse, my sword and my battles."

"And playing faro?" she joked.

"Sure, I like to gamble."

"You always did. There's only one thing you haven't gambled with..." changing her tone, she mentioned another confederate commander. "Have you seen Zaremba?"

"Yes."

"He was here, you know, and he made a very good impression. You could tell he's an experienced soldier. After Malczewski's defeats, all of the Wielkopolska region recognized him as its military leader. It's occured to me that if you two worked together..."

"Nothing would come of it."

"Why?"

"We differ in everything. I won't fight under his command, and he thinks too much of himself to fight under mine."

"You're younger," she began persuasively.

"No!" he said, cutting her off sharply. After a pause, he went on. "Zaremba is a good soldier, I admit. His men are well trained and disciplined, but not as eager to fight as mine. And he's a procrastinator."

She sat quietly for a while, toying with her pretty fingers.

"You worry me, Casimir," she said. "Promise me that you'll try to agree with Zaremba. I'm so eager to see you working together. Please try, really."

"For Your Grace I'll do everything I can."

She brightened at once.

"And now listen to me, *mon cher*. You said you came to hear my commands? Fine. You see, my uncle and I have great plans for you."

"What does that mean, my lady?"

"You've met Colonel Dumouriez. I know, you don't have to tell me, he's not the nicest person on earth. But he's French, and uncle keeps saying that Poland can only be saved by God, France, and Turkey. The Turks have disappointed us so far, but France is the most important. If France gives you advice, you'd do best to follow it. The Emperor and the Prussian king will do anything King Louis asks. And Louis also has influence with the Turks, who can threaten Russia and force Empress Catherine to step back from Poland. With her support gone, our own pitiful King will have to abdicate."

He listened in silence. When she paused he said: "For the time being we've got to fight. That Dumouriez is just a clown."

"But he was sent by the King of France, and his view of the situation will determine how much assistance Louis gives us. Under him, the

Confederation's detachments will be fused into an army and that army shall be headed by... Guess who?"

Pulaski said he didn't know.

"My husband, Karol. The Bishop decided it, but I must tell you I'm afraid. I know that's the way it has to be, but... Your army is so disorderly and undisciplined, Dumouriez says all it can do is turn tail."

"He said that?" Pulaski boiled with rage.

"I know that's not always the case," she assured him.

"That's why I think you should be at Karol's side. He admires you. He's never forgotten you."

As a boy Pulaski had been a royal page, thanks to his father's efforts, and spent half a year at court. Nothing interesting happened there, except that he met the Duchess. Even then his eyes had followed her. The fascination had remained, as Franciszka knew full well. She was too much in love with her husband to reciprocate, but she didn't spare her young admirer her help. What little trust the confederated nobles had recently begun to have in him, he owed to Krasińska.

"If the Duke takes supreme command I'll report to him immediately and put my skills and men at his service," he declared.

"That's just what I expected from you!" she exclaimed, clapping her hands. "Now if you'd agree to settle your dispute with Zaremba..."

"I'll do what I can. I'll propose joint operations. Maybe it'll be easier to reach agreement now that I hold Jasna Góra."

"Ah, yes. We haven't talked about that yet."

"Dumouriez doesn't understand: it's a much more important fortress than Lanckorona, and fairly well armed, too. I've ordered the engineers to reinforce it."

"Did you have any trouble taking it?" she asked.

"I would have, if it hadn't been for a ruse. The monks won't let anybody in, but Durini, the papal envoy, was in the monastery, so I went up to the gate and asked to attend Mass, which he was saying."

"Durini is on our side. He made a speech, and said the Poles were ready to shed their blood in defense of the faith."

"My father mentioned that speech... I asked Durini to bless my detachment, camped below the walls. He came the next day. Then I attended another Mass with my officers and chaplain. The monks didn't dare refuse us admission, seeing how friendly I was with the Nuncio, but the garrison soldiers wouldn't allow us in. They're still terrified of Drewitz, who'd been there before us, demanded money and burned some farms. Walewski spotted a bread cart, and when the gate opened for it my men stormed inside."

"For God's sake, Casimir! What did the Nuncio say? And the Prior?"

"The Nucio murmured something and pretended to be indignant, but I'm sure he was pleased. Anyway, he left shortly afterwards. Provincial Lubojeński and Prior Pafnucy began to weep and wail, especially when I ordered them to hand over the keys to the arsenal. I said I'd taken the fortress in the name of the Confederation, I was assuming command, and would tolerate no dissent." He leaned forward. "Do you know what we found in the arsenal? Almost a hundred and fifty cannon, over forty made of bronze, all in good working order. And countless muskets, Prussian carbines, harquebuses and mortars. The friars had collected them over the years. They even have their own powder stores and a cannonball foundry. We could defend the monastery for months. And that muttonhead Dumouriez –"

"*Fi donc*, Casimir. What language!"

"I'm sorry, Your Ladyship. Anyway, I hold the fortress now and I'm not going to give it up. I just need one favor."

"Ask."

"Have the council of the Confederation appoint me commander of Jasna Góra. I don't want to serve under anyone."

"You want to be free as a bird forever, don't you? But I don't know if you're aware of plans to move the leadership of the uprising to Poland with Jasna Góra as its headquarters. The shrine is so revered no one would dare attack it."

"If that happens I'll guarantee the safety of our leaders, but Dumouriez wouldn't even hear about Jasna Góra."

"I'll do everything in my power to help you, and always will. I'm counting on you when Karol becomes Supreme Commander."

"Where's the Prince now?"

"In Paris. I'm sure Louis will recognize his value and treat him well. When we win, Stanisław Poniatowski will have to abdicate. Believe me Casimir, I wish you all the best. Now let's have dinner, there're still so many things you must tell me..."

Pulaski hurried back to Jasna Góra at the end of October and the next few weeks saw considerable fighting. The Commander didn't wait for the enemy, but, as he'd promised, he went out looking for battle. Keeping his word to Franciszka, he began joint operations with Zaremba and together they crushed both Drewitz and Rönne.

Drewitz was the most dangerous of all the Russian Empress' commanders fighting the confederates. The German Protestant had left Frederick's army to serve Catherine, and although he was an excellent soldier he was also cruel and rapacious and had smashed dozens of confederate detachments. When he trapped the enemy he promised freedom, only to capture them once they surrendered. He burned and robbed manors, hanged those owners suspected of aiding the confederates, and let his soldiers rape the women. He extorted money and pocketed huge sums himself. He aroused fear everywhere. Villagers fled into the woods, the gentry deserted their mansions or humiliated themselves at his feet.

Rönne, a German like Drewitz and an infamous bandit in his own right, was an incomparably less able commander. Pulaski remembered that it had been Rönne who destroyed his unit at Włodawa, and that one of his officers, Major Castelli, had killed Franciszek and Dorota. He angrily sought revenge but Zaremba forestalled him, attacking Castelli's unit near Piotrków, routing it, and killing Castelli himself.

The collaboration with Zaremba ended quickly. The two men were of dissimilar character and had different approaches to warfare. Zaremba was a prudent, experienced officer who believed that war did not consist of endless skirmishes, he wanted to strengthen his position in Wielkopolska and set out to conquer Poznań. Pulaski, meanwhile, returned to Częstochowa, summoned by a letter from Zieliński, the Marshal of Płock, who wrote that Drewitz was in the vicinity of the monastery again and, worse still, that he might have established contact with officers from the former garrison, or even with the Paulistes themselves.

When he reached Jasna Góra, Pulaski noted with satisfaction that the French engineers, de la Serre and d'Etannion, hadn't wasted time. The ramparts and walls had been repaired, the moat dredged, and a stockade built in front of it. As requested, they had also constructed small redoubts on the approaches to keep the enemy at a distance.

Meanwhile a betrayal had been in the making, but at the last minute one of the conspirators had broken down and exposed the plot and his partners in treason; four officers and a monk had promised Drewitz that they would open the gates for him. Pulaski immediately convened a court martial which passed death sentences on the traitors and he ordered the sentences carried out. Thanks to the discovery of the plot, the defenders let Drewitz approach the walls at night and, when his troops were about to march inside, opened fire. Drewitz suffered heavy losses and withdrew into the woods.

The provincial and the prior protested the imprisonment of the Paulite implicated in the conspiracy. Pulaski suspected that the friar had been involved on the prior's behalf, and he responded by ordering the monks out of the monastery. After repeated pleas from Zieliński, Pulaski changed his mind and confined them to one corridor.

Drewitz disappeared, but supposedly was gathering his forces for a fresh assault. The news from Warsaw was that the King and Prince Volkonsky, the Empress' new ambassador, had agreed that Jasna Góra would not be attacked. But Drewitz's corps commander, General Weymar, wanted to give his favorite officer the opportunity for revenge. Although Drewitz boasted he would occupy the "comical fortress" within three hours, he wisely did not move without heavy artillery. The Duchess Krasińska wrote that Prussian cannon and mortars were arriving in Lubliniec, reportedly on loan to Drewitz, confirming Pulaski's fears that a formidable opponent would soon appear at the walls of Jasna Góra.

By mid–December another enemy had arrived and laid siege: an early winter reinforced by bitter cold. After years of fighting, Pulaski's troops were in rags. Few of the men had a decent pair of boots, and their Commander wore a short, threadbare hussar's coat. Busy preparing their defenses, the soldiers had failed to collect wood and the monastery's fuel supply was dangerously low. One freezing morning Pulaski's adjutant told him that the prior wished to see him.

"What does he want?"

"He didn't say."

"Very well. Bring him to the library."

The door opened and two friars entered, bowing deeply.

"Praise be to Jesus Christ."

"Forever and ever. Come in, Fathers, and warm yourselves by the fire."

They advanced shyly. The passionate young Commander inspired awe in them. Not long ago it had looked as though he was going to have them all hanged. Now they were encouraged by Pulaski's friendly gesture.

"Sit down," he said. "How are things? We haven't talked for a long time."

The prior, Father Pafnucy Brzeziński, a timid man with a tendency to weep at the first sign of difficulty, had been selected to negotiate with Pulaski because the Order's provincial was unyielding and his exchanges with the young Marshal of Łomża instantly developed into quarrels.

"We haven't seen you, Sir," he said, "because you ordered us locked up."

"You wanted to turn the monastery over to Drewitz. I couldn't let that happen."

"We didn't let him in in May, although he made horrible threats. He burned our estate at Gnaszyn. The convent nearly went up in smoke as well. We're afraid of him and don't want him in the monastery – he's a Lutheran! But we're not guilty of your charge, sir."

"You didn't want to let me in either."

The prior gestured helplessly and looked to his companion for assistance. The other monk was an old man with a dry, wrinkled, ascetic face.

"We were told," he began, "that the King guarantees our security if we let no one inside the walls... But things have turned out differently."

"King Stanisław may promise safety, but he can't deliver it. The Russians are doing whatever they want and Drewitz doesn't even obey Catherine's ambassador. I'm convinced he'll attack the monastery any day now. Then it'll be me, not the King, who guarantees your security!"

The prior did not seem appeased. "We've heard that Drewitz got cannon from the Prussians, and he wouldn't be planning to attack if you weren't here."

"Are you saying that the safety of your monastery is more important than the war? Than tyrannical attempts to dictate to a free nation? Than threats to the truths of the Catholic faith?" Pułaski spoke rapid-fire, swallowing his words as he always did when he couldn't control his anger.

The tone of Pulaski's voice terrified the prior. He sat mute, clasping his hands as if in prayer. The other friar spoke for him.

"It's not only our own safety that's at stake, sir. The war is being fought over many issues. It's not easy for a servant of God to decide which side to choose. We judge people not by their words, but their deeds. Please don't be angry at what I'm going to say, but we're not convinced that those who set up the Confederation are completely right while those supporting the King and the Czartoryskis are totally wrong."

"Don't you see, Father? Our King is in the pay of Moscow!" Pulaski was getting increasingly irritated. "What's your name?"

"Gotwald Olaw. I'm from Silesia. I've been the prior's deputy for some time now."

"And you think, Father, that –"

"I think, sir, that it's our duty to guard the miraculous icon. That's the most important thing to us."

"Yet Father Kordecki pushed his fears aside and fought instead. His example inspired the whole nation."

"Before Kordecki decided to fight, he prayed. Evidently that was what the Madonna told him to do. And you, sir, have you prayed for divine inspiration?"

Pulaski did not answer at once. He stared at the friar in surprise.

"We went into battle in the name of God and the Blessed Virgin," he said a moment later. "Do you think that Our Lady doesn't want the faith to triumph?"

"Maybe She wants it to triumph in our hearts first."

"Unless we want take up arms, we'll become slaves!"

"God, the Father, has various ways of opening people's hearts. If necessary, He may resort to the paternal cane to administer justice."

The conversation broke off. Pulaski sat hunched, gazing at the glowing logs. The muscles twitched on his weatherbeaten cheeks. The prior looked at his companion with growing terror.

"So what do you want?" Pulaski asked finally.

"As I said," Father Pafnucy resumed, "we have no doubt that Drewitz will be here soon. If he takes the monastery he'll loot the treasury and desecrate the Icon."

"First he has to take it," Pulaski said firmly.

"We have to be prepared for the eventuality. He has the men and he has the artillery. And what happens then? That's why we've come to request –"

"Request what?"

"Your permission to take the Icon away and to hide our treasures."

"Take it where?"

"Głogów, where it was when the Swedes attacked Jasna Góra."

"So the Madonna wasn't here then?"

"Not the Icon," Father Gotwald explained. "But She is always here. We can't associate Her presence with any picture, even the holiest one. The Icon could disappear, the monastery could be destroyed, yet She would remain among us."

Pulaski looked straight into the friar's blue eyes, then lowered his head and, lost in thought, fixed his eyes on the flames. The room was silent.

"Your request takes me by surprise," he said at last. "But I must deny it. If the soldiers found out that the Icon had disappeared they wouldn't have much heart for battle. It's important to them, perhaps the most important thing. My father and I began our struggle by giving ourselves to the Blessed Virgin, and I want to fight in Her defense. Your treasures don't interest me. What I owned once, I've already lost. And you can be sure that if you took your treasures to Prešov, you'd never see them again. Our Estates Generals need money and wouldn't hesitate to help themselves. Don't move anything that belongs to Our Lady. Seal it and leave it."

He banged his fist on the mantelpiece, adding weight to his decision. The friars looked at one another, then got up and bowed.

Father Gotwald said: "Sir, you're taking a great responsibility by putting the Holy Icon at risk. We'll pray that the Blessed Virgin watches over you. You've been daring, but then She loves those who dare."

That night Pulaski went to the chapel. He had not been there since his arrival, there'd been too much to attend to and he was on the move all the time. The friars had already finished their prayers and left. At the far end of the room a group of pilgrims from Moravia were standing or kneeling behind the grille. They'd arrived that morning and Pulaski had allowed them inside, as there had been no new reports of impending danger from the numerous patrols spread around the countryside. The Icon was about to be covered, but the prior noticed Pulaski enter and he ordered the painting kept uncovered a while longer.

The chapel was silent. The candle flames, undisturbed by any gust of wind, stood motionless like the tips of burning lances. The blackness of ebony, illuminated by silver ornaments, surrounded the Icon like a starlit night. In front of the altar was a broad antependium and, in the center, the shrine of Jasna Góra itself. Above were the symbols of authority: royal crowns, bishops' miters, cardinals' hats, and a papal tiara. All of this seemed to prostrate itself before Our Lady, who had chosen this small hilltop monastery for Her residence.

As he looked at the silver bas-relief he realized that for some time he had been consumed by a hidden anxiety which he'd never been able to articulate, not even to himself. But now this anxiety revealed itself and emerged like a mysterious foreign object breaking the surface of a stormy sea, which one tries to identify in vain until at last the waves throw it onto the shore. The monk was right: he had accepted a terrible responsibilty. Was it too bold of him to be so sure that he could protect this priceless relic?

For three years he had fought a personal, almost private war with Drewitz. They had even talked to each other once: trusting in Polish chivalry, Drewitz had visited him at his quarters. Fortunes changed regularly in this war of theirs. The combatants got so carried away at times that they forgot the cause for which they were fighting. Recently, Drewitz had suffered a series of defeats that surely must have made him furious. He would do everything in his power to capture Jasna Góra. Frederick had given him infallible artillery; if he took the monastery he would give no thought to the sanctity of the place. He was not a Russian – the Russians showed respect for religious shrines, especially those dedicated to the Immaculate Virgin. To Drewitz this would be just another objective in which a hated enemy had taken refuge.

Pulaski realized that the fortress was more than that – it was the mounting for a priceless gem. Until then he had taken it for granted that in waging a struggle that he was absolutely certain was right, he had the power of almighty God on his side. The long years of war had convinced him, however, that despite this power the outcome was still uncertain. Possibly, given Turkey's recent defeats, it was now even less certain. What had become of the foreign support that Bishop Krasiński put so much faith in? What was the use of Dumouriez's mission if he wanted to fight only according to his own methods and hated the Poles? The Estates Generals were being torn apart by disputes: some wanted to seek agreement with the King, others saw the toppling of Catherine's protege as the most important thing on earth. And what was left of his father's noble intentions at Bar?

Who remembered noble intentions after three years of a bloody war? Already some confederates preferred to have unintelligible Masonic anagrams written on their banners instead of the name of Our Lady!

He looked at the picture. The Madonna's eyes were serene, yet somewhat stern. He knew that face well. His canoness sister had once given him a gorget which he wore on his chest during the day and at night kept under his pillow. One day the chain broke and the gorget was lost; he could not calm down. It was as if the person dearest to him had deserted and all that remained was to shoot himself in the head or to run away. Fortunately, the gorget was found and he immediately regained his self-assurance. He ordered a stronger chain made and promised the goldsmith that he'd hang him if it broke.

Yet this face was not the same as the one on his gorget: it seemed to be alive. The scarred cheek actually seemed to give Her life. This was a real person, someone he'd involved in his own private war.

The sense of responsibility became unbearable. Compared to it the showdown with Drewitz was a mere trifle. Something else, something enormous, hovered on the horizon.

In the grey predawn of the last day of the year, Drewitz and some four thousand men reached the foot of Jasna Góra after a very cautious and deliberate approach. The vast majority of his corps were cavalry, supported by dragoons, cuirassiers, and Cossacks. Virtually all of the officers were German. In addition to his own artillery, he fielded sixteen huge cannon and four heavy mortars loaned by the Prussians together with their crews. Drewitz was prepared to take the mountain, or level it.

Pulaski led his cavalry out of the fortress to meet his old enemy, chased a few Cossack patrols roaming the nearby hills, and then fell upon the slow-moving column like a hungry hawk. He attacked it from the rear, from the front, harassed it, and forced it to halt. This was his kind of warfare and he was a master of it: fearless, unpredictable, seemingly everywhere at once. When Drewitz deployed his artillery, Pulaski dispersed – only to resume the attack once the column had reformed and was on the move again.

Several hours later the confederate cavalry withdrew and Drewitz brought his troops up through the streets of Old Częstochowa. Retreating under a barrage of artillery fire from the redoubts, the enemy commander pulled his troops out of range and did not mount a full scale attack until the following morning. His sharpshooters advanced across the orchards and gardens of the Old City on the lower slopes of the hill. Pulaski's cavalry attacked at once, was repelled, but succeeded in leading Drewitz within range of the cannon placed at St. Jacob's church. Despite this temporary success, the attack pressed forward, forcing Pulaski to withdraw the guns and abandon the position. Other enemy units took the Paulite novitiate at St. Barbara's church and threatened to cut off the troops manning the redoubt; the remaining force took Częstochowa. Fearing they'd reach the monastery walls, Pulaski ordered the settlement put to the torch, and the fortifications guarding the approaches to Jasna Góra were abandoned. Drewitz set up his headquarters beside St. Barbara's and immediately ordered trenches dug. The terrified townspeople worked feverishly through the night and at dawn the cannon were in position, their huge mouths trained on the fortress.

A heavy bombardement lasted throughout the day, yet the monastery suffered only minor damage, a surprising fact given the Prussian artillery's reputation of reliability. That evening, after a full day's shelling, an officer despatched by Drewitz appeared at the monastery gate with a letter for the Commander. He was led into the fortress blindfolded and taken to Pulaski who was in the library.

"Good Sir," Drewitz wrote, "I call on you to surrender before you are destroyed. Obey my demand, and I promise to intercede with Her Majesty the Empress on your behalf. She may forgive your crimes and perhaps even take you into her service. If you do not surrender, my yagers will capture the fortress and you will all face serious punishment; you most of all, for breaking the vow you made in Berdyczów. Give me your immediate reply."

Pulaski crumpled the letter and hurled it to the floor.

"What's your name, soldier?"

"Friedrich Ungern, captain of cuirassiers."

"You speak Polish?"

"*Nemnozhko.* But I prefer German."

"I'm not going to talk to you in either German or Russian, and I won't reply to that snake's letter. It's not worth the paper. Listen carefully now, and tell this to Drewitz: Everybody knows who it really is that doesn't keep his word. We remember who promises freedom in return for surrender and then drives those who've believed him off in shackles. Or who deserted his king and sold himself to another monarch for loot. So he has no business talking to me about broken vows, and I'm not interested in surrender. Tell him that if he sends another idiot with such an offer I'll have the man hanged from the gates. Understand?"

"*Habs' verstanden.*"

"Then get the hell out of here. And don't show your face here again!"

The following day was Christmas Eve in the Orthodox Church, but neither side let up their artillery barrage. A fierce exchange went on all day and again the Prussian artillery failed to cause any major damage to the stronghold.

In the evening, Pulaski summoned his officers.

"Gentlemen," he announced, "I've decided to teach Drewitz a lesson tonight. We'll raid the trenches opposite the convent gate, they're giving us the most trouble. We'll spike his guns and cut his men to pieces. I need sixty hussars and Mirów cavalrymen. Only volunteers. Pick the best. They should be well clothed, it's freezing outside. Ask those who aren't going to give their coats and boots to those who are. When we've killed the enemy we'll have plenty. Make each man a wide straw belt for easy identification in the darkness, and take spikes and hammers with you. We'll leave after midnight, in three groups. Captain Repp will lead the first, Captain Czyżewski the second, and I'll take the third. Czyżewski will head straight for the trenches and Repp's group will attack from the rear, from the direction of Częstochowa. I'll provide cover from St. Barbara's. Once we're in the trenches, have the soldiers yell: 'Zaremba! Zaremba!' Drewitz will think it's Zaremba, coming to help us."

"It wouldn't be a bad idea if he did," one of the officers said. "Catching Drewitz in a crossfire, now, that would be something!"

"He won't come because he doesn't want to," Pulaski said. "His ego won't permit it. But we"ll manage without him."

Preparations for the raid began enthusiastically. There was no shortage of volunteers; clothing presented the worst problem. In order to give reasonable protection to the soldiers going on the sortie, several dozen men stripped down to their shirts. The troops took no firearms, only swords, axes and spears. The officers stuck pistols behind their belts.

The raiding party gathered at a hidden gate in the Lubomirski bastion. The night was misty, and moonlight seemed to hang in the air as it filtered through the clouds. A thin coat of snow glittered on the ground. The cold was unbearable. As they filed through the gate, the soldiers' breaths formed clouds of steam. Pulaski ordered them to walk softly: the noise of feet scuffling on the frozen earth carried a long way in the stillness.

The party split into three sections as planned and crept toward the trenches. Ahead of them nothing moved, and the only sound was the singing in St. Barbara's church. They crawled the last fifty yards on their bellies and stopped within a few feet of the ditch. The voices in the church droned on. Spread out in an irregular line, the men looked like logs that had rolled off a passing cart.

A pistol shot exploded the peaceful silence and at Pulaski's signal the men swarmed over the gun battery from all sides, shouting: "Zaremba! Death! Zaremba!" Totally surprised, half asleep, the enemy offered virtually no resistance. The Poles slashed with swords, hacked with axes, and smashed with cudgels. They grabbed weapons and coats from their dying victims. During the melee long spikes were driven into the cannon vents, rendering them useless.

Every position was in an uproar. Trumpets sounded and drums rolled. Drewitz was too experienced a commander to surrender to blind panic; men immediately began pouring out of the church and the counterattack formed.

Pulaski had anticipated the move. While Repp and Czyżewski withdrew toward the stockade, Pulaski's group fought a hand-to-hand delaying action. Several hussars fell and the General signaled retreat, bringing up the rear and using his saber to hold off an infantryman wielding a long bayonet. He made a quick turn, caught his spur on something, lost his balance and fell to the ground. The soldier raised his carbine over his head and pointed the bayonet downward. Pulaski instinctively found the pistol under his belt, yanked it out, and fired.

The soldier fell.

Pulaski jumped to his feet and ran.

A head count showed only five men missing. Several wounded had been carried to safety by their comrades. In spite of the late hour, the triumphant commander ordered everyone into the chapel for a thanksgiving service. The chaplain said Mass. The Paulites stood along the walls, participating in the prayers.

Neither side fired a shot the following day. Observed from the monastery walls, Drewitz's troops were constantly on the move despite the holiday.

"I'm sure he's looking for Zaremba," Pulaski said, surveying the perimeter through a telescope. "We scared the hell out of him."

"We finished off quite a few of his men last night, too," Zawoyski, Pulaski's deputy, added. "They keep hauling the bodies away. I've already counted over fifty. What a fine Christmas they had, eh?"

"Let them blame that heretic. I wouldn't have attacked on Christmas Eve if it hadn't been for Drewitz."

For several days the mountain peak reverberated with the echoes of an almost continuous cannonade. Pulaski, unpredictable as the wind, used the artillery exchange as cover for another sortie. But the enemy was on the alert now and the Poles suffered heavy casualties. On January 10 the bombardment ceased and there were obvious signs of a major regroupment outside the fortress walls.

Pulaski became convinced that Drewitz was about to storm the monastery in a final, all-out effort to capture it. The Prussian guns had proved totally ineffective; most of the cannonballs overshot their targets. Drewitz had probably realized that if his operation, which had been launched against the ambassador's wishes, failed, he was in a great deal of trouble.

Pulaski ordered preparations to repel the attackers. Massive logs, rocks, and baskets of broken glass were piled on the ramparts. Great stocks of cannonballs and carts full of black powder stood by the guns. Straw wreaths were soaked in tar. While these preparations were in progress, religious music was played which could be heard beyond the Warta River. This irritated Drewitz and played on his nerves, so he ordered to attack. Every time he fired, Pulaski ordered to fire. The soldiers on the ramparts remarked that it was as though a bullet chased a bullet. This duel lasted till dusk. Commotions could be heard on the redoubts, therefore Pulaski permitted only part of the corps to rest.

The attack began at two in the morning, with the main strike coming from the direction of St. Roch church and centering on the stretch of walls between the Lubomirski and Szaniawski bastions. Drewitz committed almost all his men at once. The infantry and dismounted cavalrymen were preceded by hundreds of peasants rounded up from neighboring villages, who carried bridging supplies and five long ladders. The monastery cannon showered the attackers with grapeshot, scything down the front ranks, but the assault continued. The enemy reached the stockade, then crossed it. The peasants dropped brushwood into the shallow moat and their bodies fell on top of it as the deadly rain of bullets took a heavy toll.

When the storming party had crossed the moat and reached the walls, it was greeted by an avalanche of logs, glass, and stones. Pulaski's men poured down boiling tar and lit the straw wreaths, which they hung on long poles and threw on the milling crowd below. Ladders were placed against the wall, but they were too short and were easily pushed away.

The attack disintegrated. The invaders ran back through the moat and then withdrew behind the stockade. The battle had lasted less than an hour.

At daybreak it was possible to judge the magnitude of the victory. The moat was filled with the dead and the dying, the majority of them peasants. The confederates went down to gather weapons and clothing from the dead, and the wounded were carried to the far side of the stockade so Drewitz's men could collect them. One badly wounded cuirassier officer was taken into the fort, but he died minutes later.

Once again Pulaski ordered a service of thanksgiving. This time the friars took part; it was the day of their patron, St. Paul the Hermit. A procession with music circled the ramparts and cannon fired in celebration.

Drewitz abandoned the siege abruptly. A rumor reached the monastery that he'd been ordered to return at once to Cracow, which was allegedly threatened by the Confederates. Others claimed that the Prussians had demanded the return of their cannon. Still others maintained that Drewitz had been ordered to surrender his command and explain why he'd marched on Jasna Góra.

Several months after the siege, Pulaski received a letter from Franciszka.

"Dear Casimir," the Duchess wrote, "the echoes of your victory over

Drewitz can still be heard. The Prussian gunners wounded in the battle now praise your valor. Drewitz has been utterly disgraced. Not only has he been stripped of his command, but he's been discharged from the Russian army altogether. Hardly surprising: Suvorov charged him with maliciously refusing to come to his assistance at Lanckorona. Drewitz wanted to return to King Frederick's army, but his offer was turned down. The King told him that he had no use for an officer whose assault ladders had been hurled down by Our Lady Herself.

"After this pleasant news, I have news of another kind. Colonel Dumouriez is still against you, and Zaremba complains as well. The Colonel refers to you as a mad adventurer, while Zaremba has written to the Estates General that he can't collaborate with you because you're too eager to fight, and that you'd risk the lives of a hundred soldiers to kill just one enemy. Ah, *mon cher*, how I wanted you to come to some arrangement with Zaremba. You two are regarded as the best commanders of the Confederation, and you lose out in all disputes with him.

"Prince Karol is in Dresden now and it seems he won't assume supreme command as we'd planned earlier. Dumouriez is devising grand new schemes all the time, but his position has weakened since his protector, Prince Choiseul, ceased being a minister in France. My uncle, the Bishop, fears that France might now withdraw its support.

"This brings me to a very important matter. As I'm sure you are aware, the Estates General recently issued a manifesto proclaiming an interregnum. Ever since he arrived, Colonel Dumouriez has been explaining that this was essential, without it King Louis won't agree to help us. Not everybody is convinced that this was so important. You know yourself that many marshals and commanders have been thinking about siding with Poniatowski. You and you alone have the reputation as someone who won't ally himself to a king imposed on us by Moscow.

"Stanisław Poniatowski must be forced to abdicate, then we'll be able to tell France that its condition has been met. Besides, aren't there other representatives of the fine house of Wettin, under whose reign the Polish Commonwealth prospered? But it's premature to worry about who's going to rule Poland next. Louis will attend to that when the time is right. The thing to do now is to make sure that Stanisław steps down; he refuses to do so of his own free will. In fact, not only does he refuse, but he also has actually promised the Russian ambassador that he will despatch an army under Branicki against us.

"This, *mon cher*, is where you show your superiority over Zaremba. For while I may have a great deal of sympathy for him, I've heard that he's not really as committed in his opposition to the King as you are. It's this attitude that may win you the confidence of the Estates General.

"You will soon be visited by a certain Strawiński, a nobleman from Lithuania and a brave confederate. Please listen carefully to what he has to say, and consider whether his plans merit some attention."

Pulaski put the letter away. He had already talked to Strawiński on several occasions. The man's ideas were outrageous, which was precisely why he liked him.

The victory over Drewitz had filled Pulaski with pride and enthusiasm. All doubts he may have felt on the eve of the siege were gone. In fact, he was convinced that an interdependence had been formed between himself and the Madonna. She had helped him, while he had contributed to Her glory. It seemed that this was a blessing on everything he had done so far and was still to do. This proved him correct in his attitude towards Zaremba, the Estates General, and the King.

He did not feel any particular hostility toward the King. He'd seen him in Warsaw on a number of occasions and had decided that Poniatowski was a man of no knightly spirit, which was the only trait of character he admired. If anything, the King's brother Andrzej, the imperial general, actually seemed to be the better man. But how could the Poniatowski's compare with, say, Prince Karol Radziwiłł, who was the embodiment of chivalry and the spirit of liberty? Poniatowski was a Russian pawn. All it needed was to have him abducted and taken to Jasna Góra, and for him to renounce the crown and place the power entrusted in him by Catherine at the disposal of the Estates General. There was no need to harm him. Pulaski would earn the appreciation of the Estates General, the Duchess Franciszka would be happy, and the Virgin Mary would bless his act.

Pulaski's growing conviction that everything he did was also the work of the Blessed Virgin infected his subordinates as well. The young, daring, and wildly courageous leader, disliked by the Estates General and the other Confederate Commanders, was idolized by his troops. His officers and men were prepared to march into hell for him. The garrison at Jasna Góra decided to honor his exploits with a special badge, secretly made by one of

Frank's fellow-believers in Częstochowa, the goldsmith Herszko. The badge was a cross with a likeness of the Madonna on one side; on the other was an eagle holding a royal scepter and orb in its claws.

Presenting the badge to Pulaski on February 2 in the presence of the whole garrison at Jasna Góra, Zawoyski said: "Real virtues are rarely rewarded in this world, and while those who ought to notice them remain silent, we, your soldiers, cannot. By awarding this badge we honor your achievements and your valor, displayed in particular during the defense of the sacred castle of the Immaculate Virgin. The eagle on the cross wears no crown, as Stanisław Poniatowski has no right to wear one. We have only Her, our Queen."

The soldiers cheered madly while the cannon fired a salute. His officers embraced him one after the other. It was the most magnificent day of his life.

Pulaski decided to give his backing to Strawiński's plan, insisting on only one thing: Poniatowski must come to no harm. He was hard and ruthless in combat, acceptable traits in a professional soldier, but he'd never raised a finger against a defenseless person. Even if Drewitz had fallen into his eager hands, his hatred of the German traitor would have vanished at once. He made it clear to the conspirators that his participation depended solely on that condition, which his sense of honor demanded. Given full assurance that it would be met, the Estates General, with the Duchess' help, induced him to prepare the plot against the King.

Later, he wondered if his definition of honor differed from that of other men.

When the plot failed and those implicated panicked and started laying blame on each other, and while the Estates General disclaimed all responsibility, the bulk of the accusation fell upon Pulaski like a wall of loosely piled stones. His fortunes in war had varied; he'd suffered defeats, including an especially crushing blow at Radom at the hands of Drewitz's former subordinates: Schlippenbach, Düsterloch, and Michelson; but no defeat matched the disaster that befell him in the wake of the abortive plot. He was reputed to have always been the enemy of monarchs, and supposedly it was he who had raised his hand against the regent. He tried to explain; he issued statements and wrote letters. Everything he did actually made his case worse. He was condemned by all the courts of Europe, including the French. It was announced in the Empire that if he appeared within its borders he would be imprisoned. Frederick had issued no warning, but he could strike without one all the same. Saxony feared him like the plague. In Warsaw he was sentenced to death. It did not help that his brother Antoni returned to Poland, released from exile and hailed as the man who'd saved Kazan from Pugachev's rebellion.

When Zaremba learned that the Prussians had entered Wielkopolska he laid down his arms and appealed to the King for mercy. The only representative of the Confederation left was Pulaski, who'd become a cursed man. What little remained of the scattered confederate forces now headed for Częstochowa to join him, but the starving town could not feed them and the stocks of provisions at Jasna Góra had also been consumed. The commander realized that there was nothing left for him anywhere. His country faced the threat of partition by neighboring powers, and the most important thing – the only important thing – was to preserve what could be saved of independence. Pulaski almost envied those who were going to Warsaw and, once they'd obtained a royal pardon, were able to join in the attempt to save the country. For him, that option did not exist.

Disputes, quarrels, and senseless fights became increasingly common among the hungry, embittered, desperate defenders of Jasna Góra. The Paulites helped soothe the tense, potentially explosive atmosphere as best they could. The former conflict between the friars and the troops had by then been replaced by friendship. More and more of the soldiers took part in services and gathered for prayer in front of the miraculous Icon.

Pulaski visited the chapel often himself. His depression over his recent denunciation frequently drove him to consider suicide. In that way, he thought, he could put an impassable distance between himself and both the undeserved accusations and the succession of defeats crowding in on him. He carried the thought of a self-inflicted fatal wound everywhere, touching upon it day and night, acutely aware of it as a hungry man is aware of the last coin in his pocket. Yet it was there in the chapel, before the image of the Madonna, that those thoughts encountered the greatest resistance.

He was too occupied with his burning inner pain to pray. There was an abundance of bitterness and despair in him, but despite those feelings he persevered like a mortally frightened refugee who'd finally found the one and only safe harbor.

He raised his eyes and looked at the Blessed Virgin's face, but he turned away immediately. She looked at him, he felt, with immense sympathy and pity. And he could not bear Her gaze.

He no longer thought about the glory that his exploits had brought Her; he was more certain with every passing day that She did not need the glory of those victories. She wanted and expected something different of him. Not daring raids, not heroic stands, but a different life. The problem was precisely what form that life should take.

People from his father's generation had urged him to join their struggle, assuring him that they would be fighting for freedom and the faith. But they went to war waving the banners of envy, dissent, and blind ambition, driven by the desire for personal gain. Those who'd supported them were no different.

Like other young men, Pulaski had allowed himself to be carried away by his emotions. He was a man of great passion, prepared to give his blood, his life, and his wealth for the cause. He had fought valiantly, but he'd also carried within him the inherited legacy of weakness. What help were all the rosaries, gorgets, and scapulars? Father Marek had promised miracles, but did miracles really fall from the sky and solve problems the way an unexpected morning rain eased a summer drought? Or were the solutions created in man himself?

One day in the sacristy, Pulaski made a decision. He happened upon Father Gotwald, who was putting away the liturgical vestments used during Mass.

"I see you're heading for the chapel again, sir," the friar said, smiling. "I'm so pleased for you. The picture of the Blessed Virgin has a very special property, you know."

"What property is that?"

"It speaks to people." He chose his next words carefully. "Especially those who... are troubled and in need of Her assistance. Sometimes it may seem that we're listening to our own thoughts, but in reality Our Lady is speaking."

"You may be right, Father. I wish She would speak to me."

"If you're waiting for Her words then I presume that She has begun to talk to you already. Listen attentively. She must be heard to the end."

Pulaski looked at the friar, wondering if his thoughts had somehow been discerned. Then he said: "I've caused you a lot of difficulty, haven't I?"

"Let me just say that you didn't understand us and we didn't understand you. That's the way it is sometimes."

"I've brought you something..." Pulaski reached into his pocket. "This cross. My comrades gave it to me... Spent their last pennies to have it made. I'd like to give it to Her. I didn't save Jasna Góra – She did." He added, "Saved it from me, too."

"We'll accept your cross, of course, and put it in Her treasury. But I think you're judging yourself too severely, sir. She's not like that. She understands a man's intentions and I'm sure She's accepted yours. Whatever they may be."

"If things are the way you say, Father, then I'll meet Her again. Although it might be in the last minute of my life."

The friar nodded, and gave him a cryptic smile.

Pulaski knelt in the chapel for a long time that day, looking into the Madonna's eyes. He knew then that his decision was the right one, the final one, and he no longer tried to avoid Her penetrating stare.

A solitary rider crossed the bridge that spanned the Liswarta River and urged his tired horse forward onto the soil of Silesia. The man's clothes were dirty, his boots mud-splattered, his moustache overlong and ill-kempt. He slumped in the saddle and the horse's gait threw his weary body from side to side like the pendulum of a maladjusted clock. He avoided the main road by choosing a farm track that wound through the woods and fields, and every few hundred yards his eyes swept the surrounding area – foward, left flank, right flank, to the rear – with the practiced ease of a trained observer. His precautions reminded him of another, quite different journey over the familiar six-mile route from Lisy to the small palace at Lubliniec.

It had been September, Pulaski recalled wistfully, and the gentle sunlight had touched the wall of trees bordering the road with a delicacy peculiar to this time of year. He remembered the scent of heather and mushrooms carried by the warm autumn breeze. He'd had the company of a good friend and their rumpled appearance had merely been one facet of a subtle camouflage, a bit of theatrical cover like his brash attitude when the soldier at the bridge barrier confronted them.

Pulaski managed a smile. Yesterday's deception had become today's necessity, a matter of survival, the need to flow with the prevailing currents. The boldness he'd displayed at the barrier was not gone, he knew, but so much had happened since that autumn.

He straightened his spine and spurred his horse toward Lubliniec and his meeting with the Duchess.

Krasińska met her visitor with outstretched arms as if to embrace the wretched-looking figure, but then she froze in horror.

"Oh, Casimir, *mon pauvre...*" she said pitifully. "How terrible to see you in such condition. What's become of you, my dear friend?"

Pulaski bowed without saying a word. His thin face spoke for him, betraying fatigue, lack of sleep, and confusion. She motioned him to a couch and sat down by his side.

"I trust," she began, her voice full of genuine concern, "that nobody knows you're here? You didn't give your real name I presume?"

"Of course not. I am Rudziński now, but I'm still at your service."

"Let's hope no one recognizes you, I can't count on the Prussian officers the way I used to. Everything has changed and –"

"An understatement."

"And you carry the stigma of someone who attempted regicide."

"I'm sure you believe me, Your Ladyship," he burst out as if a time bomb inside him had been waiting to go off. "That was never my intention! I don't care if anyone else believes me, but I couldn't stand the thought of you suspecting me of such treachery!"

"I don't!" She hurriedly reassured him. "I believe you, Casimir. I always have. I've defended you from the first moment the news spread that you had attempted to kill the King. I knew it couldn't be true. I tried to convince everyone, but it's not easy to dismiss such a terrible charge. Everybody kept repeating it. The King sent letters to monarchs all over the world, and he mentioned you by name. Poor boy..." She stroked his hair. "So you've left Jasna Góra?"

"Yes, without even saying farewell. A difficult decision. They think I'll be back."

"But you're not going back?"

"Why should I? Everything's fallen to pieces."

"That's true," she sighed. "The Prussians have taken Wielkopolska and the Tsarina's forces are moving in deeper and deeper. Even worse,

Kaunitz is demanding that Estates General leaves the territory of the Empire. There's nobody left in Prešov now. France has withdrawn all offers of assistance, Saxony is powerless..."

"There's still Turkey."

"Only Turkey. My uncle is afraid we shouldn't expect much help from that quarter."

"Nevertheless, Turkey is still fighting. I've decided to go there. I'm a soldier. That's what I will do."

"Maybe that's not such a bad idea, dear Casimir. Your heroism will shine again, and those terrible accusations will fade." She leaned towards him. "When are you leaving?"

"I don't know yet. I'm penniless, I even had to borrow money to get here."

"Oh, I wish I could help you! But I have nothing myself. I'm like a tree in winter... Wait – you know what? Go to Dresden! I'll give you a letter for Karol, I'm sure he'll do something for you. He's always thought highly of you and he understands that Turkey is our last hope."

"That's odd," Pulaski said.

"What is, my dear?"

"Last hope. I never thought we'd get to that point."

They were silent.

In the past there had been so much to talk about and never enough time to say it all.

CHAPTER 8

PRINCE PONIATOWSKI

The snow had stopped, the sun shone and it was now a fine day. There was a light frost and, although it was February, one could sense the first breath of the approaching spring in the air.

The column of carriages, hansoms, and heavily laden carts moved slowly, escorted by soldiers. Before entering the woods, patrols were sent out to reconnoiter the flanks. The enemy was in fact a safe distance away and the road ran along the border with Silesia, now held by the French. Nevertheless, the commander-in-chief ordered his escort troops to be on the alert. He dismounted and joined Countess Czosnowska in her carriage.

"Do we really have to part?" the woman asked. "What will I do without you? You can't leave me on my own, Pepi."

She was young and very beautiful. Her light-colored hair spilled over the collar of an expensive fur and her sky-blue eyes were wide open, betraying a childish lightheartedness and fear of boredom.

"It'll only be a few days, Zofia," Prince Józef Poniatowski said.

"Try to make them as few as possible. I really won't be able to bear your being away. These military matters are so boring. How I'd like to be in Cracow now! And be there with you. I hope it will be a bit more lively than Warsaw."

"Then go to Cracow right away."

"Without you? Oh, no!"

"Village life will bore you to death. And I've got things to attend to."

"Ah, those 'things' of yours! What tedium!"

"Please try to understand – the army needs training, uniforms, weapons... Right now they're just individuals full of good intentions. Napoleon is demanding light cavalry from me and I have to see to it."

"Yes, you have to see to everything on your own, I know, I know!" She puffed out her cheeks like a child. "You've no time for me at all. And I love you so, Pepi."

"You'll have a good time in Cracow. I'm told they'll be organizing balls and receptions there."

"Really?" She brightened up at once.

"And Marshal Frimont is there, the commander of the Emperor's armies."

"He's such a nice man. He'll see to it that there's none of that gloomy atmosphere there was in Warsaw."

"I'm sure he will. And there'll be Bignon, too."

"But you'll come too, won't you?"

"As soon as I can," he said.

"Is it true there might be war with Austria?"

"That's not impossible."

"Horrible! It's bad enough to be fighting the Russians. The Austrians are nice. They're our allies."

"At the moment."

"And the Emperor? When will he come back again?"

He did not answer. She was not even waiting for an answer; her thoughts were already in Cracow.

Poniatowski's eyes rested on the boy sitting opposite him. Józio was four years old, his face framed with curly fair hair. He'd inherited his mother's good looks and the absence of front teeth did not make him any less charming, but boredom with the long journey showed in his blue eyes as he absently squeezed a toy horse.

"What have I given him?" Poniatowski thought. "I'll go away and disappear from his memory. She won't be able to bring him up, she's just an empty doll. She'll find amusement for herself soon enough, but the boy..."

"As soon as we arrive, I'll order a Cracow-style uniform made for you," he told Józio.

"And will it be just like real?"

"As real as anybody ever had."

"I wish I already had it."

"You'll get it."

The road climbed uphill, fell away, then climbed again. In the far distance, beyond a chain of hills overgrown with dark forests, a church spire appeared, then vanished again.

"We'll be in Częstochowa before long," he told Zofia.

"Are you going to stay on there?"

"I want to go to the monastery and visit the garrison. It's an important fortress, guarding our flanks."

"I heard there's some important picture there. Is that true?" Zofia asked.

"Yes, an old Icon of Our Lady. It's greatly revered."

"So the soldiers are there to protect the Icon?"

"No, to defend us from the Russians."

The carriage wheels began to rattle and bounce as the column entered a stretch of road paved with cobblestones. They passed between the houses of an impoverished town. Beyond their roofs, most of which were thatched, rose a snow-covered ridge with protective walls and above them the outline of a church.

They stopped outside an inn. Its owner ran out at once. He wore a gaberdine coat and a skull-cap. He moved from one carriage to another, bowing low and inviting the travelers inside.

The duty officer opened the door of Countess Czosnowska's carriage.

"Will you be proceeding at once, Your Excellency, or after a meal?" he asked.

"At once. Have them fetch a horse."

An orderly appeared with a mount. Poniatowski pressed Zofia's hand to his lips.

"Take care of yourself. I'll be in Krzeszowice in two, maybe three days.

But if you prefer, go on ahead to Cracow. You'll certainly find it more to your liking."

He put one arm around the boy and pressed his head hard to his chest. His sense of guilt only made him love his son more.

"Goodbye, Józio."

"Goodbye. Will you take me to war when I get the uniform?"

"There'll be enough wars for you, too. I'm sure of that," he said. Once more he hugged the boy and then quickly pushed him away. This is no time to be sentimental, he thought. I must have the strength to make a decision.

Supporting himself with a cane and dragging one leg, he walked along the line of carriages. The injury he'd suffered at Vitebsk still caused him problems, especially when he rose after sitting for a time.

"At Sabach I nearly lost a leg," he thought, "yet I recovered somehow. Now every wound festers... A rest would do me good. A long rest away from everything. A long, endless rest..."

Henrietta and his sister, Teresa, were in the next carriage.

"*Au revoir, chère amie*," he said as he kissed the Countess' yellowish bony fingers, adorned with loose rings that jingled each time she moved her hand.

"I hope, Pepi, that you're not staying here to be with some lady friend," she said jokingly, wagging her finger at him. "I know you, and you know that I've always helped you in your conquests. But now you've got to save your time for your old friends. You mustn't leave us alone..."

"*Soyez tranquille, Henriette.* I'll be with you in a few days."

"Don't forget."

Once he had expected women to give him joy and relaxation, now the tide had turned – each of them demanded his time and attention. But he did not have that time, nor did they offer him the peace and calm he needed. Instead, they burdened him with their own fears, concerns and longings. "You must come," they said, "we must talk, I have so much to tell you..." And they dismissed his worries with an impatient shrug.

When he had said goodbye to Anetka in Warsaw, she, too, forgot for a while about her malicious gossip and the story she loved to repeat again and again (and which she herself had heard from Colonel Wąsowicz); the story of how, during his retreat from Moscow, Napoleon had at all costs wanted to make a detour to Walewice to see his mistress, the Countess

Walewska, and how Caulaincourt had objected to the plan. Anetka was sad that he was going, that the Austrians had gone (they were not as nice as the French, but were much better dancers), that so many Polish soldiers had not returned from Russia, and that she did not know when she was going to see the peerless Wąsowicz again... He'd started to say that he had a feeling he would never return to Warsaw, but she did not let him finish. She was greatly moved when he made her a gift of the Jabłonna estate, and asked him to kiss her children – August, Natalia and Maurycy, a mere infant. She had consoled herself by recalling how nice Tsar Alexander had been when she met him eight years ago.

Teresa leaned out of the carriage and kissed his cheek.

"Don't push yourself too hard, Pepi. We all beg you. Watch your health. Don't take risks. And think of some sensible way out of this tangled situation." Then, quietly, as if confiding a secret, she added: "In his last letter, Prince Talleyrand asked me to plead with you to show some prudence, too."

"I'll take care to heed the Prince's advice," he said with polite irony in his voice.

"Oh, Pepi, Pepi... We worry about you. So many women care for you. We all love you... Remember that."

"I never forget it."

She looked at him tenderly, and despite the fact that what she said annoyed him, he bowed and kissed her hand affectionately. She was a good sister. He could never forget that one of her eyes was made of glass, and that it was he who'd caused her disability by his wild horseplay. She had never said a word of reproach for that sin, but he couldn't erase it from his memory. He had been reckless many times in his life, but had never fled the responsibility for his recklessness.

His adjutants approached him: Potocki, Kicki, Axamitowski, Szydłowski, Skórzewski, Szumlański. He thought for a while, then nodded to Potocki.

"Only you, Artur, will be coming with me. You," he turned to the others, "shall report to Różniecki. He'll need your help in organizing the general staff. And forget about your amusements – get down to some hard work."

They saluted and clicked their heels together. Despite their years at war, they still lacked the proper military bearing. They were no longer young, but still gave the impression of gilded youths dressed up for fun. After the return from Russia, each had ordered a new uniform replete with elaborate braiding and decorations of their own design. These costumes made them look rather like Murat and his Neapolitan staff. What a contrast to Poniatowski's modest general's uniform, which only bore the ribbons of the French Legion d'Honneur and the Polish Virtuti Militari.

An aide helped him mount his horse. He wrapped a greatcoat around himself and set off, half a platoon of lancers riding in front and the other half behind. Small wooden houses stood along the street leading up to the monastery. The town had barely been rebuilt from the great fire of 1770 when it was razed to ground again in 1809. Its population had shrunk considerably.

As he rode, Poniatowski was lost in thought. The sun lit up the snowcapped houses and fences with a glare that already betokened spring, but he was too troubled by doubts to notice.

He was like a man caught in a collapsing house: the walls and ceiling were caving in around him, he was trapped, half-buried, but still alive. Previously he had been commander-in-chief and minister of war, but next to him there had been the King, the government of the Duchy of Warsaw, his friends and advisors. Now everyone was gone. He was on his own. It mattered little that the government still existed, its ministers were already negotiating with the Tsar's envoys. The King had gone to Prague to negotiate with the Emperor and there was every indication that even his loyalty, which Napoleon regarded as the deepest, was wavering. His friends were deserting him one by one. Generals and colonels were leaving the army, the only ones left were the former companions of his youth. He had surrounded himself with them, assigning them important posts and offices. They could perform their duties but had no advice to offer. His counselors had either been struck dumb or kept changing their minds. Others appeared, sent by Radziwiłł and Czartoryski. Everybody suggested a different line of action. The only thing they agreed on was that he had to break with Bonaparte as soon as possible.

Again and again he was told, even though he knew it well himself, that the country had had enough of the French – of their ruthlessness, their plundering and looting, and their demands. When the last French unit had retreated across Poland, the peasants had to be restrained from seizing scythes and axes and wreaking their own justice on the robbers and rapists. With the French and their German allies gone, the poverty of a whole country robbed of its people and food became starkly apparent. And it was in this ravaged country that he now had to form a new army and requisition provisions from what little stocks were left. Fathers refused to give away their sons, whose brothers had been left in the snows of Russia. Desertions multiplied. Poland was paying a heavy price for its seven years' truncated statehood as a French military camp.

Even so, the most painful sacrifices would have been forgotten had the French stayed. East of the Vistula the Duchy was in Russian hands. When the French armies left, the forts had been garrisoned by the most motley units imaginable. Napoleon had entrusted the defense of the Duchy to the Austrians! That was pure mockery. Poniatowski had know Schwarzenberg too long and too well not to know what he really thought, despite his diplomatic phrases. One day the Austrian commander pulled his line of defense back behind the Pilica. Poniatowski realized then that he had to leave Warsaw. With nobody left to guard the river, the Russians soon crossed onto the west bank of the Vistula. Vinzigerode, the Russian commander, caught up with the French near Kalisz and routed them. The Russian army was already cooperating with the Prussians, who had now openly changed alliances and were turning against the French. The area between Cracow and Częstochowa was the last island not yet flooded by the oncoming tide, the last patch of land on which the Polish forces could regroup for their final battle.

Modlin, Toruń and Zamość were cut off and besieged. Those fortresses could offer him no assistance, nor could he go to their aid. In view of the French rout, someone else had to cover the northern flank of the forces now concentrating near Cracow. He could expect only Jasna Góra to provide this cover. In 1809 it had withstood an Austrian siege. This time he had to demand much more from it.

The horses' hooves rang on the white lime stones, which looked like chunks of frozen snow. The street reached the foot of a hill dotted with a sparse growth of trees, then turned in a wide arch along the ruins of burned houses which nobody had tried to rebuild. They entered a vast open space, and, crossing it, they reached the gate of the fortress.

The alarm sounded at once – they had been spotted by the guards posted on the walls. Their commander delivered a report to Poniatowski.

Listening to the lieutenant's words, Poniatowski studied the soldiers. The war in Russia had made him tolerant as regards to the appearance of his troops, nevertheless, he found the sight of these men deeply embarrassing. Not one had a full uniform. Some had only the jackets, others only the trousers, while the majority wore civilian clothes or foreign uniforms, ragged and torn. Their boots were even worse – cracked, full of holes, tied up with string. They were armed with a sundry assortment of rifles: Prussian, French, and Russian. Some kept the cartridges in special pouches, other simply carried them in their pockets. The caps, too, came in assorted shapes, but most were ordinary peasants' caps made of sheepskin.

Having received the report, he rode into the fortress. In the courtyard he was met by the commander, an artillery colonel named Górski. He dismounted and followed him into the building. A huge room with a vaulted ceiling and thick walls housed the chancellery, which doubled as the quarters of the commanding staff. Camp beds stood along the wall, and uniforms and coats hung above them. In the center was a long table littered with papers. Trunks were piled haphazardly in a corner.

He sat down on the best chair in the room. The colonel stood stiffly in front of him. He was middle-aged, a short and bulky man with a face pitted by smallpox scars. The top of his head was totally bald.

"How many men have you got, Colonel?" he asked.

"One thousand two hundred and six, Your Excellency."

"What kind of soldiers are they?"

The colonel spread his hands helplessly.

"You can hardly call them soldiers at all. Raw recruits, every one. Most have never held a rifle in their hands before, or seen a cannon at close quarters. On top of that they weren't the best material to begin with: the younger and stronger men were sent to frontline regiments. The Fortress got the leftovers."

"And the officers and the lower ranks?"

"They're not too bad. Most of them were in Russia, and some have been at war since the beginning of the Duchy. Two were in Spain, but they're cripples. They're doing what they can to train the men, but it's not easy given their state of health."

"I see. What about weapons?"

"That's a problem, Your Excellency. I only have enough rifles for half the garrison and each one's different. And there's precious little ammunition. We've got twelve cannon, but some are really antiques. And this is all the ammunition we've got for them –" he pointed to the trunks in the corner.

"How long would that last if the fortress came under siege?"

"Two days, maybe three..."

"Well, you have to take that possibility into account. The Russians are already in Kalisz."

"Won't we be getting any more ammunition?"

"No."

Silence. Colonel Górski stared at the floor.

"What are your orders?" he asked at last.

"Defend the fortress for as long as you can. How's morale?"

"It's hard to say... You know yourself, nobody trusts the French any longer."

"There's no need to trust them. Let's just remember that thanks to them we were able to form the Polish army and fight for our cause."

"I quite agree. But now that they've been beaten and have fled..."

"We're covering their rear so they can regroup for a fresh attack."

"The Russian Emperor is said to be very well disposed toward us."

"That may be so, but we were in bondage until Emperor Napoleon came along. I don't remember your record right now, but if I'm not mistaken you fought in the Insurrection. Is that right?"

"I fought under your command even earlier, Your Excellency, at Zieleńce. Then in the Insurrection. I was wounded during the siege of Warsaw, then I joined the army of the Duchy and got another wound at the battle of Sandomierz. Now I'm back from Russia."

"I don't have to tell you then, you know yourself what you're fighting for. About morale..."

"It's improved since they got here. Jasna Góra counts for something. The Black Madonna... The great tradition... The priests and friars talk to the soldiers a lot, and I'm sure that gives them strength. But at the same time", he lowered his voice, "it's being said that Napoleon's defeat was the

Lord's punishment for holding the Holy Father prisoner, for the ransacked churches, the lewdness and blasphemy."

"Let's not pass judgement on the God, Colonel, when God hasn't asked us to do so. Let's just try to conduct ourselves properly."

"The Austrian officers who came here said that their Emperor worshipped the Blessed Virgin greatly and respected Her image."

"Show that we revere Her even more, and have even more respect for the Icon that our fathers surrounded with so much love."

"But if there's a siege..."

"I'm perfectly sure that you'll carry out your duty. I'm leaving you to defend the fortress for as long as you have the means to do so. Every single day you hold out counts. Do you undersand?"

"Yes, sir."

"Now I'd like you to take me on an inspection of the gun emplacements, the fortifications, the soldiers' quarters, the kitchens, and the dressing station. And before I leave I'd like to address the garrison."

Although his leg ached, Poniatowski walked around the ramparts with the colonel. As he walked he reflected on the situation: "Will they fight? That Górski is an excellent officer and a superb gunner. Now he's lost confidence... Yet he hasn't deserted like Chłopicki, Kniaziewicz, or Sanguszko. He confided his misgivings to me, that means he trusts me. If Bignon heard his words, he would report him for treason at once... Bignon is friendly toward us, not like Serra or the repulsively servile Pradt! But in his heart Bignon cherishes the idea of Poland incorporated into the Kingdom of Prussia. An old French idea... We're not thought important, it's Brandenburg that has always been France's favorite."

"But why should I bother with all that? I'm a soldier, not a politician. But now I'm alone, bearing sole responsibility for everything. There was a time when some people accused me of being overambitious... that's never been true. Today they leave it all to me and I'm expected to make all the decisions. I'm on my own, with the weight of the Duchy on my shoulders – no, the weight of all Poland. I'm supposed to make an army out of nothing and then decide its fate. Napoleon has given his orders: stay put and fight. But that's just not possible. The Russians will crush us with an army ten times larger than ours. The Austrians will sell us out. Guerrilla warfare? That was all right for the Spaniards, with their mountains and wilderness. The terrain is different here. I have to defy Napoleon's order. I have to defy

Bignon, who's stopped trusting me and started trusting the Austrians instead, with Sacken, who could order an offensive at any minute, only a dozen miles away. I have to negotiate with Frimont, who mouths assurances about our alliance while in reality getting ready to betray us. And the country is embittered and on the verge of despair."

Absent-mindedly, he listened to the information given by the colonel. Yet all the time he kept asking himself the same question: "Will they fight? I can't expect much of them. The soldiers are poorly trained and the fortress has hardly any provisions, and every day they defend this place will be important. Every additional day means getting another step closer to forming the corps. An extra day might bring salvation... But is salvation really still possible?"

He leaned on an old bronze gun which remembered the days of the Confederates. Below the fortress a vast snow-covered square sloped toward the town. Far beyond the buildings he saw a road and a column of troops. He stopped listening to the colonel. Nothing mattered any more. It was too late. There was no point in wearying himself. Better to close his eyes...

He'd had such moments of sad hopelessness when he was a little boy. He had run to his mother, put his head on her knees and closed his eyes. She stroked his hair and quietly, tenderly said: "My little Pepi, my little boy..." Then he'd fall asleep under his mother's caresses and forget about everything.

Now everybody was making demands on him. It was impossible to deal with everything. His hopeless toil bred weariness. Closing his eyes and trying to sleep was not enough. Not even sleep afforded an escape from reality.

He always kept a pair of pistols received from his uncle in the holsters by his saddle. They were beautiful weapons, with silver-studded mahogany grips. He thought about them increasingly often now. He laid them by his bed and often took them in his hands. The grips fit neatly into the palm of his hand. The cool muzzle seemed so friendly when it touched his cheek. "In those barrels," he thought, "was rest, and peace..."

The inspection was drawing to a close when the prior of the monastery, Father Szuffranowicz, appeared and asked Poniatowski and his senior officers to dinner. The Prince accepted the invitation and followed the prior into the refectory.

A magnificent Gothic ceiling, decorated a long time ago for the wedding of King Michał, covered the huge hall in a sea of colors. Stucco arabesques tangled above their heads. The meal was modest, and despite the worries besetting him Poniatowski could not resist casting a derisive glance in the direction of his adjutant, grimacing over a bowl of buckwheat. Zofia's brother had quickly forgotten about the hunger they'd faced in Russia. He himself had never been very choosy about food, a fact his friends joked about openly, knowing that he never took offense at jokes about his person. His enemies, on the other hand, mocked him viciously behind his back and used the opportunity to make some remark about the little-known origins of his family.

After dinner, the prior leaned over toward Poniatowski and said: "Would you like to see the Miraculous Image of Our Lady of Jasna Góra, your Excellency?"

This was the second time he had been at Jasna Góra, but he'd never entered the chapel containing the Icon. Some strange nervousness had stopped him. It was as though he felt there was something improper in raising one's eyes to look at the Virgin, She who was called the Immaculate.

He had not prayed in a long time. When his mother had been alive, she'd grieved over this. She had first blamed Stanisław August and then Henrietta for his departure from the religious traditions of the house of von Thun. Mothers always look for someone to blame for their sons' sins... His uncle had often talked about God, but they were just words. He would not make any sacrifices or do anything to back them up. Henrietta had brought with her the climate of parlors in which people ridiculed the faith of the simple folk and spoke of God in impersonal and misty terms. She had no need of religious experiences, she was too busy thinking about herself to have the time or will to think about anything else. She felt no need of faith. With the King, it was different, he was too clever not to feel that need. But he feared for his comfort too much not to realize that he would complicate his life greatly if he did not ignore these calls. This was not to say that Henrietta's behavior had had any influence whatever on Poniatowski. His attitude toward her had something fatalistic about it: she did not attract him in any way, everything having ended after the time they spent together in Brussels. That had been when the obligations arose, which he could not free himself from. In fact, he'd never been able to free himself from any obligations. As for his uncle, the influence was much stronger – the King did not even try to carry out some of his desires, but his nephew regarded himself bound by them nevertheless, and the King's fears left an uneasiness in the Prince's heart. He too felt that faith might demand too much of him. He preferred to believe that having taken so much upon himself he had a right to some consolation.

He had no wish to see the Icon, but, constrained by his innate tact, he was unable to think up a suitable excuse for refusing the invitation.

"Very well, Father. I'd be glad to."

Father Szuffranowicz rose from the table and led him along the wide corridors of the monastery.

The black altar, embellished with silver bas-reliefs, resembled a giant catafalque. The Holy Picture had been uncovered and Mary's face appeared like a stained-glass window letting golden sunshine pour into the murky chapel. Now the altar was full of life. The silverplate glittered. Countless strings of pearls and coral beads seemed to form a garland in the national colors. The pearls must have been donated by women of noble birth and rich burghers' wives, while the coral had come from country women who donated their finest jewelery to get their sons and husbands back. They took the white and red necklaces off and brought them here, as if showing that they understood that love of country took precedence over human love; at the same time, they knew that the One in front of whose likeness they knelt was the Protector and Guardian of this exchange. Theirs was not a desperate gesture of rejecting everything else once what was most important had been taken away from them; this was a trust born in the hearts of women who realized what the heart of Our Lady was like.

Poniatowski raised his eyes – only to lower them again at once. He, who had been able to look so boldly and conqueringly into the eyes of women, now lacked the courage to look into these eyes. People came here, he thought, with their heartfelt pleas and made the greatest offerings. They rushed here as if to a treasury, to deposit their pennies. They received consolation, and also the strength to act. But he – what did he have to offer?

He forced himself to lift up his head. The Madonna looked at him. Although he evaded Her gaze, it rested firmly on his face. Her eyes seemed to be waiting for something.

If Szarlotta hadn't died... That was no explanation. A beautiful childhood love had died, but he had not remained faithful to it. While not shirking great and difficult tasks, in this one area he had chosen the easy way out.

Life had been hard as long as he could remember, ever since the romantic days in Vienna and Prague had ended. The life chosen for him by his uncle – not by Poniatowski himself – had laid a heavy, seemingly crushing burden on his shoulders. Initially, his uncle had been beside him. But then, having pushed him into this great adventure, he had drawn back. He first infected his nephew with his dreams, only to abandon them later himself. Although Poniatowski often felt disenchantment, he had not given up. But yes, he had looked for consolation.

Now the burden was no lighter – indeed, it had grown even heavier. His grandiose plans had collapsed. The Catonian characters had proven to be more dwarfish. The love affairs he had used as a substitute for love over the years had burned themselves out. Women demanded more and more from him but offered nothing...

All this made the pistols so tempting. When everything else loses its sense, death assumes a special meaning.

His mother used to say to him: "At least promise me, Pepi, that you'll say the Hail Mary from time to time. Do it for me. You see, the Lord is great, holy and awesome, while we are so weak. But She, His Mother, knows how to speak to Him on our behalf. In Poland there's a miraculous image of Her, if you happen to see it some day..."

Now he had the Icon in front of him, for the first and last time. He was certain he would never come here again. He had arrived at the end of the road. Everything has to end... It was not possible to carry the burden any further. There was only one way out.

When he said this to himself he at once felt the urge to raise his head. He had the impression that the Madonna's eyes had seized him and were forcing him to look at the Icon. He saw Her penetrating gaze fixed on him. He tried to escape those eyes, but they held him fast.

Very well, so you reach for the pistols, and then what? Without its commander, the corps will fall to pieces. The ephemeral state created by Napoleon will cease to exist even before Europe starts to consider Poland's destiny. History will record that the Poles had not deserved their own state, that it had taken a foreign power to make something of them. When that power was no longer there to help, they had fallen back into oblivion.

An hour earlier he had met a group of officers on the ramparts. Górski was right – all of them had been crippled in the last campaign, that was why they'd been selected for the less demanding service at the fortress. Greeting them, he had looked at their faces. He remembered almost every one: this one from Smolensk, that one from Borodino, another from Moscow, another from the battle on the Berezina. Their worn and tattered uniforms were adorned with medals and crosses. They stood at attention before him as proudly as they could. At the end of the line he saw a smooth face with wide cheekbones and graying hair falling in locks on the forehead. He stopped in amazement.

"*Tiens*, can it really be you, Madame Żubrowa?"

"It's me, Your Excellency."

"Back in the ranks? I'd heard that you'd been wounded, Madame."

"I was but I scraped through somehow. And I was promoted."

"That's right, I remember signing your commission."

"But I don't have the strength I used to. I can't go charging off into the attack like I once did."

"I remember it well. You fought alongside the most valiant of men. I pinned the cross on your jacket myself. And now you're still with us."

"They wanted to discharge me altogether, said I was an old woman and had better go home. But I said: send me to Częstochowa. I'll be all right serving in the fortress."

"With you here, Madame Żubrowa, I've more confidence they won't surrender Jasna Góra."

"We'll do all we can," she declared solemnly. "Won't we, boys?" she turned to the other officers, who nodded their approval. "Weak and unworthy though we are, we shall defend our Virgin. If only you, Your Excellency, could stay with us."

Poniatowski stroked his moustache.

"As an old soldier, Madame, you know very well that I can't shut myself up with you in the fortress."

"Yes, we all know that. That wasn't what I meant. You must stay with our army, Your Excellency, wherever it may be. With you in command, we see the point in fighting on. Even if it means death or captivity, we'll defend Jasna Góra to the last."

"They trust me," he thought now. "But if there's a siege, I won't be able to help. There's no point deluding myself. I'll fail them even though they trust me."

"But won't I be failing them even more if I put the pistol to my head?" Żubrowa had said: "Even if it means death or captivity." She's an experienced soldier, she understands what I'm asking of them.

He raised his head again, and again encountered the eyes gazing at him. Slowly, he began to recall the words: "Hail Mary, full of grace, the Lord is with Thee... Holy Mary, Mother of God pray for us now, and at the hour of our death." He shifted his thoughts like the beads of a rosary: "You who have trusted us, help us. Be by our side today and tomorrow, when we'll be dying. When we'll be dying..."

He felt a sudden chill. He had looked death in the face too often not to realize that it had come up to him, softly yet noticeably. But if death were so near, why stretch his arms out toward it? Why die to flee death?

"No," he thought. "No! I won't use the pistols. Neither now nor later, when I'll find things even harder."

His leg ached so much he couldn't genuflect. He just bowed deeply and left the chapel."

The garrison was assembled in a square in the monastery yard. The motley gathering of soliders looked more like a band of robbers or partisans. Only the huge eagles clumsily cut out of sheet metal and stuck onto headgear of all kinds, and the standards bearing the likeness of Our Lady and the emblem of an eagle, obviously sewn by some local women, indicated their military affiliation.

Leaning on his cane, he walked into the middle of the square. Commands were issued. The soldiers stood at attention. Pairs of eyes, young and old, peered out intently at him from underneath the eagles.

"Soldiers," he began. "I am entrusting you with the defense of this venerable place. The tides of ill fortune have engulfed the rock on which the monastery and the fortress stand many times before, and each time they have rolled back, having achieved nothing. You have to gather up all your strength. The defense of these walls is a dire necessity. Every day of your defense will help your comrades consolidate their ranks. Don't be afraid, for even if the enemy tide floods over you for a while, it will not submerge this place. Whatever the outcome of this war, our strength lies here. Wherever history takes us, we shall return to this rock... Nothing is lost if it has not been lost here."

CHAPTER 9

ARCHBISHOP FELIŃSKI

"Please follow me, Your Excellency," said the friar. He led the way across the church and opened the door to the chapel.

Feliński entered slowly, full of excitement: it was the second time he had been there. Until recently, he'd spent his life far away from central Poland – in Volhynia and Podolia, then in Russia, Paris, and Russia again. Only now was he getting to know the Congress Kingdom. He had dreamed of seeing Jasna Góra ever since he'd put himself in Our Lady's care, begging Her protection from the danger of corruption during his school years at Klewań. Jasna Góra symbolized the history of Poland, which had always been his one and only beloved motherland although he lived far away from its heart.

He knelt down in front of the Cross. Squeezed between columns, Christ's body hung heavily against the background of silver sheeting. Above Him were a sun and moon with human faces. The Savior's head had dropped onto His right shoulder, with His black, curly beard resting on His chest, down which rivulets of blood flowed. Jesus's lips were parted and His eyes closed. His legs were flexed stiffly and His toes nearly touched the rock symbolized by solid spheres.

The cruelty conveyed by the detail of the sculpture was terrifying. An unearthly chill wafted from it. For an instant, Feliński recalled his disputes with the followers of Towiański. The initial point that had put him off were their crosses, which bore no figure of Christ. Their leader had insisted that the cross itself was enough to evoke divine thoughts, but Feliński was too attached to the figure of Jesus on the Cross that he remembered from village churches, both Catholic and Uniate. In the West, he'd been both shocked and excited by Medieval sculpture; Jesus on the Cross, he thought, was an absolute necessity. There was a dangerous tendency to surrender to imagination and to invent symbols, but the suffering Jesus was real and He wanted us to understand the sense of that pain.

He prayed for a short time and then rose and walked to the altar in the center of the chapel. The friar pointed to a faldstool placed near the steps. Leaning over to the Archbishop he whispered: "We'll uncover the Icon in a minute."

Behind Feliński, on the other side of the grille, silence prevailed. As he'd walked to the altar he'd seen several women wrapped in shawls, kneeling in humble anticipation. Someone must have told them that the Icon would be uncovered at this unusual hour for the benefit of the distinguished visitor. A man in black knelt behind them; the burning candles reflected in his glasses.

He tried to pray but the thoughts which had been awakened in conversation on the train and subsequent deliberations during the carriage ride rushed through his head like a wild mountain stream. He could not concentrate.

Feliński had come there unexpectedly. Only his closest associates knew of the intended journey, a desire that had presented itself quite suddenly. He would have preferred to arrive incognito but could not risk possible recognition and the ensuing comment, so he'd simply asked the prior, Father Kapiczyński, to keep the visit a secret. He wished only to pray before the Icon, have dinner with the friars, say Mass the next morning and return to Warsaw.

Recent days had passed very quickly in a succession of meetings, discussions, and conferences. The situation was extremely tense. His arrival in Warsaw the previous January, full of hope, had been like a magnificent sign from the Lord, the sudden fulfillment of his dreams. He had trusted others and received much encouragement, but within a year everything had gone wrong. He tried in vain to control the raging storm of conflicting desires and passions that embroiled everyone around him; the impetuosity of some people engendered obstinacy among others, and he sensed that no one was aware that the gathering storm was bound to end in a whirlwind.

He had tried to influence those delirious minds. His patient explanations of intricate matters usually encouraged people to admit that he was right, but as soon as they went away they changed their minds and negated their promises as though yielding to some mysterious force that directed their actions. Eventually he grew to loathe those conversations; once his hopes were aroused the subsequent disappointment was all the more painful. Ideally, he would have preferred solitude but people flocked to see him and ask his advice – most of which he knew would never be taken. Others brought Jobe's news, whined about their despair, and demanded consolation. But there were a few who brought warnings and thinly veiled threats.

Worst of all was that he had to face all of it on his own. His associates listened to him but only grumbled and complained and took no action. He found it necessary to keep up their spirits as well as his own, to prevent them from falling to pieces under pressure.

Events moved so quickly that he rarely had enough time for his regular pastoral duties. He'd only started an inspection tour of Skierniewice and Łowicz when the Viceroy sent a messenger to summon him back to Warsaw. His secret and hurried sidetrip to Częstochowa was not connected with any urgent business, although there were matters which demanded his personal attention. For some time now, disturbing reports had reached him that the local clergy had established a close relationship with the Committee, supporting its decrees, allowing churches to be used for demonstrations, and honoring its requests for assuring the faithful of the Virgin's blessing.

His life, he thought as he tried to pray, seemed always to have been one of struggle and turmoil.

Since childhood he had known what it meant to fight for freedom. The Felińskis were patriots who cherished the tradition of the Napoleonic era and the November insurrection. Then Janusz Hejbowicz appeared in their home and drew his mother into clandestine activities; they were preparing an underground printing shop when the project was discovered. Hejbo-wicz's real name was Konarski, an ardent freedom fighter. He was executed and Felińska, a widow, was hauled away by the police. Her six children, the eldest of which, Paulinka, was barely nineteen, were taken to Berezowo. The family estate was confiscated and the children, together with their ailing grandmother, found themselves destitute.

They were brought up thanks to kindness, occasionally that of total strangers. They lived separated from one another, and poor Paulinka paid with her life for her efforts to help her brothers and sisters. Many years passed before they saw their mother again. The Tsar, Gorchakov, and others now talked politely and graciously, and it appeared that the country was about to embark on the long road back to independence.

Unlike those who imagined that it was enough to demand that all of Europe, led by France, intervene militarily on Poland's behalf, he knew that things were actually much more complicated. After all, he'd had the opportunity of spending three years "undergoing treatment in Aix--la-Chapelle"–which was what he had written on his passport application when he'd gone to Paris. He had witnessed the February revolution and seen how easily the revolutionary government had betrayed the Polish cause, which Lamartine dismissed as "the cause of a dead people." In Paris he'd come into close contact with the Polish emigrés and got to know their hopes and bitter disputes. The principles he observed prevented him from succumbing to Towiański's charisma, but he grew deeply attached to the lonely-genius son of Mrs. Salomea Bécu, his mother's friend.

Słowacki understood the real France better than his compatriots, who said that when the French engaged in revolutions they did it for themselves alone, because other nations meant nothing to them. The French revolutionary spirit was fed by *imperateurism*. Słowacki had realized that the era of France in world history – also applied to the rest of Western Europe – had ended and would never return. He fervently assured his friend that the time drew near when the Slavic people would take the fate of the world in their hands. One day he showed Feliński a poem he'd written:

> Amid the quarrels
> The Lord sounds a great bell,
> vacating the throne for the Slav Pope.

It takes so much to save this world of God –
coming to do this is the Slav Pope,
the friend of the people.

"You'll see," he had insisted. "A Slav will become pope, probably after I'm dead. He'll call on our people and they'll come forward to sacrifice themselves. And he'll arm them with love. You'll see, Szczęsny... You'll see it yourself, but I won't."

Słowacki knew he was dying, but he was so carried away by a surge of religious emotions that he seemed not to notice the disease consuming his body. Feliński did not dare correct his friend's views, which sometimes were far removed from those of the Church, but he knew that his faith and zeal were those of a child.

When the uprising broke out in Wielkopolska, both Feliński and the ailing Słowacki set out to join the struggle. Feliński was able to take part in only one battle, but it enabled him to see the insincerity of Mierosławski and his cohorts. The experience left a deep impression, making him highly critical of those who were now preparing for the final battle and once again drawing inspiration from Mierosławski and other leaders.

He returned to Paris and spent several weeks at Słowacki's deathbed. The poet had been right: the June revolution produced only the bloodthirsty Cavaignac, while the Poles were once again blamed for all the evil that had befallen the Parisians. Then he witnessed the coming to power of Napoleon III...

Those three years had stripped him of all illusions. The age of France was past, but the age of the Slavs had not yet arrived. Who could he turn to for help? An unrequited love had left him at the edge of despair, and he felt that he wanted to die. But Our Lady must have been watching over him. He found the true path and decided to enter the priesthood. He wanted to dedicate himself and his work to the only cause which he now considered just, the spiritual rebirth of the nation, and he reasoned that they could not call themselves "the Christ of nations" when they were still an unrepentant Mary Magdalene. One could not demand freedom from the Lord without first being worthy of that freedom; or expect God's blessing when one accepted suffering badly and bitterly, filled with hatred and the desire for revenge; or lock oneself up in egotism and refuse to acknowledge that even one's enemies were called upon to serve. He wanted to work to change people's hearts and knew that he could do that best as a priest. He gave himself to the Church and let it use him for the greatest good.

Stopping in Częstochowa en route to Warsaw on that brilliant, sunny January afternoon one year ago, wishing to offer himself to Our Lady, he'd received a warm welcome and been urged to lead the coming struggle or go back to St. Petersburg. The rush of attention following his unexpected elevation had overwhelmed him. It was as if a great miracle had occurred: how could he, after working in relative obscurity in the St. Petersburg Theological Academy and serving as chaplain to the Family of Mary since his ordination seven years earlier, have anticipated the meteoric rise to Archbishop of Warsaw! On what merit? By whose insistence? It was true that on occasion he'd dispatched secret reports to Rome on certain aspects of the Church's situation in the Russian Empire, but those who'd used the information hadn't revealed its source and perhaps did not even know it. His friendship with Fr. Lubieński might have accounted for the suspicions that he was in the service of Moscow, yet his nomination had been endorsed in Rome at lightning speed and although he tried to accept it calmly, he was both elated and filled with anxiety. The elevation meant negotiations with the Tsar, his ministers, Margrave Wielkopolski. He did not give way to enthusiasm, nor did he share Lubieński's hopes, born in the parlors of the Gagarins and other Russian Catholic families.

A year ago it had seemed that he had received confirmation of his aspirations. He was going to Poland to fulfill the enormous mission of freeing minds of vain illusions that threatened to destroy the nation. Work, not illusions, was needed; hard work to rebuild the kind of faith that had once guided the nation and dictated the words of the Lwów oath to Jan Kazimierz.

At the border of the Congress Kingdom he'd encountered roads made impassable by snow. The guards allowed him to take a circuitous route across Prussian-occupied Poland, by way of Częstochowa. He had interpreted this as a special sign. One might have thought that the Church barred his way in order to receive its tribute.

His decision to return to Jasna Góra now had not been prompted by a desire to involve himself in controversy, for he lacked the time. Tension caused by the Margrave's decree on conscription into the Tsarist army was running so high that even a few hours' absence from Warsaw could have incalculable consequences. Nevertheless, he had come. His mother and his beloved Paulinka had taught him devotion to the Virgin Mary, and he desperately needed Her assistance. "When all else fails," his mother had told him, "go to Her. She will always be there for you."

Suddenly, the curtain slid down with a quiet rustle and the Icon appeared. Behind his back he heard quickened breaths and a woman's brief sob. He fixed his eyes on Our Lady's face. On his other visit he'd been surprised to see no joy in those eyes to match the joy burning in his heart. Again he saw only a solemn, vaguely sad expression. Two marks – sword slashes on the right cheek – distorted the face and aggravated the look of suffering. The small lips were pressed tightly together. Yet the face seemed to demand something of him. He hadn't sensed anything like that before, and he did not know what it could be.

"Do you want me, Blessed Virgin," he thought, "to tell You about the disasters looming over the country? The naive joy I brought with me to Poland has been crushed by bitterness and fear. At the Theological Academy and the orphanage of the Family of Mary, I had no idea how intricate life could be. I realized quickly that even my best intentions couldn't untangle the knots. I trusted people too much: kind words are not honesty. I took the Tsar's gracious words for truth and his vague promises for pledges. In Warsaw somebody called me 'the St. Petersburg bishop' and the words stung like a slap in the face. They wanted me to copy Archbishop Fijałkowski and Father Białobrzeski, but how could I when I knew they'd closed their eyes to the lunatic activities of the conspirators? In St. Petersburg, I'd been informed that the conspirators were fighting against the faith, while actually they'd been joined by countless Catholics and almost all the young priests! They trusted their leaders, just as I had trusted the Tsar and his ministers."

"But was trust possible any more?" he asked himself, recalling the conversation on the train and an earlier exchange with Zamoyski.

At the Warsaw station, the conductor had respectfully led Felinski to an empty compartment; apparently one of the priests accompanying the Archbishop had told the railwayman who he was.

Putting the luggage on the overhead rack, the conductor said, "You'll find it comfortable here, Your Excellency. Want me to close the compartment?"

"No no – I'd be glad to have company on the trip."

"As you wish. But I'll only let decent-looking people inside. No clowns. And no spies." He smiled broadly, displaying yellowed teeth below his bushy moustache. "Plenty of them around these days, nosing into everybody's business. Expecially those going beyond the cordon. They check passports and search suitcases. But don't worry, I can spot a swine like that a mile off. To hell with them!"

"That's no Christian way to talk."

"You're saying that because you're an excellency, but I'm sure you think the same as me. That scum doesn't deserve one good Christian word. It's a good thing our boys have begun sorting them out. One of 'em gets spotted, a minute later he's got a knife between his ribs."

Feliński did not respond. He'd talked about this from the pulpit constantly. Hardly a day passed in Warsaw without someone being murdered. Sometimes the victims were police agents, more often they simply were people accused of treason. Were the accusations well-founded? Was there someone who ordered the executions? When he asked priests about the slayings, they swore that the Committee passed death sentences only in exceptional circumstances, and then only after close examination of the charges. One could understand the assassination of Lüders, but what was the point of shooting at the Tsar's brother just as he was bringing hopes of a welcome change to Warsaw? Some lunatic tribunal was destroying everything that might have been achieved by compromise. The conspirators had made two attempts on the Margrave's life, which only increased his determination to hunt them down. When he emerged unscathed from the second, somebody stuck a sign on his carriage that read: "Let no one raise a hand against this lackey of the Tsar. There would be more harm than profit in this pig's death." Feliński himself had received several warnings and threats. He'd had difficulty dissuading the authorities from detailing a platoon of Cossacks to follow his carriage as they had for Wielopolski.

Two other passengers entered the compartment. They bowed respectfully. One was a middle-aged nobleman with a walrus moustache and a bald pate. He sat opposite Feliński and told him that he came from near Poznań, but because of various difficulties he'd been forced to sell his estate and move into the Kingdom. He leased an estate near Radomsko, but things were not easy there either.

"That peasant rabble drives a hard bargain over the rent," he complained. "And they've become so high and mighty, too. They quarrel with you, make demands. The reds have given them ideas, My Lord, promised them God knows what. How can you run an estate in these conditions? You toil until your head aches and still get nothing to show for it. I can see I might have to move to town for good..."

Feliński listened to the man's words without much conviction. The squire did not strike him as someone who took proper care of his land. At Wojutyn he'd known many owners who treated their lands merely as a source of income, squandering whatever they earned on clothes, card games, hounds, and other amusements. The man seated across from him seemed to fall into that category.

The other passenger was a young man in a student's uniform. He had a dark, full beard, thick lips, a crop of curly hair, and large black eyes. He bowed stiffly and sat down in a corner without introducing himself.

The second bell had already rung when a plump man in a splendid fur coat and pince-nez rushed in, panting heavily. He exchanged exaggeratedly polite greetings with Feliński, bowing repeatedly and gesticulating widely. He gave his name and said he was a barrister.

The bell rang a third time and the train pulled out.

"I'm sure Your Excellency has already heard the news," the lawyer began. "The whole of Warsaw is shocked. Miniszewski was stabbed to death, right outside his house!"

"Yes, I know. Will this terror never end? It pains me terribly. Assassinations have never been a Polish tool."

"That treacherous scribbler got what he deserved," the student unexpectedly interjected. "That dog worked for Moscow and Wielopolski. His own wife didn't have the guts to walk behind his coffin."

Everyone turned their heads in amazement.

"That's bold talk," the squire said. "And what if somebody overhears?" He got up and looked out into the corridor.

"Anyway," said the barrister, "he was a journalist. They report the information they're provided with."

"All he ever wrote were lies!" the student retorted. "If someone wants the truth they shouldn't read 'Powszechniak.' It's a dirty rag."

"And what, in your opinion, is the recommended reading material?" the barrister inquired.

"True patriots," the student's voice became even more arrogant, "know the trustworthy papers appearing underground. I suppose you've never seen them, sir?"

"Lord, what kind of a question is that? One can read them, but there's no need to shout about it," the barrister said, waving his arms. "Besides, I really have no time for reading. Travel takes up too much of my time, and I've got so much work on my hands. Once in awhile I hear this or that in a cafe..."

"And you call yourself a patriot, or a friend of Moscow?" the student pressed him.

"What do you want from me?" said the barrister indignantly, "I don't even know you." He was upset, his arms flailed about more violently and his pince-nez kept sliding down his sweaty nose. "I don't have to explain myself. I fulfill all my patriotic duties. The whole bar knows me. Of course I'm a patriot – I paid the national tax! Our curate himself collected the money." He nodded to the archbishop.

"Everybody has to pay the tax," the student went on firmly. "That's no great achievement. Those who don't pay will be ostracized and their names made public. If people weren't so fearful, the whites and the renegades wouldn't be where they are. Anyway, they'll get what's coming to them very soon... You'd know about all this, gentlemen, if you read the Committee's press. The French Emperor and Prince Napoleon have their eyes on us. The heroic General Mierosławski will turn up one day..."

"Maybe so, but you don't have to talk about it in public," the squire burst out in terror. "And certainly not so loudly! Before he gets here, we'll have rotted in prison."

"You're quite right, sir," the barrister came to his support. "We know that Napoleon is friendly toward us. He not only thinks about us – he does the thinking for us, too. I sometimes take a look at 'Czas' and the French papers."

"Back when I lived in the Duchy of Poznań, I read the papers there," the squire boasted, "and I have to tell you, gentlemen, that the Prussian have a lot of sympathy and understanding for us, too. The Germans are disliked here, but they shouldn't be. They've changed a great deal."

"I have to agree with you," the student conceded. "When the need arises, the Prussian government will definitely help us. We've got to work with everyone, so long as they're against Moscow. The Russians' behavior has to be condemned publicly at every opportunity. We have to be firm with them, then they'll give in!"

"You can't be too firm, either," the lawyer observed. "Last year the army opened fire on the crowds. The police are making arrests, throwing people in prison, torturing them. And then we had that trouble with the churches.. Father Białobrzeski was sentenced to death... Wasn't it you, Your Excellency, who reopened the churches?"

"Yes," Feliński replied. "We couldn't consent to the faithful being denied access to their Creator."

"Yet things didn't go the way they should have," the student said accusingly. "Your Lordship should've demanded guarantees of Father Białobrzeski's safe return. The church service should have been changed, to make it a huge demonstration of the people's will."

"With your permission, young man, as a bishop I have to conduct the act of reconciliation in accordance with Church rules, not according to the wishes of some individual. The church is a house of prayer, not a meeting place for political demonstration."

"Once, people of different faiths prayed together. Even nonbelievers sang religious songs. Now you've banned that."

"Yes, I have," Feliński replied politely. "The singing of religious songs alone hasn't made a Christian out of anybody yet, nor has going to church. As Catholics, we want to convince everyone that ours is the true faith, and we rejoice at every conversion. But when people profess a different faith, the Church does not encourage common prayer. Perhaps some time in the future, when we're closer to unity, that'll be possible. But for the time being, let everybody pray before his own altar."

The student kept up his attack.

"You say Mass for the Tsar, but bar Jews from your churches, and you won't give absolution to a servant girl working for a Jewish family. Yet there are many Jews among the true patriots, and rabbis have always taken part in our demonstrations."

"It's a Church custom to pray for those who rule us, even if they're of a different faith. Perhaps the Jewish population is really capable of expressing its attachment to our country, but when a naive coutry girl works in a Jewish home, amid totally different customs, she often ends up going astray."

"You have an answer for everything," the student said ironically.

"You're worried about every peasant girl who comes to town. But when the whole nation is suffering persecution and there's nothing other than prayer and hymns, Your Lordship denies it even that much consolation. Father Mikoszewski at St. Alexander's, on the other hand..."

"Excuse me," – contrary to his intentions, Feliński's vioce betrayed impatience – "but Father Mikoszewski is not authorized to present the attitude of the Church. That's not his responsibility."

"Yet Father Mikoszewski invited everybody to come and join in."

"He did, but only until he had to face Russian police superintendent. When he started to fear for his own skin, he banned singing without waiting for my orders."

Feliński regretted his words a bit. What he'd said was true, and the silver-tongued curate from St. Alexander's aroused neither his sympathy nor his trust. Nevertheless, he wished to be the shepherd of all, including those whose activities terrified him. They, too, had been entrusted to his care.

"Father Mikoszewski is only a priest," the student said. "But you, Your Lordship, govern the whole Church."

"And I have to tell you it's an enormous burden. I've faced endless accusations and objections ever since I came here. The underground press you've mentioned keeps attacking me, and I've been denounced in the 'Polish Priest's Voice'. I've been called a renegade, yet, we're talking to each other and you're not afraid to say anything that might land you in jail if I notified someone. Which means you know I won't tell anyone, don't you?"

"Of course I know that," the student admitted. "You aren't a traitor, Your Lordship. You're simply living under illusions." He made a dismissive gesture.

Feliński smiled and looked away. The passions of youth had always amused him. Outside, the browns and golds of the autumn countryside flashed by.

"Who knows where the illusions are?" the lawyer said. "I would never criticize Your Excellency's actions. When we took to the streets of Warsaw, the priests marched side by side with pastors and rabbis... It was all so beautiful. But when the army opens fire on a crowd and the police go into churches, drag people out, beat and torture them... I heard they dragged a girl from the Capuchins' church, took her to the town hall and stripped her naked. She died of shame. These are terrible things... It's better to stop singing and wait. Maybe things will change."

Feliński had talked to Andrzej Zamoyski immediately before the meeting of the gentry which led to Zamoyski being despatched to St. Petersburg. Zamoyski had spoken in a similar vein: "If we can't achieve everything we want, then let's at least seek a gradual improvement. Let's grit our teeth, keep silent and wait."

"Wait for what, Count?" he asked.

Zamoyski shrugged.

"That's a difficult question, Your Excellency. I'm not a prophet, all I can think about is independence. But there's one thing I'm sure of – if those madmen start an uprising it will mean suicide for the country."

"If you think that, why don't you join hands with the Margrave?"

"Wielopolski is selling us to Russia. If we follow him, one day we'll be surprised to find we're no longer Poles."

"The Margrave has remained a Pole. If we would help him..."

Zamoyski shook his head.

"That's impossible. Besides, Wielopolski won't accept assistance from anybody, he's too proud. He doesn't want cooperation. He has definite plans, but he's keeping them to himself. No, there's no point talking to him."

"He's done a lot of good for the country."

"I don't deny that. But these things are just pacifiers, they don't satisfy the people."

"What would?"

"A Kingdom of Poland, incorporating Lithuania and Ruthenia."

"And who would be the king?"

"The Archduke."

"The Tsar wouldn't agree."

"That's why we have to grit out teeth and wait."

While his thoughts wandered, the Madonna had been looking at him as if expecting something.

His reverence and respect for the Mother of God had never left him since childhood, but there'd been times when they could have. He had looked to Her for salvation as a high school student in Klewań, and then later during his studies in Kiev and Moscow. He'd been surrounded by a group of friends whose love of their homeland overshadowed everything, and who read every book on Polish history they could lay their hands on. They combined prayers with words of hate, they had no idea what demands real faith made of them, and their behavior had little in common with the requirements of religion. But he remained faithful to Our Lady. Not only did he call on Her for assistance, he wished to be Her servant. Not only did he never allow anyone to profane Her name, he wanted Her to lead him.

The more he knew about Poland's history, the more he was convinced of two fundamental truths. The first involved Mary's continuous protection, shielding the nation from approaching dangers and rekindling new strength in it. The other concerned the succession of the faith acts against what had brought the nation to the verge of disaster again and again. It seemed that no other nation's history was so full of opposites: periods of disaster and periods of glory. Two momentous events marked the intersection of these two lines: the salvation from the Swedish "deluge" and the vows taken by Jan Kazimierz. But despite the great Grace the country had received, breaches of faith prevailed, bringing inevitable punishment and censure. Seventy years before, they had forfeited what little independence they had. They fought in vain, engaged in vain efforts, vain struggles and vain plots. They suffered in vain, as Feliński's mother had suffered in distant Berezowo and her children had suffered, scattered and looked after by kindly strangers.

Both at home and in exile, some people had begun to reason that the pain was undeserved, that the nation was suffering innocently, as Christ had. So Towiański's followers erected crosses with no figures of Christ on them, as if suggesting that this was the cross on which Poland was being crucified. Feliński saw this as hypocrisy and false humility. We must repent, he thought, not take pride in our suffering. Towianskism was so dangerous because it carried the tempting sin of arrogance. The Resurrectionists were right in taking up a struggle against them. Feliński understood Jański's disciples better since his own brother Julian had become a Resurrectionist. There was a time when there were misunderstandings, now a thread of communion had been formed. They had vocally backed his appointment in Rome, opposing Antonelli. They also understood that his pastoral letters, written in St. Petersburg with no knowledge of Warsaw affairs, and which someone had sent to 'Le Monde', had in fact appeared in the press against his wishes.

In battling Towiański, the Resurrectionists sought to keep the cult of the Blessed Virgin within the bounds defined by the teachings of the Church. They feared that the theories of this mysterious charlatan combined heretical errors with a worship of Our Lady bordering on deification. While still in Paris, Feliński had shared those fears; when he returned from the West, he dismissed them. He believed that, even if exaggerated, love of the Mother of God could never be a man's undoing. She Herself would not permit it. And if Towiański was sincere in his cult, the cult might spell redemption for him.

Feliński often thought that those who entrusted themselves to Mary's care were taking the shortest path to Jesus. As if anticipating the future, the Pope had announced a new dogma of the extraordinary choice, and four years later Mary Herself had confirmed this verdict to a small shepherd girl in the Pyrenees. He had received Holy Orders from the dying Archbishop Hołowiński on Our Lady's birthday, regarding this as a sign ordering him to dedicate his priesthood to the service of the Blessed Virgin. He gave the name of the Family of Mary to a congregation he had set up, then, when already an archbishop, he looked after the nunneries. He also brought the nuns of the Order of St. Mary Magdalene to Warsaw, introduced May services dedicated to Our Lady in Warsaw's churches, personally blessed the pilgrims setting out for Częstochowa, and visited the shrine of the Blessed Virgin at Studzianna.

He looked into the Madonna's eyes for a sign that She was satisfied with him, but once again he failed to find one. The small lips were painfully contracted. The face seemed sad and serious, offering him no solace.

"Did She want to reproach him for something? I haven't done much," he thought. "I've tried, though. But with all this hostility toward me... The endless disappointments... I always think I can trust someone, then there's dissent all around. First they branded me a renegade, now they think I'm just a simple fool. The young priests have been drawn into conspiracy and the old ones are only interested in their own peace and comfort. Neither possess sufficient knowledge of religion. When I brought Father Golian to preach, his sermons immediately got him into conflict with the conspirators... It's so difficult to talk to them. They're young and absolutely convinced that they're right. They commit the most insane acts in the name of faith. I can't condemn them, but I can't join them either. I freed the churches from demonstrations that had nothing to do with religion, but what was the outcome? The conspirators burrowed further underground. People once came to church to sing, now the priests go to secret meetings and collaborate with the Committee's activists. What is this Committee like? Can it be trusted? Where does the revolution end and the struggle for national freedom begin? That struggle will erupt any day now, and how will it end?"

"Blessed Virgin," he whispered. "I'm sure you know..."

Although Wielopolski was outwardly rather brusque, he had a lot of sympathy for Feliński. After all, it was he who'd wanted Feliński as Warsaw's Archbishop. At the beginning he'd even asked for Feliński's blessing, but as time went by their conversations had grown increasingly difficult. Feliński had not found it easy to become intimate with the huge, morose and taciturn man, who only uttered truisms and orders. Any objection or even attempt to suggest something different only made him more determined to stick to his own plan. He was detested by both his compatriots and the Tsarist bureaucrats. The former found him contemptuously repulsive; the latter considered him stubborn and rude. He seemed to be the personification of force, yet there was something in Wielopolski's grey eyes that contradicted that.

One day Feliński entered the Margrave's office and saw a tray full of medicine bottles on his desk. Wielopolski quickly covered it with a newspaper. During the conversation he inquired about the Margrave's health; Wielopolski muttered that he felt fine. Several days later the Archbishop asked Wielopolski's sons about their father's health, but they were unable to tell him anything. Their father was a mystery even to them. Feliński did not know if there was anyone capable of looking behind the mask of the man, who was engaged in a great battle against the country's youth.

Contrary to the advice of his aides, the Margrave pushed through the plan of forced conscription: it was precisely the conspiring urban youth who would have to don army greatcoats. Although he was put off by the Margrave's inflexibility, Feliński went to him once again to try to persuade him to change his mind.

Wielopolski turned in his chair as he listened to the Archbishop's arguments. His lips were pressed tight and he stared at the floor. He waited patiently for Feliński to finish, and the he said: "Please leave those matters to me, Your Excellency. You are the Lord's servant, but I know the people. Forbearance has made them arrogant, and if they're allowed to do as they please they'll set the country ablaze and unleash a bloodbath like the one in Galicia. The exiles are stirring them up and they're also being encouraged by France and Prussia. This boil has to be lanced. If they're taken by surprise they'll either step back or start a struggle, but then they can be crushed with a single blow. They may have inflamed the country but they're not capable of putting up a real fight. All they're good for is talking about revolution, and the only way of dealing with them is by force. I didn't need more then a stick to disarm the one who tried to kill me. Do trust me, Your Excellency, I understand your position. Ramsay doesn't like my decision either, he'd prefer to exaggerate the danger and bring troops into the Congress Kingdom. We don't need them. Those revolutionist dogs will run away with their tails between their legs!"

"What could he say in reply? Wielopolski was adamant that he knew everything about the people, but did he?" thought Feliński. "He hardly ever leaves his office or listens to the people. I don't have many opportunities to talk to them either, but at least I listen to the priests. This isn't a boil on the body of the nation, but a fever that has infected everyone. I have no trust in such men as Mierosławski, nor in Napoleon nor the Prussians. I'm afraid of revolutions like those led by the Carbonari and Garibaldi, but I feel that the rising tide is not aimed at the Church, it only expresses the desire for freedom."

The Vatican did not understand that. Antonelli and other advisers had suggested to Pius IX the warning he gave Feliński in a letter. The Pope wrote: "Be careful not to make any pacts concerning the elementary structure of the Church until you receive the appropriate instructions..." They feared he might become implicated in revolutionary activity through his naive goodwill. Kajsiewicz promised a letter which would deliver a blow to all the "Mazzinites and Towianites," a letter Feliński feared greatly. He wrote Cardinal Antonelli a polite and cautious reply, telling him that "the revolutionary party, which does not want to consider any kind of compromise with the Governemnt, is almost wholly composed of youngsters with no political experience and only a superficial knowledge of religious principles. I would not say that they've hatched a plot to overthrow society and the Church."

Earlier he had approached Primate Przyłuski, asking advice on how to solve his predicament. The Poznań Archbishop sent a letter in reply, saying, "We should take a clear view of our matters, refuse to be carried away by illusions, and be guided only by our faith, common sense and experience. We all love our Motherland, both those who see its salvation in mad undertakings and consider themselves the only loyal citizens, and those who, like us, see those hopes about to be dashed..."

The primate's letter confirmed his own views. And yet he felt that if he'd made a similar statement in public in Rome, his arguments would be taken as an unconditional condemnation of priests cooperating with the underground movement, and as an indictment of Polish Catholicism.

"I have not come here to condemn," he prayed. "I wish to defend, not accuse. These are impetuous and reckless people. They do not possess true knowledge, they allow themselves to be carried away by emotion, and are too quick to heed bad advice. But their hearts are aflame with love of their country. They remind me of Juliusz... I don't want to be harsh on them. They've been entrusted to me. They are my children now, and how could anyone accuse his own children? No matter how badly they behave and how much suffering they cause me, even if they renounce me, I shall not renounce them! Oh Blessed Virgin, have mercy on them! Reach out Your protecting hand. Tell me what I must do to save them. If the faith is our future, I must save them in order to save our future. When I first put on the vestments of the Archbishop of Warsaw, it occured to me that this privilege of wearing red could signify blood. Sometimes I think it's easier to offer blood than to tolerate pain that consumes the body slowly day by day. If I can give my pain for them, pray take it..."

In the last few days the Archbishop had felt even lonelier than before. Zamoyski, whom he regarded as his dearest friend, had been forced to leave. He was not even permitted to say farewell to his sick wife. Without a leader, the whites became divided: the older people went back to their estates, while the younger ones began to lean increasingly towards the reds. Duke Konstanty had changed. He had previously seemed sincere, open and forthright, now he'd withdrawn into himself. It was obvious that he weighed every word he said. He was no longer the same man who only half a year earlier, after suffering a minor injury in an attempt on his life, had said that the blood would seal a friendship.

Terrorists were being hanged on the slopes of the Citadel. When they aimed their pistols at the Grand Duke and tried to stab Wielopolski, the people were horrified. But once hanged they became symbols of self sacrifice and martyrdom. Strands of the ropes were collected like holy relics; people looked for signs in the sun and brought flowers to the gallows. Masses for the hanged men's souls were said for weeks on end.

Feliński allowed the Masses to take place in defiance of the authorities' demands. He prayed for these men himself. It was one thing to condemn assassinations, he reasoned, but another to care about souls. He thought about Jaroszyński the would-be assassin, whom he had tried in vain to save. The poor man had been deceived into believing that he was carrying out the Committee's orders, and at the last moment had decided not to pull the trigger when he saw that the Archduke's wife was pregnant.

"I am also asking for intercession on their behalf," he whispered. "They, too, have been put in my care. I haven't been able to reach them. I judged them too harshly at the beginning, and afterwards it was too late..."

The candles flickered, alternately casting shadows and patches of light on Mary's face. Momentarily the Icon seemed to disappear in the darkness, only to reemerge the next instant showing a face full of sorrow.

"Won't You tell me anything?" he thought. "Advice from You is the best there can be. Shall I return to the problems that proved beyond my abilities? The burden that fell on my shoulders was more than I could bear, but I was proud of the dignity it bestowed on me. Perhaps I should have refused? Perhaps I was not humble enough? I've come to ask Your assistance. You look at me sorrowfully, as if in sympathy, yet You haven't spoken. Still, I feel that You are listening, trying to tell me something, but I don't understand. Can't You say it more clearly? Punish me if I've abused my office, but save those infected with the fever of action and those who doubt. Those who have been wronged so terribly and those who respond with hatred. Those who suffer and those who will suffer in the future."

He raised his head. He felt shame for having come there like a resentful child wanting to be comforted. Shouldn't he have remembered that Mary knew about everything and that She was never indifferent to what happened?

Now it appeared that Her eyes pointed to the Cross. Feliński had accused Towiański of refusing to see the Body of the Lord Condemned, who had won redemption through His humiliation and suffering. When Feliński looked at the Cross he saw the suffering, not the reward for that suffering.

Perhaps this was what Her eyes wished to tell him: "You want to fight by word and deed. My Son could do nothing more on the Cross. He endured the suffering until death. When something is too great for a man to cope with, all he can do is try to endure."

A painful thought shook his body. He was barely forty, still in his prime. A man of forty did not step down and leave the stage...

But then he remembered Słowacki again. He, the greatest poet of all, had so much more to say yet he did not rebel in the face of approaching death. He slipped away peacefully, as though convinced that the miracle of the Slav pope would occur together with his death. Didn't Jesus say that the grain of wheat must die in the ground?

The door opened and a sudden gust of wind sent a ripple through the candle flames. A shadow flitted across Mary's face, creating the illusion that it had twitched, and that the half-closed eyes were signaling approval.

A friar leaned over the faldstool.

"With your permission, Your Excellency, we'd like to cover the Icon. It's eight o'clock..."

"Please go ahead," he replied.

Slowly, the Icon disappeared behind its silver screen. He did not take his eyes off Our Lady until the last moment, but he no longer looked for consolation there. His entire life had passed before his eyes during that amazingly short hour, as it was said that people saw their lives a moment before death.

He rose and walked towards the door. A friar rang his keys, gently urging the people on their way. They rose from their knees and filed through the doorway. The women sniffed back their tears.

Feliński noticed a clean-shaven man whose hair was cut short. He wore spectacles and held himself stiffly erect, and he bowed as he passed. The

Archbishop thought he recognized the man, but he could not recall where he'd seen him before.

He leaned toward the friar. "Who is he, Father?"

"Some nobleman from Kobryń. I didn't quite catch is name... Tugutt, Traugutt, something like that. It sounded German."

"What else do you know about him?"

"Very little. He's a former officer. He arrived yesterday, asked for shelter in the monastery, and went to confession. Then he ordered a Mass for the souls of his grandmother, his wife, and his sons."

"He seems so young to have lost those closest to him," Feliński said. "And you say he's from Kobryń?"

The friar nodded. "But he also said he used to live in Saint Petersburg."

That was where he must have seen him, Feliński thought. Probably at St. Catherine's. He was sure the man had worn a uniform then, although he might have been just another army deserter who'd joined the conspirators. Yet the fact that he had come to Jasna Góra spoke well for him.

The Archbishop walked slowly down the unlit aisle. Supper and an evening of conversation with the friars awaited him. He would have preferred being left alone with the thoughts his prayers had awakened, but is was important to see to other matters.

He left the chapel in a mood of tranquility he had not experienced in months.

13*

CHAPTER 10

JOHN

Wheezing with every step, the squat, heavy-set priest plodded deliberately along the row of gates that stretched from the mouth of St. Barbara Street to the entrance of the basilica. The afternoon heat seemed to penetrate even the soles of his shoes. He wiped his neck and forehead with a damp handkerchief, and with a resigned look on his flushed face he glanced into the cloudless sky. His companion, a slim young priest who moved with an easy gait, reduced his pace.

"Your Excellency must be tired," he said in Italian.

"Don't worry about me, Father, I'm just an old mule who's been stabled too long." He gave a long sigh and patted his sweaty face again. "I never wheezed when I was in the army, but I wasn't fat then. Maybe this is God's punishment for not exercising." He added: "Except at the dinner table."

"Your Excellency was in the army?" The priest expressed surprise. "Was that during the war?"

"Oh yes," the Archbishop said.

"Did you see any action?"

"I comforted the wounded in the hospitals at Bergamo and Turino. There was no one to fight there except the non-believers who took pride in their lack of faith. But they were all good men and I'm sure Our Lord helped them see the light in time." He passed through the monastery gate, paused, and looked around the courtyard. "Is it always so crowded?"

A tide of pilgrims flowed constantly to and from the monastery. Several fatigued women sat in the gateways to escape the sun. There was a line of pilgrims outside the office to request Masses, and another at the door of the luggage room where visitors left their bags, knapsacks and bundles.

"It's like this all through the season," the young priest explained. "They start coming in April, the crowds swell in May, and it stays that way until November. Between Christmas and Easter it's relatively quiet."

Insolito a meravigliosamente. The Archbishop shook his head in admiration. "Your bishop told me that over two million people visit Jasna Góra every year. That's almost hard to believe. There are other places where Our Lady is just as deeply revered."

"Ostra Brama, Kodeń, Ludźmierz, Swarzew, Wysokie Koło..."

"Yes, yes, you're an extraordinary nation. The Holy Father told me that he got to know your people fairly well. He said I had to see Częstochowa –" he nearly choked on the pronunciation – "and pay my respects to your Madonna."

In front of the altar beneath the galleries, a stream of worshippers received Holy Communion. Another lined the aisles outside the confessionals. Several young Paulites guided the faithful skilfully as they stepped back from the altar rail, knelt down at the side and, after a brief prayer, headed for the basilica.

The titular bishop of Areopolis surveyed the scene with a benign smile. The pilgrims were poorly dressed. Here and there a few flowery peasant headscarves and colorfully striped aprons stood out against the drab background. The people seemed tired and were not very clean. The pungent odor of sweat hung in the air, but it did not disturb the Apostolic visitor to Bulgaria. He was a peasant himself and had taken part in many pilgrimages, traveling on foot with his mother and brothers, often carrying his shoes in his hand. He knew what is was like to walk all day along a dusty road under a scorching sun. He'd slept in barns and risen early to wash at a well and wait for Mass to be said in a patch of shade. He remembered the tiring drowsiness and the buzzing in his ears. But that weariness had also brought joy. Then there was the trek back home, to a village perched on the side of a lone mountain which rose up out of the plain. The Roncalli family home was like all the others, built of brick and roofed with weathered tiles. The life of the extended family was concentrated in the broad arcades upstairs from which a row of doors led to tiny dark rooms. People only slept there. That was where children were born and old men died. The people here at Jasna Góra were just like him and those dear to him.

The priest led Archbishop Roncalli through the gate below the clock and across a small yard that was an extension of the chapel of Our Lady. Beyond the entrance, adorned with antlers and old paintings, steep stairs led up to the Knights' Hall. At the far end was the monastery gate. Notified of the visitor's arrival, two friars fluent in Italian greeted him.

"Does Your Excellency wish to tour the monastery, or will he perhaps rest a moment first?" one of them asked.

"No, I ran out of breath coming up the hill but I'm not really tired. If you'd be so kind as to show me the marvels of this place, we could start at once."

They descended the stairs and went to the sacristy. Here, too, there was a great deal of movement under the vaulted ceiling. Several priests prepared to say Mass, others were removing their liturgical robes among a throng of altar boys. A few pilgrims shyly approached the priests and friars.

The Paulites motioned everyone aside and led Roncalli into the narrow passageway that led to the altar in the chapel. He felt like a camel passing through the eye of a needle. No mass was being celebrated at the moment, but the Icon was uncovered. Roncalli knelt down on the á prie-dieu the monks offered him.

"Bene," he said. *"Molto grazie.* And now please allow me to pray for a while."

The friars stepped back. Angelo Roncalli turned his eyes to the picture. The chapel echoed with the sound of breathing and whispered prayers. Candlelight reflected in the silver ornaments of the Icon, the strings of amber beads, the votive offerings. The dark face of the Madonna looked down calmly from underneath the golden gown held up by angels. Her features could not be seen from a distance. Kneeling only a few feet away, he saw the long slender nose, the narrow half-closed eyes, the scars on the cheek and the small lips which seemed slightly contorted, as if from the pain of the wound.

He could not stop looking at that face.

Before Roncalli left the Vatican to assume his duties, the bespectacled Pius XI told him: "It would be a good idea if Your Excellency made a detour to Poland during your travels between Rome and Sofia. It's a very unusual country indeed. I grew attached to it and am fond of the people. Go to Częstochowa. The Black Madonna is quite extraordinary. Nobody knows how it got there... You know, when I look at Our Lady of Częstochowa, I think I see a similarity between Her Face and the Face of Jesus on the Turin Shroud... Go to Częstochowa if you can. When you look at that face, you won't be able to take your eyes off it. Unusual ideas will come into your head."

The Pope had been right. The longer he looked at the dark face with the forehead covered by a creased scarf, the more he was swept away by a raging current of thought.

Several years before, when he was in his forties, Roncalli had reached an important crossroads. After his return from the army he stayed in Rome and worked in the Congregation for the Propagation of the Faith. He liked the work. Slowly, he was drawn back into the well-oiled machinery of the Vatican state. He knew from that moment on that he would be climbing the ladder of success. He had never been short of ambition; from the beginning of his career in the priesthood he'd had to suppress it. He knew that what he lacked in talent he could make up with hard work and dedication. He believed that he could go far. His bridled ambitions struggled to break free.

Unexpectedly, he'd been summoned to the Pope. Pius XI announced that he was sending him to Bulgaria as Apostolic visitor and he cautioned that it would not be a simple mission. The Bulgarian Catholics were few and widely scattered, lacked priests and were caught up in internal disputes. The odd position of the King, torn between two denominations, only made matters worse.

"You'll have to find the various Catholic groups," the Pope told him, "establish contact with them and define the principles of ministration to their communities. This won't be easy. But I want to entrust this important mission to you in particular, Father. I remember how you once told me that you thought it our primary duty to spread the Gospel in the world.

And that's exactly what I expect you to do."

On the day of St. Joseph, his most beloved saint, Roncalli was ordained an archbishop *in partibus infidelium*. It was only a title, one which was to ennoble somewhat the modest position of a visitor of the Holy See to a non-Catholic country. It did not hold the promise of educating, stirring consciences, or winning people's hearts, but could he refuse the Holy Father's request?

Before he had accepted the words *Oboedientia et pax* as his maxim as bishop, from the moment he entered the seminary, he had decided that it was his absolute duty to obey the Church authorities. He was already struggling against the desire to make decisions and impose his views on others, the inclination to argue, discuss and, most of all, to talk too much. These things cropped up every time he examined his conscience. Striving to control himself, he requested the assistance of Our Lady. Having decided one day that he still did not love Her enough, he resolved to strengthen his love by keeping Her permanently in his mind. He prayed to Her stubbornly and repeatedly. He prostrated himself before Her, confessing his lapses and begging Her to teach him humility and obedience. Above all he prayed that he might learn to love. He realized how much self-love there was in him, and knew it prevented him from loving others more strongly.

He wanted to learn to love because he wanted to be a saint. He reasoned that a Christian, especially a priest, could aim for nothing less. Day after day he practiced rigid self-control. He complied with every rule of seminary life; he said every prayer he was instructed to. He was convinced that when he'd done everything in his power, the God would grant the assistance necessary for victory. The early failures and defects in his spiritual life worried him, but the time came when he understood that this concern was not defeat but a sign of the conceit still in his heart. In his diary, he wrote: "When I get too talkative – even without seeking glory for myself – I later feel bitter and discouraged. This is how self-love pains over self-love. My tears are then crocodile tears..."

When he became bishop, his persistent work found expression in his motto, "Obedience and peace." Obedience to everything the Church taught and commanded, everything required by its eternal wisdom, which had allowed it to bring forth so many saints; but also peace of spirit and peace of heart, control over the feelings of regret, anger or impatience.

201

Obedience and peace were two features that had distinquished St. Joseph. Three centuries earlier Cardinal Baronius, the hero of a book Roncalli had written, had chosen the same motto.

And what a useful motto it turned out to be when he arrived in Bulgaria. The task assigned to him by Pius XI proved to be almost beyond his powers. He started his work by touring the villages inhabited by Catholics, which were strewn over wild, mountainous terrain. If a place could not be reached by car, he traveled on horseback. Not being fond of exercise, he found the journeys terribly exhausting. Yet he was satisfied; for the first time he had a taste of genuine missionary work.

His satisfaction was short-lived. The trips made him realize how very dispersed and diversified the Catholic population of Bulgaria was. It was futile even to dream of uniting it and organizing a Bulgarian Church! Whatever he managed to put together soon fell apart like a sand castle. On top of that he had to face all the difficulties on his own. He had neither enough help nor enough funds, and he soon realized that he could not expect them from the Holy See. The Vatican did not seem bothered about the troubles of its visitor: his reports went unanswered for months. Finally, the Archbishop reached the conclusion that Bulgarian matters evidently were troublesome to the Vatican bureaucrats as well, and that the Vatican must want its envoy to manage affairs on his own as best he could.

He struggled against overwhelming bitterness. Letters from friends said that life in Rome proceeded as usual. New people were squaring up to new tasks, while his own efforts and struggles were producing no tangible results. He lived on his own, deserted and forgotten, but he did not give up.

Finally something began to take shape. The individual factions stopped fighting and pledged to cooperate, and at last he found a man who seemed to be the right candidate for bishop. Stefan Kurtev was ordained quickly. He was young, bursting with energy, and full of ideas. But would this promising bishop manage to maintain control of the still tangled situation once Archbishop Roncalli left?

Leaving Rome for Bulgaria, Roncalli had imagined his exile might last a year, two at most. Four years later he was still there, longing for Italy and his family and friends. Loneliness, combined with an awareness of how little he'd accomplished, pained him immensely. Now that a bishop had been installed, the Apostolic visitor could report his mission fulfilled. But was he really entitled to say that? Could he leave Kurtev by himself?

The Archbishop read voraciously in his tiny Sofia apartment. He frequently reached for the writings of Francis de Sales, whom he respected greatly. Since he himself became a bishop, St. Francis had been an example that he wanted to copy. In one of his works he read: "I know that nothing in this world is so inferior as to be completely useless. One only needs to put the thing to proper use. The Lord has given me the Grace to understand that I was made for Him, by Him and in Him... Therefore, wherever the service of the Lord's glory may call me, there I will go with no objection."

"This is the approach I should adopt myself," he thought as he put away the book. "I also have received everything from Him and for Him. Whatever He asks of me I should do without a trace of dissent. If it was His will that I should work here, what does it matter that great events are taking place in Rome? He wants me here."

He reached for the book again: "Bishops have a special responsibility to work for the purification of souls... They could make no better use of their time than to pursue precisely this goal..."

"I wasn't made a bishop because of my own personal merits," he thought, "but in order to serve Him. In Rome there are opportunities and friends; here in Bulgaria I'm alone in the face of mounting obligations, difficulties and disappointments. There is so much to be done and so little that I can do. And yet – this is why I've been sent to this place."

He knelt down and began to pray. He called on Our Lady to provide assistance, then he decided that he would go to Rome and submit an application for an extension of his stay in Bulgaria."

His internal revolt had been suppressed, but a feeling of regret and uneasiness lingered in his heart. He knew that his decision was right and proper, nevertheless he was unable to free himself of fearing the days and years to come when he would have to abide by that decision.

Now he studied the dark face in front of him and thought that Our Lady returned his concentration and anticipation. There was so much strength there, but at the same time so much peace. It was the peace he missed; the peace for which he had prayed in vain during his retreat prior to going to Bulgaria, and throughout his stay there. Thanks to those prayers he had endured, but now it seemed that his reserves of peace had been totally depleted. The sea on which he sailed was becoming stormy again. The storm raged and the foaming waves rose higher, yet he felt solid ground under his feet. If only he didn't lose hope!

He looked ardently at the Madonna, whose narrow eyes seemed to assume growing gentleness and kindness. He recalled St. Francis's words: "And if the Lord orders you to walk on the waves of adversity, fear not. He is beside you..."

"What does it matter that my work in Bulgaria has produced so little?" he thought. "Peace, peace above all. What may seem nothing to me, must certainly mean something to Christ. He wants that 'something' and is using me in my incompetence. I am there to work, but the result depends on Him. It's of no importance whether I see the fruit of my labors. Peace and patience! Only of peace and patience can true love be born. And without love I shall never become a saint."

Since his years in the seminary, his desire to achieve sainthood had never left him. He counterposed this desire to the luster of worldly ambitions. "God," he thought, "never promised that I would live to be eighty and receive honors and dignities. Over the years, God has only told me that if I want to love Him, I must trust Him to the point of saintliness, as the saints did. They put themselves wholly at His command without expecting consolation in return. And He gave them peace – His peace. Not the peace of the world or the peace of oblivion, but the peace of trust, the peace of patient anticipation."

"Oh Mother of the mysterious Icon," he prayed, "grant me that kind of peace. Let my heart tremble and suffer, but let my faith remain unshaken. I'll reject all earthly desires. I'll do nothing to change my situation. I'll live from one day to the next, obeying the commands of the Holy Father. If only You will look after me and lead me as You have all these years..."

A priest arrived to say Mass. The people behind Roncalli came to life. He heard whispers, sighs, and sobs. The voices merged into a noise resembling the roar of the sea. This was not merely a crowd of the faithful, the Icon and the people together were like a mighty force capable of changing history.

He compelled himself to rise from the faldstool and leave the chapel. The Paulite assigned to assist him waited in the sacristy. He followed them out, suppressing his natural inclination to talk in order to hear the history of the Icon and the monastery.

"So that king of yours proclaimed Her the Queen of Poland? I read about that – a book by Sienkiewicz, wasn't it? What a magnificent decision! Others have made Her their queen too, then they forgot about it. But you've remembered despite the enslavement and partitions that lasted so many years. *Molto bene, molto bene.* I know only a little about your history. In Brescia we remember that some of our people assisted in your struggle for liberty."

When they asked him to sign the visitors' book in the library, he wrote: "*Fiat pax in virtute Tua, Regina Poloniae et abundantia in turribus Tuis.*"

The Paulites invited Roncalli to dinner. Seated under a great crucifix hanging on a wall covered with paintings and crowned with arches, he listened to the history of the huge refectory. Exhausted by the tour of the monastery, he ate with gusto. Later, one of the friars told him that the car sent by the bishop to take him to Cracow waited outside the gate.

"Very well," he said. "I'll leave in a moment. But with your permission I'd like to visit the Madonna once more."

He was led into the dark, silent chapel. Without fanfare, the Icon was uncovered. Again he knelt down at the same spot. The Virgin's face seemed to be very dark and smooth at close quarters. He could barely see Her features, but the eyes seemed to be as full of kindness and peace as before.

"Bless me, Our Lady," he begged. "Bless me, Queen of a nation I have grown so fond of. I don't know if I'll ever visit this shrine of Yours again, but I will never forget this day. Don't ever let me out of Your care. And if You wish to show me that You are by my side, then, at the end of my days, wherever I am, let me see those most gracious eyes of Yours again."

CHAPTER 11

FATHER MAXIMILIAN

On the eve of World War II, a balding friar wearing a black cassock girded by a white rope entered the sacristy with obvious hesitation, as if intimidated by the row of priests donning their liturgical vestments. He had a thick salt-and-pepper beard that fell to his chest and his head was inclined slightly to the right, which gave him a look of pained fatigue. One of the Paulites noticed him at once and hurried to greet him.

"*Laudetur Jesus Christus.* Who's come to visit us at Jasna Góra! How are you, Father Maximilian?"

"*In saecula saeculorum.* I was on my way to Cracow and decided on the spur of the moment to stop here for a few hours, to bow before the Virgin. Could I possibly say Mass?"

"Of course! Let me check the book and see what we have today." The Paulite opened a small ledger. "Right now there's a Hungarian priest saying Mass... Then... Yes, you can say yours in forty-five minutes, Father."

"Thank you."

"And how are things going at Niepokalanów? I hear it's been one anniversary after another."

That was all over now, Maximilian Kolbe said. Last year they had celebrated the twentieth anniversary of the Militia of the Immaculate and the tenth anniversary of the founding of the house, now they were nearing the end of the first of the last five years before the quarter-centenary.

"We haven't achieved much so far," he said modestly.

"Oh, but you're really too demanding of yourselves. You're doing an amazing amount of work! We hear about you so often. The eyes of all Poland are on you. Everyone reads 'Rycerz Niepokalanej' and 'Mały Dziennik', and I hear you're going to start a radio broadcasting service soon."

"We'd like to begin on our feastday, but there are problems."

"You've coped with problems before, Father. You're very good at it."

"The Immaculate Virgin overcomes the difficulties, not me. Niepokalanów is her achievement, She watches over it. All we know how to do is spoil things. Sometimes it seems that developing Niepokalanów means more newspapers or better equipment, but in reality it means souls won over to Her. I keep repeating this to myself and the others. I suppose that even if we were scattered to the far corners of the earth and had to flee without our cassocks, there would still be growth if each of us saw love develop inside himself."

The White Friar raised his hands in mock terror. "Who could scatter you? It looks as though the storm is abating now, after that Czechoslovak business."

Kolbe wanted to say something – his lips moved impatiently underneath his beard, but he did not speak.

"Will you be going back to Japan, Father?" the Paulite asked.

He shook his head. "The Order wants me here, not in Mugenzai nor Sono. It appears I'm of more use in Poland."

"Of course, of course. It's all just beginning in Japan, isn't it?"

"Yes. There's a lot of resistance but also a great deal of interest in Christianity, lots of fervor and devotion. If only we didn't disturb one another and if the times were a bit more peaceful. Although, maybe it's precisely because of that –" He abruptly denied a thought that had formed in his mind. "If you don't mind, I'll go to the chapel now and pray."

"I'll come for you when it's time for Mass."

He left the sacristy, passed the stairs leading to the Knights' Hall and went into the chapel. The Icon was uncovered and Mass was ending in

A view of the east front
of the Paulite Church
and Monastery at Jasna Góra

The Paulite Church.
View of the High Altar

The Church Sacristy, 1649–51, with stucco work and murals, after 1690

Refectory of the Monastery
with the vaulting decorated
in stucco work, before 1670, and polychrome, 1696

Pope John Paul II presenting a portrait
of Bishop Stanisław Hozjusz in 1987

Painting of Father Maximilian Kolbe.
Gift to Pope John Paul II during
his second visit to Jasna Góra in 1983

Pope John Paul II
with Cardinal Stefan Wyszyński
in Cracow, 1979

Apartment of Pope John Paul II
during his first visit in the Paulite Monastery
at Jasna Góra

Monstrance endowed *ex voto*
for the defence of Jasna Góra
against the Swedes in 1655, 1672

Miraculous Image of Our Lady
in the Ruby Robe

front of the altar. As usual, the chapel was full of people, standing and kneeling in front of the grille and in the narrow side passages.

Father Maximilian found a vacant faldstool and knelt down. He had a sleepless night behind him and found it hard to pray standing. His legs trembled and his body seemed to sag. He had had trouble with his health all the years he'd been in Japan. When he returned he was better at first, but recently he'd begun to feel weak again. The ailment was as obstinate as a mule. His doctor had already told him to spend some weeks resting in the mountains in Zakopane.

But how could he go when developments unfolded with the speed of an airplane – or rather an etheroplane – while the atmosphere became heavier and more stifling with every passing day? In Nagasaki, immersed in his ardous but intoxicating missionary work, he'd had no time to listen for the thunder of approaching events. He neither read newspapers nor listened to the radio; the letters he received from Poland were like a voice from a totally different world.

On his return, however, he'd found himself in the midst of events that developed at a feverish pace. A sense of terror wafted over Poland from beyond its western frontiers. He immediately understood the danger. Descended from a Silesian family, he knew all the various brands of Germanism – that same Germanism that had once deprived his forefathers of everything they had. More than many other people he was conscious of the lands subjugated centuries ago, which still waited for liberation. Busy with his missionary work, he suddenly noticed one day that the danger was nearer and crueler than ever before.

When he left Poland, next to the great cause that guided him – conquering the whole world for Our Lady – he was also motivated by a smaller, private desire. Deeply involved in impassioned journalism, and excitable in his struggle against evil, he too often spoke out against those who personified that evil. He knew it wasn't easy to separate people from ideals, yet he felt that She did not want that struggle. She demanded opposition to evil combined with love of one's fellow men. In order to understand Her injunctions, one had to submit totally to Her will and renounce the militancy which too often made one go too far.

His forebodings proved correct. In Japan there had been no lack of difficulties, but there was no struggle that had to be suppressed. There were opponents, but no enemies. The opponents were ready to listen. Through exchanging arguments, he began to understand his fellow men more fully and became more indulgent towards them. Previously, he'd tried to impose on others the rigid standards he set for himself, now his attitude was more moderate. He began to realize that if Mary wanted to surround the whole world with care, She wanted this accomplished differently than he had first believed when he began his work and when every month more copies of his magazine left the Grodno printer.

"So is this the way it is?", he asked himself as he raised his eyes to the Icon.

Mary's narrow eyes looked at him from above Her bejeweled gown and beneath the golden crown supported by angels; the same eyes that had looked at him years ago from the plaster figure on a small altar behind a wardrobe in his family home, and that had promised him two crowns – one white, and one red. Later he'd searched for that look in the figure of the Blessed Virgin at the entrance to the Massabiele cave, which had enraged Bernadette because it bore no resemblance to the Blessed Virgin she had seen there. He had prayed that he would see it in the chapel, searching for it above the red armchair in which a pious Sister of Charity had once seen Our Lady and received a holy medal from Her. He had prayed to see it each time he passed the figure of the Immaculate – a plain, sugary one – that stood outside the makeshift chapel at Niepokalanów.

For the first crown, the white one, he'd fought for years. It had not been as easy as it might have appeared to the friars around him. He had to reject every temptation that came his way, push it aside when it still appeared harmless. The zeal and enthusiasm with which he infected others and which depleted his strength was an attempt to rechannel the flame that burned within him and would have turned into a huge, uncontrollable fire were it not for his redoubled vigilance. His missionary work also helped to extinguish that fire and he exhausted himself through constant action. Although just forty-four years old, he already felt mortally drained. The strenuous work and a succession of illnesses had made him feel like a fruit from which the last drop of juice had been squeezed. That was the condition he'd been in when he returned to Poland.

His illness had subsided, but the exhaustion remained. While once he'd been bursting with energy, he now had to gather all his strength in a superhuman effort for every action. Not even the tense atmosphere could awaken him. Several years before he would have plunged into it headfirst, writing, proclaiming, organizing, and struggling for his ideals. That he still fought today was thanks to his relentless willpower. He fought, while at the same time restraining himself, afraid of hurting his fellow men. His former enemies were enemies no more, he only considered them to be unfortunate souls who had lost their way. He was able to see some good in every man and to love everyone.

Despite his permanent exhaustion, fever, and sleeplessness, despite the apathy he overcame a hundred times a day, he sensed something terrible in the air. Something he thought of as a mysterious monster creeping out of the darkness. Others did not sense it. Still others saw the approaching danger but tried to believe that it would disappear by itself, just as it had appeared. Yet he was convinced it was getting nearer and nearer all the time.

Kolbe wanted to finish as soon as possible the tasks he considered most important in his life. Mugenzai no Sono needed him no longer, but there was still the problem of Amalam, the Niepokalanów of India. Almost everything was ready to start work there, he just had to get the people together and set out on a journey once more. However, he knew that he would not be able to go. The original Niepokalanów near Sochaczew had become a huge machine that required internal organization, and there was the need to prepare people for the day it would have to run without him. Up to then he had always run it himself, no matter how far away he might have been. He feared that should he disappear, his successors would succumb to the temptation of erecting huge, solid buildings and continually installing more advanced equipment, while the only idea that Niepokalanów was really meant to serve, that of winning people's hearts to Mary and through Her to Jesus, would fade into the background. Material expansion did not matter to him. Plain wooden-frame houses were better than massive buildings that could only arouse the envy of those living in poverty. Father Francis had rejected everything to be able to go to the people, and his sons took to the roads of Europe as itinerant missionaries with no possessions of their own, to bring divine joy to the people. Today this joy was carried by newspapers dedicated to the glory of the Immaculate Virgin.

"Tomorrow", he thought, "it would be broadcasted over the airwaves. Yet print and the radio were merely tools that would change in time. It was not the tools that mattered, but the message."

There was something else he wanted to complete. For many years he'd harbored the idea of a book in which he would present the role of Our Lady in the contemporary world. Lourdes, the medal, the forgotten writings of Louis de Montfort... These were the milestones on the path along which his thoughts traveled. He wanted to go even further. His mind was already conceiving the unimaginably great role of the Immaculate Virgin in the contemporary world, the One who passed each human prayer to Her Son and transmitted all Grace from the Holy Spirit. He wanted to write about who She really was, what She desired, and what She could offer people. He wanted to create a work that would be the song of life.

He was always preoccupied with such thoughts, yet the daily problems which absorbed him prevented a quiet formulation of his views. He dissipated his energy constantly, writing popular articles for "Rycerz Niepokalanej", educating the friars, assigning duties at Niepokalanów, and attending sessions of the various committees to which he was invited with increasing frequency. Afterwards he found it difficult to gather his scattered thoughts.

"Does this mean I'm not going to be able to write my book about You?" he asked himself, and looked at Mary's face for an answer.

The scarred face of the Mother of God was full of tranquility. She seemed to be telling him to leave everything to Her: "Don't you remember saying so many times that everything only becomes what it should be once it's entrusted to Me?"

"But what if my life is nearing its end?"

He had thought about death since adolescence; it followed him step by step. How he would hate to die in bed! Shouldn't a knight of the faith perish like a soldier, struck down by enemy fire on the field of battle? If he were to die the ordinary way, a victim of consumption perhaps, what would happen to the promise of the red crown?

Three of his brothers, Walenty, Antoni, and Józef, were dead. He always remembered them in his prayers, as he remembered his father, killed in rather mysterious circumstances. Only one brother was left, but the news of Franuś that reached him from Grodno filled him with pain. Franuś needed his prayers more than the others. Only his mother found a peaceful refuge with the nuns in Cracow.

And how much he had to pray for his fellow friars, the hundreds he'd summoned to one Niepokalanów and the other! So many of them fell

under the burden of temptation and hardship. Some just walked away...
And the Masons? Since war had been declared on them, it was his duty to
fight, firing the missiles of his prayers. And Poland? His great plan of
conquering the world for Mary centered on his native land, which may
have been why he'd wanted so much to visit Jasna Góra and pay homage to
the Immaculate Virgin. After all, nowhere were the causes of Mary and
Poland so strongly bound together.

Kolbe was so engrossed in thought that the White Friar had to clear his
throat several times to attract his attention.

"Father Guardian... It's time to go to the sacristy."

Without a word he rose and followed the Paulite.

Two boys wearing red capes offered to serve at the Mass. They looked
at the priest in amazement. They'd seen many clergymen, but never one
with a beard. Father Maximilian noticed their curiosity.

"Looking at my beard, eh?" he asked, smiling. "You see, I've just
returned from Asia, where all the missionaries grow beards. This identifies
us to the locals. But now it's time to shave it off, as I probably won't be
going on another mission."

He put on a chasuble and followed the altar boys along the narrow
passage. Now he had the Madonna's face directly in front of him. Her gaze
rested on him like a soft yet firm touch.

Each time he said Mass, he opened with words of gratitude to Our
Lady. If it were not for Her Grace, if the water of Lourdes had not healed
his gangrenous finger he would not have been ordained. He had become
what he was through Her Will, and he owed everything he'd ever
accomplished to Her.

His work had always been connected with the desire to serve Her. He
repelled all weakness with his determination to repay Her for the Grace he
had received. And extraordinary things had happened: although permanently infirm, he was able to achieve more than others. Despite many
difficulties and much envy, his work grew before his eyes.

"What does it mean that my strength is now beginning to fail?" he
wondered. "Am I no longer to be a tool in Her hands?"

Uneasily, he raised his head and looked at the face of the Blessed
Virgin. But he found no reproach nor anger there.

"Do You want my work to come to an end?" he thought. "It is You who decides everything. I was foolish and vain to think that I was the one You had chosen to spread Your glory all over the world. I know: You want something else. You want us to be like runners in a relay, passing the baton from one to another, each contributing to people's knowledge of You.

"I've told my brothers many times that there are three stages in a man's life. First he learns and prepares himself, then he works and acts, finally he suffers. I had a feeling that was the way things were, but, as often happens, I didn't notice this division in my own life. You have accepted my division, and now You are telling me that my work is over. Now comes the time to suffer, and to act through suffering."

He shivered. He knew what it meant to suffer. He had learned about the suffering of the spirit when he'd encountered opposition, been called a madman, been mocked and suspected of trying to generate publicity for himself, been envied, been disappointed, and when he'd been betrayed and deceived. He was also acquainted with physical suffering: fevers that sapped his strength, coughing, aching lungs, sore throat, toothaches, nervous trembling, stomach upsets, sleepless nights, and drowsiness during the day. But could all that even be compared with his suffering of recent months? Wasn't something about to happen that would dwarf everything he's known so far?

Father Maximilian finished Mass and returned to the sacristy. The White Friar appeared at his side again.

"Can I invite you to breakfast, Father Guardian?"

He looked at his watch. "I'd be delighted. I still have some time before my train."

The Paulite waited for him to finish his prayer of thanksgiving and then led him through a hidden door in the corner of the sacristy to the part of the monastery that was off limits to women. They entered the huge refectory with its magnificent Gothic ceiling. A giant crucifix hung above the main table. Groups of friars and laymen sat along the rows of long tables stretching across the vast hall. A friar immediately approached with a jug of steaming coffee.

The Paulite sat down beside him. "Have you heard, Father, that the Germans have set an enormous levy on the Jews for Grünszpan's attempt on the life of their ambassador in Paris?"

"I have."

"What they're doing is terrible. They're persecuting them in the cruelest manner. Where will it all end? Your writings, Father, are sometimes none too friendly towards the Jews..."

"I've tried to distinguish between those Jews who have done Poland harm and those who are honest and decent. But now I'm worried that the latter may suffer for the sins of the former. It isn't easy to write when you have to fight for the things you believe are most important yet at the same time love your fellow man. I sometimes think that St. Louis de Montfort may not have been totally right when he wrote that the legacy of the Immaculate Virgin will only be bestowed on those whom he called predestined to receive it, the successors to the chosen people. No, no... She watches over everyone."

"Do you really think so, Father?"

"I'm convinced of it. She wants everyone to find salvation. And, like Jesus, She has the most love for those sheep who've strayed from the fold."

"You can't mean the Nazis?"

Kolbe did not reply at once. He touched his wire-rimmed glasses and gazed off into space.

"Perhaps they're the ones who know not what they are doing."

After breakfast some time remained before his departure, so he returned to the chapel. The last Mass was drawing to a close. In a few minutes the majestic sound of trumpets would fill the church and the Icon would be covered. He looked fervently into Our Lady's face, trying to memorize every detail, feeling certain that he was seeing if for the last time.

He had once dreamed of a military career, and despite the love he felt for the Blessed Virgin he'd come close to leaving the Order to join the armed forces as his brother Franuś had done in those years of rebirth of independence. But She had kept him by Her side. Nevertheless, he quietly envied his father and brother, and when he formed his organization devoted to the service of Our Lady he christened it the Army of the Immaculate. He still wanted to die for Her in battle.

Now it seemed that the Virgin had never promised him the battles and death of a soldier. He was to die differently. At the back of his mind he thought he could see a dark dungeon with steel-barred windows and naked, twisted bodies...

The trumpets sounded and the silver curtain started to descond slowly. He looked at the Madonna until the very last moment. He was tempted to wave his hand, the way people waved after a departing train, and call out: "Whatever You command me to do..."

CHAPTER 12

THE OLD MAN AN THE CHILD

Before passing through the gate crowned by the figure of the Archangel, Tomasz took a leisurely stroll through the souvenir stalls along the walls. The trash that vendors peddled would have done credit to a village fair. Down below were decent stores and kiosks, but the top of the hill was dominated by itinerant traders dealing in hopeless rubbish – children's whistles, rosaries made of biscuits, holy and not-so-holy pictures that were the height of artistic bad taste, highlanders' moccasins, teddy bears in the most bizzare colors imaginable, crosses and scapulars, disgusting brooches and jewelry made of 'American' gold, mirrors with photographs of smiling girls on the back, wooden picture frames, plastic toys...

He'd been there many times before and he had very old memories connected with the market. Once it had stretched over a wider area, incorporating the hole-in-the-wall shops lining the street that climbed the hill. He remembered the first time he'd walked along the road: a little boy bewildered by the noise, the calls of the streetsellers, the gaily – colored stalls. He recalled the whistling of clay roosters and the flutter of paper snakes which sprang to life when one blew into a mouthpiece at the tip of the tail. Now and then he'd stopped at a stall and then run on the double so as not to lose sight of his father walking on ahead.

Doctor Bielicki had walked slowly with his hands clasped behind his back, ignoring the stalls. His gaze soared higher up over the ramparts, the walls, the spire. His father had been an extremely energetic man, bursting with ideas and initiative. He organized, established, and worked in countless associations and committees which sprang up everywhere like mushrooms after a summer rain. There was an enormous amount of work to be done. The country was impoverished and ravaged by the World War, but the exhilarating awareness of independence released extraordinary strength in people. The resulting surge of joy made them forget their own shortcomings and mobilized them to work for the good of their reborn homeland. Poland was feverishly assimilating the achievements it had been denied for so many years. A health enthusiast and dedicated doctor known for being equally eager to treat the poor as the rich, Bielicki had rolled up his sleeves and not only spent hours by his patients' bedsides but also began laying the foundations of a modern organization of health care for children. He put his own theories and methods into practice, believing that sunshine, fresh air, and fun and games were a more effective cure for tuberculosis than medicines and surgery.

Bielicki's eldest son had spent little time with his father, whose days were filled with speaking engagements, inspections, and instructing the personnel of the newly–founded establishments. House calls took up his evenings, and sometimes he was so tired that he fell asleep at the table waiting for supper to be served. Occasionally he took a day or two off from his feverish activities and took Tomasz with him out of Warsaw, time he set aside for rest and conversation with his first-born. His wife, who stayed home with the younger children, used to say that between their oldest boy and the rest of the children there was room for a sister named War.

During one of these expeditions to Jasna Góra, Tomasz discovered that his father's debilitating work had not deprived him of sensitivity and ability to experience deeply the times in which they lived.

"You, Tomek", he used to say to his son, "are not grown up yet but you're big enough, I think, to understand the great good fortune that has come our way. We've regained our freedom. Could I have dreamed of that when I was your age? Now you'll be able to live an ordinary life and, God willing, it'll be different from mine, or my father's and grandfather's." His grandfather had been a white lancer in the November insurrection. Wounded, he'd fallen ill and died. His father was captured and deported to Siberia after being wounded in the uprising of 1863. He wasn't even twenty then, and was a mature man when he came back. Only then did he marry. His life wasn't easy: the family estate had been confiscated by the Tsarist authorities, and the small piece of land his wife received as her dowry didn't provide enough income. He hadn't been in good health when he returned, and the hardships finished him off. His wife died shortly afterward and the property was grabbed by creditors. Bielicki's brothers were at the university then, but they somehow managed to complete their studies and start their own homes. He was the youngest and was still at school. "Some distant relatives took care of me. I pray none of you have to live that kind of life... I was thrown out of high school for speaking Polish, and the relatives managed to send me to another town to finish. But I've had my share of poverty. I wore shoes full of holes and ate dry bread and onions. But I was stubborn, and I graduated at the university despite everything. How great it is that you can speak our own tongue freely and study in Polish too! The last time I was here, a statue of a Tsar still stood over there by the wall where the figure of Our Lady is now."

A photographer had set up shop below the monastery wall. Opposite a tripod topped by a box camera hung a piece of canvas with the monastery painted on it and the Blessed Virgin levitating above the walls. „Souvenir of Częstochowa – 1922" was embellished on the heavy clouds.

Tomasz stopped, struck by a sudden idea. He caught his father by the hand.

"Daddy, let's have our photograph taken."

"But it's horrendous!"

"That's why we should do it. We'll show Mummy and we'll all laugh."

They stepped in front of the garish screen. The doctor placed his hand on Tomasz's shoulder, and the photographer, a short, balding man with a turned-up nose streaked with purple veins, dived under the black sheet behind the camera. He held up one hand and snapped his fingers, signaling his clients to freeze for a moment. While he made the prints, the father and son continued their walk along the stalls.

He now recalled that long-lost photograph of a well-built man in a straw boater and a lad in a broad-brimmed schoolboy's hat.

"Why did I ask him so few questions then?" he thought with regret. "There was so much to learn from him... Why did he feel so close to this place?"

His father had been very familiar with the shrine and had led him from one historic sight to the next with an air of confidence, showing him the Swedish cannonballs embedded in the walls (for years Tomasz thought they'd landed there centuries ago), the statue of Father Kordecki, the treasures of the armory. Standing atop the walls they'd looked down at the vast meadow stretching towards the trees in the park that hid the town from view.

"I wonder where the giant cannon was," he'd asked, "the one Kmicic blew up."

His father shrugged. He never voiced an opinion on matters he did not know well.

"You could buy yourself out then," he said. "It wasn't a Polish army. Now everyone will be eager to join up."

In the last year of the war, Tomasz remembered, his father had worn the red, white, and red armband of a Civil Guard officer. Many years later, as they walked together hurriedly to reach home before curfew, the old man said to his son: "Please tell your friends that maybe I could still be of some use to them. I'm too weak to march, but I could dress wounds with an ambulance team. And if they don't want me as a doctor, maybe I could help with the horses. As a boy I worked a lot with horses."

"That's another thing I should have asked him about," he thought.

They had reached the chapel just as the Icon was about to be uncovered. A fanfare sounded and the silver screen began to slide down slowly. His father crossed himself with a quick, broad movement of his hand, peasant-style. He prayed in a whisper.

When they left the chapel, Bielicki took him to the sacristy. From a vest pocket he produced a gold heart wrapped in pink tissue, and he walked up to one of the monks. Tomasz heard him say: "I'd like to offer this to Our Lady as a token of thanksgiving. You see, Father, I used to come here many times before the war, begging that..."

He had not heard what his father had begged for.

Tomasz was at the university when his parents decided to make a family pilgrimage to Częstochowa to mark the occasion of a wedding anniversary. They went for two days, stayed with nuns they knew well in St. Barbara Street, and rose early to be in the monastery for the first uncovering of the Icon.

The trip could not have come at a worse time for him. He was torn between his studies, his work in the organization, and love. He'd discovered the opposite sex relatively late, and each girl he met was a revelation to him. He loved them all in a romantic, sentimental way. He collected mementos – scented letters, ribbons from their dresses. He wrote poems, too, although he never showed them to anyone, not even the girls to whom they were dedicated. He was terribly shy. His studies were not going well either. His father wanted him to become a doctor, but the very thought of the dissecting room terrified him. Eventually he chose law, although he did not find it at all thrilling.

On the other hand, he was greatly absorbed in ideological activities and his greatest commitment coincided with Halina's appearance in his life. They were united by their common work and studies but she thought of him as an intimate friend, a brother almost, while he loved her madly, as befitted his melancholy, romantic nature. He wanted to conquer her, and the desire released some hidden energy in him, perhaps inherited from his father.

Although he wasn't an outstanding student, he made quite an impact on the life of the university, an interesting, tumultuous life dominated by the struggle for ideas. Tomasz became one of the most passionate of activists. Like many others, he thought the national flag hung too low: it had to be raised to the very top. And the men who ruled the country were unacceptable: their one-time merits seemed to be merits no longer. The youths did not think about the old struggle, the fight for independence; they were looking for an ideal that would electrify the whole nation. What form this ideal should take was not always clear, but everyone felt that reality had become irritatingly petty and did not measure up to their expectations, and the world of the self-contented petite bourgeois evoked their contempt. The struggle for greatness often degenerated into brawling as passion took the upper hand. The fanatics suddenly found themselves the target of charges by mounted police and were doused by water cannons. They responded by singing their battle hymn: "The golden sun is shining bright, the white eagle soars on high..."

For a while the situation became so tense it seemed blood would flow at any moment. But the successors to Piłsudski (who was charged with not having made independent Poland great enough), were not sufficiently sure of themselves to engage in a struggle against the younger generation. Or perhaps they realized that such a struggle would weaken the country just as it was facing a terrible threat.

Once the passions subsided, a certain idea, until then very vague, began to take shape. The noisy slogans were dropped and hate was forgotten. The conviction was born that the lack of greatness that had appeared so irritating was not merely related to the personal qualities of those running the country, but reached back generations and could be found in everyone's heart. Everybody developed a sense of guilt, which bred the desire for renewal.

One day the idea of new vows at Jasna Góra was born, and several years after his visit to the monastery with his parents, during which he'd constantly been impatient to get back to Warsaw, he went to Częstochowa again. With Halina by his side, he marched in a huge crowd along the Avenue of the Blessed Virgin. The street was swept by a tide of student caps of all colors, which had not always symbolized an attitude of piety. Former enemies now walked side by side. This new ideal united and conquered, rather than dividing.

As they went, they sang: "We want Our Lord, O Holy Mother..."

It was a fine September evening in 1939, one of those magnificient warm nights when the fading glare of the sun seems to bathe pines in soft streams of light, but clouds of smoke rising from the woods darkened the clear sky and the silence was torn by the thunder of artillery and the chatter of light machine guns.

Lieutenant Tomasz Bielicki rode along a sandy track at the head of his platoon. They'd already had several days of fierce fighting, beginning with a bloody battle in a clearing near Mokra, and the previous day their regiment had barely managed to escape encirclement. Tomasz's platoon, which had been sent on a reconnaissance mission, could not find their comrades when they returned to the rendezvous point. For a whole day, they searched in vain. They ran into the Germans several times, and he lost some of his men. Only twelve, all of them utterly exhausted, were left. The horses, too, were tired and limping. Night was coming and Tomasz did not know what to do.

A crowd of refugees swarmed along the road, groaning and lamenting as they walked. Crying children sat on top of horse-drawn carts and handcarts loaded with bundles; cattle followed the carts and terrified dogs ran about between the wheels. From side roads, new groups of refugees joined the column continually. Nobody knew where he was heading. Tomasz was disturbed by the fact that he had not seen any army units, and an unpleasant conviction grew stronger and stronger within him that he was behind the lines of the rapidly advancing enemy forces. Now his task was not only to link up with his own regiment, but also to find the Polish forces wherever they were.

Lt. Bielicki spotted a soldier sitting in one of the carts. "Stop!" he ordered the peasant urging on his skinny horse. He turned to the soldier: "Where are you from? Why aren't you with your unit?"

The confused soldier looked at the women sitting in the cart, as if expecting delivery from that quarter.

"Well, you see, sir, my regiment's had it. Shot to bits. Anyone that didn't get away was killed. It's all over."

"What's over?" he asked menacingly.

"This war, I think," the soldier muttered. "Them Germans are so damn strong..."

"And that's why you threw away your rifle!" Tomasz boiled with rage.

"I didn't throw it away," the soldier defended himself. "They never gave me one. They said there's not enough to go around."

For the first time in his life Tomasz wanted to hit someone straight in the face, but he overcame the temptation. The man could have been telling the truth. Although he was in uniform, he did not look much like a soldier. He was short, dark, and petrified. His heavy lips trembled. His uniform looked as if it had been borrowed from an older brother, and there was nothing military about his conduct.

"Where have you come from?" Tomasz asked.

"Częstochowa."

"You've been there? What's happening?"

"There's Germans there. They came in and set fire to the place and started murdering... A lot of them here," he pointed to the crowd, "are runnin' away from Częstochowa."

"And the monastery?"

"Bombed. All burned down."

Tomasz felt a jab of pain in his chest. He waved his hand for the cart to move on.

Several days before the war broke out, a group of pilgrims en route to Częstochowa had passed through the village in which his regiment was stationed. He looked in amazement at peasants who'd left their homes and set out to pay homage to Our Lady as if oblivious of the impending danger, yet he was proud to see those weary pilgrims walking shyly along the edge of the road.

"There's a great cause here," he thought. "Those who're thinking of attacking us aren't even aware of that greatness."

He began to convey his impressions to the regiment's chaplain, a fat and somewhat dull priest from a parish in Volhynia. The priest nodded politely, but Tomasz could see that his enthusiasm was much less than his own.

"So," he thought, "Częstochowa has been taken. The enemy is winning everywhere. Can Jasna Góra really have been destroyed? That man couldn't have seen it with his own eyes..."

In the last few days he had often noticed how panic-stricken people exaggerated their stories, but there could be no doubt that the monastery was in German hands. The awareness of this fact compounded the worries that had troubled him since morning. Until now he's been waiting for something extraordinary to happen, a miraculous reversal of fortunes. Now he could only count on himself.

He motioned to the soldiers behind him to ride into a tiny clearing in the birch woods. The party turned and drew up their horses. Tomasz dismounted and walked off to one side, onto a small mound, where he unfolded his map. He studied it carefully for a while, then he called his corporal over.

"I have to decide what to do now, Corporal," he said. "I'm afraid the regiment has turned north and we're getting farther away from it. There is shooting ahead and it looks as though we're behind the German advance. We haven't met a single Polish unit the whole day. I think we should get onto the main road, through these woods here, and find out what's going on. What do you think?"

"Well, sir, I do believe that's just what we should do."

"Do you know these parts?"

"A little. If we go through these woods, the main road is two, maybe three kilometers away. There's a village along the road."

"Won't we get lost?"

"No, all these forest paths lead to the highway. But Fritz might be in the village."

"We'll have to move cautiously. We'll cross the main road if we can. I don't expect them to be guarding it, the Huns like to get their sleep."

"We should be able to break through somehow, sir."

"Very well then. We'll leave in an hour. Tell the men to get some rest, water the horses if you can find any water, and feed them too. Have the men got any food?"

"Everybody has something in his pack, mostly apples. Want one, Lieutenant?" he asked, offering Tomasz a big red apple.

"Thanks. Post a few men to keep watch and set up the machine gun here, facing the road. Did you hear? That apology-for-a-soldier I talked to said the Germans had shelled Jasna Góra."

"Those animals are capable of anything."

"I'd like to get my hands on them for that."

"Who wouldn't?" the corporal said.

"All right, see to the men. We move out an hour from now."

The day was slowly coming to an end. The pines changed from red to grey, the smoke above the gently swaying branches disappeared in the twilight, but the sky glowed and there were fires everywhere. The roar of artillery did not cease although it seemed to be getting farther away.

Nothing disturbed their rest. From time to time, groups of refugees passed by along the road, but the previous tide had been reduced to a trickle. Everyone apparently preferred to hole up somewhere for the night.

The soldiers mounted up. He told them where they were going and that they could meet the enemy at any moment. They crossed the road and set off down a forest track. He sent scouts into the darkness ahead and rode immediately behind them.

At the far end of the tunnel formed by overhanging branches he heard the sound of engines and he was afraid that German tanks were headed in his direction. But then he dismissed the thought, knowing that they would not venture into the woods at night. The path must reach the main road somewhere just ahead, and the tanks or trucks would be there. He was now sure the enemy was on the main road.

His corporal had been right: after riding for about two kilometers they reached the edge of the forest. The scouts stopped at the treeline. There was a field on the right, covered with stubble, and a potato field on the left. Farther away were dark outlines like beasts lying in wait. They had to be the cottages of the village.

He ordered the men to dismount. Two stayed with the horses while the rest formed a loose extended line. Making as little noise as possible, they began a slow advance toward the houses and were already near the first when they heard a human voice. Tomasz halted and signaled his men to drop to the ground.

Someone was singing calmly to himself.

He motioned to the nearest soldier to accompany him. Clutching his pistol, he started to creep forward, trying to avoid the source of the singing. It was lighter out in the open and the gloom had a greyish tinge because of the glow in the sky. Tomasz spotted a stack of firewood and a man behind it, a German, wearing the standard bulbous helmet and long coat. Sentry duty evidently did not concern him greatly, for he had laid his gun aside and was leaning against the woodpile quietly humming a sad, gentle song.

"Take care of him," Tomasz whispered, "so he doesn't utter a sound." He knew he would not have been capable of doing it himself. He was prepared to shoot the enemy, but not to stick a bayonet in his back.

"No problem, sir," the soldier replied. "Pay them back some for those they've murdered." He put down his rifle after detaching the bayonet and moved off to approach his quarry from behind.

Tomasz stood motionless, his eyes glued to the German, who still stood with his back against the cordwood, singing to himself. It sounded like a religious song. Suddenly the song broke off and the German's head disappeared. Tomasz heard a quiet tussle, some gasps and snorts, then silence. Pointing his pistol, he made for the heap of firewood. His soldier knelt over the German.

"Good work," he said. "Bring up the rest of the men."

For a while he was left alone with the dead body. The man's throat had been slit and his mouth gaped open. It was not a pleasant sight.

The platoon joined him, and he said: "The corporal will stay here with three men and the light machine gun to cover us if we have to retreat under fire."

They moved ahead, past the houses and out onto the village street. Several trucks were parked there, ordinary trucks covered with tarpaulins. Some unit was evidently billeted in the village. There was no sign of a second sentry – either he was posted by the highway or the Germans did not think it necessary to have more than one. They obviously did not expect to come under attack. The village must now be far behind the front line, which had moved deep inside Polish territory.

He realized that his platoon could make it safely across the highway where, according to his map, a vast forest began. By going through it he hoped to catch up with their regiment. But another idea also crossed his mind: Why not kill the enemy here and avenge Jasna Góra? The Germans no doubt outnumbered them, but surprise would be total.

He went back to the corporal, leaving two men to guard the road. The village seemed to be asleep. He issued his commands in a whisper. The horses were quietly brought up and then they launched their attack, hurling hand grenades into the trucks and at the soldiers running out of the houses. Minutes later the vehicles were ablaze and in the glare he saw several corpses. They bolted for their horses, crossed the highway at lightning speed and stopped only when they had reached the depths of the forest.

He ordered a rest. Nobody was hurt or missing. Before blowing up the trucks someone had managed to grab a sack of tinned meat and they ate greedily, excitedly recounting their experiences.

"A whole bunch of them ran out of this house, so I tossed a grenade at them. It landed right dead center. They leaped about like frogs..."

"There were few asleep in the trucks. They jumped out and dived into the bushes. I unloaded a full magazine into them."

"That'll teach them to bomb Jasna Góra!"

"And that's only the start. They'd better not think that we're going to fall on our knees just because they've got so many tanks and bombers."

"Just wait a little, lads, and the whole situation will change around."

"We'll give them a hammering until there's nothing left for them to do but go back where they came from!"

Only one soldier was quiet. Banaszczyk, who'd killed the German sentry, looked pensively at the sky, which was still tinged with red.

When the others stopped boasting for a moment, he said: "You know, the one I knifed had a cross around his neck."

The train was crowded. People stood in the corridors and in the vestibules between the coaches. The compartments were dirty and damaged, and the luggage racks sagged under the weight of packages, sacks, and baskets. The chilly March wind blew in through the broken windows.

People talked, laughed and told crude jokes, but there was an uneasiness underneath it all. Every journey carried a mortal risk: one could land in trouble even if one had no illegal merchandise and their ID and passes were in perfect order.

Tomasz had been ordered to take part in an operation whose objective was to blow up a section of railway tracks between Częstochowa and Radomsko. The sabotage was to be synchronized with the actions of another group, which was to storm the prison in Radomsko and attempt to free the prisoners. The Częstochowa group was to carry out the actual operation, and Tomasz had been appointed as a liaison officer. He also was bringing a pack of fuses for the explosives. Two similar suticases lay on the overhead rack. The heavier one contained the fuses, the other held Tomasz's personal effects and a dozen bottles of a caramel-based ersatz tea. Before leaving, he'd been given an Ausweis identifying him as a textiles salesman.

He was alert and nervous. So far his activities had been restricted to Warsaw, where he'd become quite good at dodging street patrols and spotting approaching trucks, which could mean a round-up. But here on the train all he could do was wait passively for danger to appear.

The train had been going slowly and now slowed even further, as if the engine were running out of steam. The wheels clattered over the numerous connecting points of the maze of tracks and through the dirty windows he saw a large station. They passed empty trains, some damaged wagons, and a few rusty locomotives standing on sidings. Strange-looking signboards gave the station's name as Tschenstochau.

"*Achtung, Achtung,*" barked the loudspeakers. "*Personenzug aus Warschau...*"

The passengers crowded the windows, afraid the train might be met by a cordon of police. But the platform was empty, save for the standard two-man patrol at the exit. The station master, wearing a red cap and a red belt diagonally across his chest, ran to and fro along the coaches.

The crowd rushed off the train and hurried away, as if running for their lives. Tomasz took his suitcases and walked casually toward the exit, where a ticket collector stood in a narrow passageway with the police behind him. He stood in line, trying to appear relaxed and pretending not to look at the Germans, although his eyes never left them for a moment.

The policemen stood motionless. Suddenly one cried out "*Halt!*" and stopped a man carrying a heavy basket. They drew him aside and started to question him. The ticket collector, eager to exploit the fact that the Germans' attention was distracted, did his job faster and Tomasz passed straight through.

As prearranged, he had a newspaper sticking out of the left-hand pocket of his coat, a white scarf, and a phosphorescent button in his lapel, the kind used when walking after dusk. A slender girl stepped out of a group of people outside the station. She wore dark clothes, a headscarf tied below the chin, and heavy lipstick and mascara.

"Excuse me," she asked. "Are you bringing tea for Mr. Kowalski?"

"I only have samples."

"How many varieties?"

"Four."

She smiled confidentially. "Then everything's fine. Please follow me. And give me one of those cases."

She reached out to take a suitcase. It was a recommended procedure to pass incriminating materials to the couriers, but Tomasz never complied.

"Please take this one," he said, offering her the case containing the tea.

She made no attempt to argue, although she probably guessed that the dangerous cargo was in the other one.

They walked quickly on, side by side, crossed the bridge over the railroad tracks and turned onto the Avenue of the Blessed Virgin. Tomasz shuddered in anger when he saw the street sign: Adolf Hitler Alee. At the far end of the avenue the monastery spire rose up, silent and lonely.

"We've had a few problems here," the girl said. "They're arresting people all the time, and only a few days ago there was a massacre on Wieluńska Street."

"Has the group been broken up?"

"No, we're managing somehow."

They walked in silence. Patrols roamed the streets and one had to be careful. Near the park they turned left into a street leading up the hill toward the monastery, then they turned left again. The girl suddenly took him by the arm and pulled the scarf from her head. They passed under a low arch outside a small, old house and went into the courtyard. Baby carriages were parked along the dilapidated wall at the rear; to the left was a two-story building. A woman in the lobby gave them a look of utter contempt. They climbed the damp-smelling stairs in semi-darkness and stopped outside a door. The girl made certain that the windows were blacked out before she turned on the lights in the apartment, and then without removing her coat she built a fire in the coal stove. She did this expertly and after a while there was a roaring fire.

"It'll be warm in a minute," she said. "As you can see, this place is pretty miserable, but it could be worse. They threw us out of our apartment when they marked out the German quarter. We were allowed to take only what we could carry."

"So this is where your family stays now?"

"No, only me. My family's scattered. My father was arrested, then taken to Auschwitz... He's dead now. My mother was ill, and I persuaded her to take my sister and go to my uncle's, out in the country. At least they'll have something to eat there."

She busied herself preparing a meal.

"Aren't you afraid?" he asked.

"It's impossible not to be," she sighed. "The worst thing is that people can't be trusted. Not because they're informers, they've just got big mouths and adore gossip. If anyone knew that I work for the underground, the whole town would know by now. Stupid talk is the worst danger." She laid out bread, jam, and even some sausage. "My aunt sent the sausage. Help yourself. It's a delicacy now... You'll have to stay here tonight. That's what Adam decided. Some of our safe houses have been lost, but we think this place is safe enough. Tomorrow I'll put you in touch with the right people."

"The fuses are in the heavier suitcase."

"Good. They're badly needed. I've got a hiding place for them."

She left the apartment with the suitcase and was gone for quite a while.

Tomasz looked around the kitchen, which was fairly large. The smaller adjoining room contained only a shabby sofa, a table, and a ramshackle armchair. There were a few books on a shelf and a wooden cross on a wall next to a picture of Our Lady of Jasna Góra. He stared at Her, recalling the long ago visit with his parents. Both were old and in poor health now; his father still ran an organization to combat tuberculosis. "Life had taken many turns," he thought.

He'd married Halina two years before the war began. Their son, Marek, was born before hostilities broke out and his sister, Ania, came along after Poland had been occupied by the Nazis. The war changed Halina. During their student years and afterwards she'd remained a passionate activist and an excellent organizer, but later she refused to be involved with anything political. When Tomasz returned from the September 1939 campaign and tried to provide for his family, Halina supported him fully. But when he contacted former collegues from the old organization and became active in the underground, she had a decisive talk with him.

"I've thought this over carefully," she began. "We've got to split up. I can understand your involvement with the underground – I wish I could do the same, believe me, but we've got the children to think of... Somebody's got to take the resposibility. We need money to survive and I won't have them exposed to risk. We'll live with my parents, I can work and my mother will look after the kids. If Dad manages to open his construction business he might even help us financially." She paused. "You and I will pose as a divorced couple and meet from time to time – on neutral territory."

Tomasz knew that his wife was right, although his heart objected to the arrangement. He regarded his work in the underground as a duty, but it did not guarantee a living for his family. If only he could be sure that Halina had thought up the separation with nothing but the children's safety in mind. He did not suspect her of being unfaithful, but he realized that their relationship was not what he'd hoped it would be. Friendship had not grown into love. Their confessor priest assured them that it was only a question of time and patience, but had they married in different times, Tomasz was convinced, times that would have allowed them to grow accustomed to each other in peace and quiet, their difficulties would have been overcome long ago. And now, on top of everything, separation.

"What will happen to us," he'd thought, "if we only see each other once in awhile?"

But he'd gone along with her plan.

Feverish years followed; years loaded with danger, struggle, and tension. He rarely saw Halina and the children. She never asked about his life or his work, although she freely talked about hers. Her father had been permitted to take on various building contracts and they were quite comfortable financially. Ladies with a rather liberal outlook on life, the kind Tomasz could never stand, visited her mother. Halina had once shared his attitude, but now she gaily related the talks they had.

"The gap between us is widening," he had thought then.

The courier let herself into the apartment, and Tomasz noticed at once that she'd wiped off the make-up.

"More tea?" she asked from the kitchen.

"No thanks," he said, joining her. "What's going on at Jasna Góra?"

"The Paulites aren't having an easy time of it with the Germans right there in the monastery. It's even hard to get in touch with them. Hitler was there, you know. Back in '41. Nobody told the monks, but they recognized him from photographs. The soldiers thought a general was coming, and one did – with Hitler. He signed the visitor's book. Not his own name, of course."

"After the battle of Mokra we heard that the monastery had been bombed."

"That's not true. Częstochowa was abandoned without a shot being fired and the Germans wanted to show how much they respect holy places. But as soon as they entered the town they started making arrests, taking hostages, staging executions... My father was taken right at the beginning."

She threw some coal onto the fire.

"When you want to go to sleep, just tell me. I'll set up a camp bed and you'll sleep here in the kitchen, it's warmer, and if there's an emergency you can jump out the window – there's a low roof outside."

"What would happen to you then?"

She smiled roguishly. "I'd explain myself somehow."

"They don't listen to explanations."

She shrugged. "I've never been detained. I don't know what it would be like, and I prefer not to think about it."

"You'll be cold in the other room."

"I'm used to that."

The girl was beginning to interest him. In Warsaw he'd met various female couriers, young and pretty, but, save for a passing joke, they'd never talked about anything apart from the matters they were engaged in. He knew they had homes and families, as he did.

"Do you really have no life of your own?" he asked.

"No, I don't," she admitted. "Mum and Zosia are far away, and the only other people I know are those I work with in the organization." After a pause, she added, "I used to have a fiance. He's dead too. Killed in September. He was a cadet... But I wouldn't be able to live two separate lives, one for the cause, the other just for myself."

The interest she had aroused in him was evolving into sympathy, admiration, perhaps more. He wanted someone who would cherish the cause for which they fought while at the same time being dear to him, and this girl was extraordinary. He no longer remembered the blood-red lipstick and heavy mascara. Talking to her was easy, almost as if they'd known each each other for years, and it was easy to tell her secrets that he'd been ashamed to tell someone else.

"I don't have much of a family life, either," he confessed. "Our struggle has taken everything. I'm not complaining, that's the way it has to be. But sometimes there's a moment when you want to talk, to tell somebody about it all, to feel the presence of someone who loves... I rarely see my wife now. Since I'm in the underground she decided to devote herself to the children. Leaving me came so easily to her... That's her nature."

The girl listened with her head bowed. When he spoke the last words, she seemed to stiffen.

"Why are you telling me all this?" without looking at him, she asked.

By now he was carried away by his own words.

"I felt good talking to you. Wouldn't it be better if we called each other by our first names?"

"No," she said curtly, "it wouldn't. And there's no point talking about the things you're talking about. Nor listening to them, for that matter...

We've got a dangerous day ahead of us tomorrow, we'd better get some sleep."

She rose without waiting for a reply, pulled the camp bed out of a corner, and began to unfold it. He walked over to help her.

"I thought," he began, "well, I thought that you –"

"You thought what?" she said without raising her head. "You thought that because I'm alone, I may be a loose woman?"

"I didn't say that," he replied indignantly. "The idea never crossed my mind. All I wanted –"

"You're only tempting yourself, and maybe also... But let's drop the subject." She made up the bed and banked the fire. "It'll get very cold by morning, so here's another blanket. I've got to get up early and go out, but don't be concerned if I'm gone a long time. I should be back by seven. We'll have breakfast then. And if anybody knocks, don't answer the door. Goodnight."

"Goodnight."

She went into the other room and closed the door.

He heard the key turn in the lock.

During breakfast he looked carefully at her. He was a bit upset by her behavior last night, but at the same time he felt even more attracted to her.

"Mind if I ask where you were off to so early? It must have been about five when you left."

She smiled like a mischievous little girl.

"One of the monks at the monastery had something to pass on to me."

"Do people still go to the chapel?"

"Yes, but not so early in the morning. They're scared of the Germans who wander around there." She changed the subject. "Have you finished? You're not hungry? In that case, we'll go and meet Adam."

"What about the suitcase?"

"We'll come back for it."

Before they left she disappeared into the toilet for a minute. She came out wearing heavy make-up again. In the courtyard they met the janitor, standing in the door with a broom in his hand. The girl took Tomasz by the arm. The moustached man looked at them and ostentatiously spat in disgust.

Half an hour later he was talking to the man whose underground alias was Adam and who commanded the organization's Częstochowa group. Adam had the reputation of being one of the most energetic commanders, yet he was also very careful. He was an older man with a square peasant's face, grey eyes under bushy brows, and he was very cool and composed. He calmly outlined the situation.

"Either the Germans have gotten wind of something," he said, "or they're excited for some other reason. At any rate there's an atmosphere of terror in town. Looks as though they're out to intimidate the population. There've been a lot of arrests and round-ups, and there are more patrols in the streets than usual."

"But the operation can't be postponed," Tomasz said. "Our orders are clear. We have to do our bit for the other one to succeed."

Adam nodded. "I wasn't thinking about postponing it. We're ready to take the risk. What's involved is the life or death of our friends in prison. Were you all right at Marysia's place?"

"Yes, fine. She's a very brave courier."

"Brave? She's magnificent! Believe me, if we've managed to achieve anything here, it's only because of her."

He stayed at Adam's house until afternoon, when Marysia joined them.

"Isn't it time to get my suitcase?" he asked. "Adam said we'd be off in an hour."

"It's already where it should be," she said, smiling. "You shouldn't be seen wandering around town. The Germans are still on the alert."

"You carried that heavy case on your own?"

"It's best to go alone. If you get caught, you don't endanger anyone else." She spoke matter-of-factly. "I've brought your personal things. You won't be coming back to Częstochowa afterwards, Adam will find you a hiding place out in the country somewhere. I really wanted to go along with you, but... So it's goodbye, then."

She shook hands with him like a man. He would always remember her as she was then: with a smile on her face, and the lurid make-up.

An hour later, a rickety truck powered by gas from a wood-fired stove pulled up outside the house. Tomasz was handed an Ausweis saying that he worked for the Społem retail chain and was going to Piotrków to pick up merchandise. A short distance from Kłomnice they stopped by a small wood. A group of people detailed for the operation were already there. It was cold, but Adam would not allow a fire. He ordered everyone to sit in a ditch and the long wait began.

The explosion occurred at midnight and the group dispersed at once. Tomasz and Adam went through the woods to a place where a peasant cart waited for them, and after several hours riding along back roads they reached a manor house where they could rest and get some sleep.

At noon a courier arrived by bicycle to see Adam. Tomasz watched him discuss something with the commander. His whispers were very agitated.

"Any trouble?" he aked when the courier had gone.

For a while Adam stroked his balding head.

"The mission," he said at last, "was a success. Rail traffic was blocked, but something very bad has happened. They've taken Marysia."

"A coincidence?"

"No, they were waiting for her at our meeting place."

Tomasz sat in stunned silence.

"Maybe you can get her out?"

Adam shook his head.

"No. When people like her get caught, they die. She won't say a thing, so they'll torture her to death... She was a master of disguises. People thought God knew that about her, and she sneaked out of her house every day at dawn to be in the chapel for the morning uncovering of the Icon. We've lost someone irreplaceable."

He did not visit Częstochowa again until the late 1950's, when he went with Halina. After his release from prison, he'd found that his wife had changed once again. The deportation after the collapse of the Warsaw Uprising when the entire burden of feeding the children and her own parents had fallen on her shoulders, then her mother's disease – all had sapped her strength. She was gaunt and sick. It was as if twenty years had been ripped out of her life. She tried to be good and warm to him, but at the same time she worried about Marek and Ania, who were growing up and breaking away from her influence. To his amazement, he discovered that Halina's years of self-sacrifice had not produced a close emotional bond between her and the children.

"Let's go to Jasna Góra," she suggested. "When the vows were held I was ill and you couldn't go. They're really a sequel to the vows we made before the war. God, this is so important! Let's go together. We'll apologize and thank Our Lady for saving us despite our sins, and ask Her to take care of the children. I'm so afraid for them... I can't do anything for them any more. I feel so old. Almost forty! I'm sorry for you, Tomek. If I die, you should remarry."

"What are you talking about?"

"I think you should have married somebody else. I wanted it to be a success, and so did you, but it just didn't work out..."

Not long afterward they walked through the stalls and even had their picture taken near the wall. Who knew, maybe it was the same camera that took the photo of him and his father?

Kneeling beside his wife in the chapel, he looked anxiously into her haggard face.

"Oh Blessed Virgin," he prayed, "could she really leave us so soon? Have mercy and save her. I'll never complain or grumble again. What would I do if I lost her?"

The Madonna's face, dark and inscrutable, showed neither sympathy nor anger. It was only a face in a picture with a frozen expression that was hard to describe.

He recalled Marysia, the girl he had met fifteen years ago. "A master of disguises, Adam had said. At dawn, when others were afraid to leave their homes, she had run to this chapel and prayed. What had she prayed for? Had she prayed for him after the night he behaved so stupidly?"

Earlier, he had asked Halina to walk with him to the small house in which he'd spent that night. It was still standing, but was in even worse repair. The plaster was peeling, and a thick beam shored up the ceiling in the stairwell. The courtyard was overgrown. Parts of baby carriages rusted amid the weeds, perhaps the same ones from the previous visit. On the stairs he saw a stooped old woman – the same woman who'd looked at him and Marysia with such contempt? He told Halina about Adam and the operation, but he could not bring himself to tell her about Marysia.

He cast one more sidelong glance at his wife. Her thin lips moved and her eyes were fixed on the Icon. She had often said: "I'm such a terrible realist. I'm sorry, but paintings or sculptures don't make any impression on me at all."

When they were engaged, they'd gone to Wilno to pray to Our Lady of

Ostra Brama. Tomasz had stood before the picture suddenly ashamed of his violently awakened emotions, while Halina said she felt nothing. This time it was the opposite. He felt only a growing despair at the thought of losing his wife, while she seemed to be experiencing something.

Today he'd come to Jasna Góra alone.

Halina had died years ago and her death cut him off from the rest of the world; she was the one who'd kept up their contacts with friends and acquaintances. The business he'd worked for since his return to civilian life had dismissed him as soon as he became eligible for a pension, which rather surprised him. He'd become quite friendly with his fellow workers and thought they would not want to see him leave. It all happened quickly, without objections or proposals, and he was left completely alone.

Halina's foreboding about the children proved to be correct. Marek, a successful actor, changed partners like others changed shirts and had recently married for the third time. Tomasz had met only the first wife, a pretty woman with whom he had no idea what to talk about. Their daughter, Ivetta, now lived with her mother and, if Tomasz's count was right, her third stepfather. He'd never seen his granddaughter. Ania lived with him but he seldom saw her. Her brief relationships with men began in euphoria and ended in depression. She was very unhappy, and blamed her misfortunes on him. Whenever they talked, Ania only complained.

"It's all your fault, father," she would say. "Don't look so surprised. It's because of you that Marek drinks. You finished off Mum and you'd finish us off too, if we didn't defend ourselves."

He realized that he could be blamed for many things, but not those that Ania accused him of. He was shocked by her cut-and-dried assessment of him, and in his loneliness he often thought about his granddaughter he had never met.

For a while he analyzed his past, looking for some great evil he had committed, something that would explain his defeat. He almost wanted to find that something. It would have been better to know that he'd been justly punished for something than to live amid endless accusations he did not understand. At last those feelings grew into a bitter rebellion that drove him to Jasna Góra. It was not a rebellion against faith; he was still sure of the Reality hidden behind the mysterious Icon. That Reality remained itself, and yet it had rejected him, turned its back on him and allowed him to lose everything.

Kneeling in the chapel, surrounded by a crowd of pilgrims, it was difficult to concentrate on the Icon. It took on a strangely dull sheen in the candlelight. The Madonna's face said nothing, and he looked at Her in desperate anticipation.

"I'll go away and return to my loneliness," he thought. "I'll be like a man condemned to bear a heavy burden with no hope of help. Bearing a burden... Might this mean bearing a cross?"

He looked at the Madonna again. Her eyes now seemed turned toward somebody standing beside him.

A middle-aged couple with weary, tormented faces stood by a girl in a wheelchair. She was about sixteen and had a delicate, very pretty face. Far more attractive was her expression of absolute cheerfulness, almost joy, which contrasted sharply with the expressions of the two adults, who must have been her parents. Her big blue eyes were not turned toward the Icon, but seemed to stare vacantly into space. Her parents looked shattered, while she smiled.

Tomasz nearly stopped breathing. He forgot about the surging crowd, and the grief he'd brought there died on his lips. He could not take his eyes off the girl, then he finally turned to the Madonna.

Her eyes seemed to focus on the girl in the wheelchair and Tomasz had the feeling that they were requesting him to do the same, to try to comprehend the hidden sense of something that seemed nonsensical.

The desperate parents prayed. "Have mercy on her, heal her..."

Perhaps the Madonna was speaking also, he thought, but only the blind girl could hear Her: "I beg You, my beloved Child... For what will happen to those other children?"

A tear rolled down his face, the face of an old man.

He had not wept since childhood.

CHAPTER 13

THE PRIMATE OF POLAND

The sleek black automobile sped along a road flanked by broad, flat fields full of fresh-cut rye, puffing tractors and patient horses drawing plows that turned the soil after the harvest. Farm workers looked like colored specks in the distance. The harrowed soil took on the appearance of a bolt of corduroy unrolling itself across the earth. Carts overflowing with stacks of sheaves left the sidelanes and pulled boldly onto the highway, forming a broken chain of slow-moving obstacles that forced the chauffeur to cut his speed drastically. He swung the car around one cart and passed it.

"I'm sorry, Your Eminence," the driver said, glancing into the rearview mirror. "But these wagons..."

Wyszyński had traveled the road many times and knew the sights well, yet they never bored him. He lowered the window and filled his lungs with the warm August air, letting his eyes wander across the fields. How he loved those distant horizons...

Stefan Wyszyński's three years of confinement had been doubly painful due to the lack of space. At first there was a lonely room behind thick walls, where he was held under lock and key. A single window looked out onto a tiny yard surrounded by a barbed-wire festooned wall. Two grim men with whom he soon became quite familiar were posted at the gate. After two monotonous years he was notified of a change in the conditions of his confinement. The change occurred on a Saturday in May, the month of the rosary. He had always considered Saturday, the day of Mary, to be the holy day in the week and the news took on special significance for him. He was moved to a place where the door was unlocked, he had free access to the balcony, and he could even stroll in the nearby woods. He was permitted to send and receive letters, eventually to borrow books, and, finally, to have visitors.

Bishop Klepacz, Bishop Choromański, and Father Padacz came to see him. Klepacz, with his broad peasant face and protruding ears, resembled a laborer more than a bishop. But Wyszyński knew that the man's powerful physique concealed not only the romantic soul of a dreamer but also an advancing disease. Choromański, meanwhile, always, seemed to have an ironic glint in his half-closed eyes, which were set above fat cheeks and hidden behind a pair of glasses. Wyszyński knew about Choromański's fondness for cigars but the bishop also knew that he disliked them strongly, so he never lit one in his presence. Padacz, a modest man, always spoke in a low voice. He hadn't changed in the past two years; he still calmly defended people and found some good in everyone.

Wyszyński was now surrounded by dedicated nuns, serving him as best they could. They looked after his health, badly damaged by the lack of sunshine and fresh air and exercise. Whenever a nun entered his room, he rose from his chair. He stood up in front of every woman, for the sake of his mother's memory and out of love for the One who was the Mother of all people.

The nunnery in Komańcza was poor and primitive. It was often chilly inside even with a fire crackling in the fireplace. When he wanted to read or write, he had to light a kerosene lamp. But there was a chapel, and nuns prayed when he said Mass. He took long walks. He found a stout stick, similar to a shepherd's crook, and used it as a walking cane. Again he was in wooded hills, and he occasionally saw a human silhouette among the trees. Those now guarding him at least tried to be discreet...

But that was all past. Today he breathed freely. Sweet scents wafted over the fields. The priest sitting next to him, his secretary, had dozed off. The driver handled the car with reassuring confidence. Familiar sights appeared: the thick birch forest, the town with the elongated marketplace in the center. The road began to twist, they passed one hill after another, then a church spire appeared ahead. They would soon pass a second spire, he remembered, their destination. He reached into his pocket for his rosary. As he prayed, the beads brought recollections of the past.

"Hail Mary..."

At home, the rosary had been said every night. His father recited the prayer, and his mother, Nastka, Wacek, himself, the younger girls and the faithful Ulisia all answered. Every year, his mother made a pilgrimage to Our Lady of Ostra Brama at Wilno, while his father went to Jasna Góra. A replica of the Black Madonna hung over his bed.

Stefan was barely ten years old when the disease that had afflicted his mother for many years made her bedridden. Everyone in the house realized that death was approaching. At school he often listened for the toll of church bells, the sign that he would never see her again. During the breaks between classes, he shared his anxieties with Nastka.

One autumn day when he came back from school his father told him to go to his mother's bedside. She looked at him with an expression that was half expectant, half threatening. Abruptly, she jerked up in the bed and said: "Stefan, get dressed."

He went back for the heavy coat he'd taken off a moment earlier, expecting his mother to ask him to run an errand.

But when he returned, she shouted: "No! Not that way! Get dressed differently!"

He looked at his father uncomprehendingly.

The man whispered: "I'll explain later."

Those were the last words he heard his mother say.

Later his father said: "She wanted to tell you to dress yourself in faith, fidelity, dignity, and love. You'll need all of those in your life, my boy."

He was still a young boy when he first became aware of what his future held. On the night preceding one Good Friday, which he spent in an all-night vigil in church, he realized that he would become a priest. Several days later he told his father, who unexpectedly opposed him. Not long before, Wacek had drowned while swimming in the Bug. Stefan was the only son left, and although his father was deeply religious he was not eager to give him to God. After great insistence he finally obtained consent, but not until his father, an organist at the Andrzejewo church, had decided to remarry to make sure his four children were properly cared for.

"Full of Grace...'

He went to school in Warsaw. Next came a lower seminary, then a senior one. Poland regained independence while he was attending Pope Pius X High School. He feared for his family during the war of 1920 and prayed fervently to Our Lady, whose scarred image always hung above his bed. Four years later, before taking his vows, he visited his grandmother at Kamieńczyk.

The old lady stared a long time at the young seminarian's face, and then said sternly: "Remember, if you make a bad priest, I don't ever want to see you again!"

On the day of St. Peter and Paul, when Włocławek seminarians traditionally took their vows, the young deacon lay in the hospital with a fever. His mother had passed her frailty onto her son. He was to be ordained on August 3rd instead, which happened to be his birthday.

Arriving at the church early, he was delighted to learn that the ceremony would take place in the chapel of Our Lady of Częstochowa. The old sacristan, Mr. Radomski, looked at the deacon, who was so weak that he staggered into the chapel and quickly slid onto a pew (he'd always had trouble kneeling down).

The old man nodded his head.

"So you're the one who's to be ordained today?"

"Yes, that's right."

"Well, well... You're actually pale and you can barely stand. You'd better be thinking about a cemetery, not the priesthood."

When he lay prostrate on the floor some hours later, he said to himself, "Allow me, Oh Blessed Virgin, to be Your priest for just one year. I leave the rest to You. I dedicate everything to You."

The following day his beloved sister Stasia took him to Częstochowa. He was so weak he was afraid he would not survive the trip. It was there, in front of the Icon of the Black Madonna, that he wanted to say his first Mass. Something attracted him irresistibly to the monastery, whose Lady seemed to have been calling him since childhood. He celebrated Mass in front of Her image. Her eyes somewhat resembled his mother's eyes when she had said: "Stefan, get dressed."

"So many of the words spoken by those closest to us pass unnoticed," he thought, "and only their final words remain etched in our memories, evoking remorse that we did not listen carefully enough."

"The Lord is with Thee..."

That thought came back to him many times during the years he spent at Rywałd, Stoczek Warmiński, Prudnik and Komańcza. Our Lady had never ceased being a part of his life even when, as a student of the Górski college in Warsaw, he said a daily Hail Mary in front of the figure of Our Lady of Passau in Krakowskie Przedmieście. All the important events in his life happened on days dedicated to Her, and it was on the feast of the Annunciation that he learned from Cardinal Hlond that he'd been appointed Bishop of Lublin. Frightened, he tried to refuse the office, which he believed would be a greater burden than he could shoulder.

The Cardinal insisted on a reply.

He still tried to resist. "I'd be the youngest bishop of all."

"The Holy Father knows that," Hlond replied in his slightly nasal tone, a strange depth in his voice. "You can't say no to the Holy Father."

At Jasna Góra he took the highest of holy orders and became a bishop.

"Blessed art Thou amongst women..."

Less than two years after taking up his pastoral duties in Lublin he was stunned to hear of the Primate's sudden death. At the funeral he learned about the last moments of Cardinal Hlond's life, his apocalyptic vision, his assurance that victory would come, and that it would be the victory of Our Lady. In the autumn of 1946, the dying Cardinal had entrusted Poland to the Immaculate Heart of Mary. Wyszyński was particularly grateful for this dedication; it was the fulfillment of his desires, his plans, and his love of Mary.

"And blessed is the fruit of Thy womb, Jesus..."

The next blow was even more powerful: Wyszyński was asked to take over the two metropolitan sees vacated by Hlond. The old title of Primate, brought from Constance by Mikołaj Trąba centuries ago, had regained its luster and weight. The office was not only a dignity, but a responsibility as well. It meant being the conscience of the nation. He knew Cardinal Hlond had thought that too in proposing him as the only candidate to succeed him.

On May Day, he looked out the window of his residence on Szucha Avenue and saw countless red banners. He remembered another May Day, when he'd stood by that window surrounded by a halo of red and talked to a man whose understanding he sought, even though he sensed that the other had not matured enough to understand the matter.

"No," he'd said, "I'm not angered by the red. I'm not against it as long as it signifies the desire to bow to the needs of the working man, who knows the bitter taste of life. I share these aspirations and recognize the need for social justice, those at the helm of power must tell the whole truth, right to the end, everything. If they don't I will be forced to speak, it's my duty as Primate. I cannot stay silent!"

"Holy Mary..."

Even among those who were close to him then, many asked, smiling ironically, if he knew where he was living, in what kind of state. But he was firm in his belief that there was no other option. The Archbishops of Gniezno and Warsaw had the right to a red soutane, even when they were not cardinals, and a red cassock denoted the readiness to shed blood for one's beliefs. He had never been afraid of that.

"Mother of God..."

During his months in Stoczek he'd composed an act of personal dedication to Mary: "I dedicate to You my body and soul, my inner and outer possessions, even the value of my acts of kindness, past, present, and future, leaving You the full and complete right to do what You will with me and everything I have without exception." He also decided to forgive those who kept him prisoner.

Life was hard in Stoczek, but in Prudnik things were even worse. The guards were malicious and annoying; all his complaints and protests came up against a wall of silence. And yet, he thought he heard Our Lady's voice of consolation there: "Think not of the injustice, think not of the men who oppress you. Let your mind forget your suffering. Give your concerns to me. Do not look to people to help you. Neither hope that your tormentors will grow weary of their anger nor count on those you have left behind in a world that is closed to you, a world you might think does not exist. Think of one thing only: that I love you, that you are Mine forever. I want you to achieve much, much more. This is not the end. You will return to your work, I promise you."

Despite that promise, doubts crept into the locked room. One thought kept coming back: there were so many important things going on out there, the future was being decided while he was locked away as if in a tomb. He often thought of John in the fortress of Machaerus. John knew that somewhere, out in the sun, there lived and worked the Promised One, the One whose arrival he himself had announced. But while the Other Man acted, he remained in chains and darkness.

"Pray for us sinners..."

The 300th anniversary of the siege and defense of Jasna Góra found him in Prudnik. He'd often thought about this defense, and read the relevant chapters of *The Deluge* many times. As he admired Sienkiewicz's prose, a thought suddenly came to mind: Jan Kazimierz was in Głogowa then, while today the place is called Głogówek, which is twenty kilometers away. While the exiled King was there his painful meditations produced the great idea of vows that were to become an expiation for the years of injustice toward the peasantry, the people who served the Mother of God most ardently and faithfully.

He also remembered what one of the Jasna Góra monks, the chief historian of the Order and the monastery, had said: "The miraculous painting was not at Jasna Góra when the Swedes laid siege to the monastery. Sienkiewicz did not know that, because we don't tell everyone. Not everybody is capable of understanding that the presence of the Mother of God here is not necessarily connected with the physical presence of the Holy Icon. Thanks to millions of prayers, She is here even when the Icon is hidden. When the Nazis came, the painting had to be walled up. But back in 1655, our provincial, Fr. Teofil Borowski, loaded the Icon onto a horsecart and took it away to Silesia. First he kept it in Lubliniec and then in a monastery in the vicinity of Głogówek. This was done in the greatest secrecy, but Nuncio Vidoni must have known about it, and the King could have known as well."

So had the Icon been there, he pondered, so near to my prison? Perhaps Jan Kazimierz prayed before it? And who knows if it wasn't then that the prodigal monarch realized that She Herself wanted those vows? And that in this way She would lead the nation to reconciliation with Jesus Christ? Looking for a way out of the most difficult – seemingly hopeless – predicament, one had to entrust one's fate to Her.

The tribulations continued. In his heart he felt rebellion, anger, bitterness, and doubt. He could not stop being himself. He also visualized helpers coming to him and consolidating his growing conviction that 1956 was to be the year of a renewal of the vows. Amazingly, people outside were also thinking about it. A smuggled letter told him that all Poland waited and prayed for him, and expected his return.

"Now and at the hour of our death..."

Somebody had once drawn his attention to the great similarity between himself and Archbishop Feliński as portrayed on his tombstone. The resemblance was not limited to facial features, there were other common traits in their lives. But his imagination drew his attention to another fact: Feliński had performed the duties of archbishop for less than a year, then he stayed in exile for the next twenty. If they resembled one another so closely...

The thought had disturbed him until the war, when he was staying in Żułów with a group of blind people. One day, in the company of Father Korniłowicz, he went to a tiny spring beside which a picture of Our Lady hung from a tall pine. As they walked, they talked about the horrible times in which they were living. Suddenly, Fr. Korniłowicz proclaimed, "We shall survive, you'll see. But if our reverence of Mary were to die, if we allowed Her to be taken away from us, that would mean the death of the nation's spirit."

Some years later he discovered exactly the some words in the text of one of Feliński's addresses, when Feliński was being forced to leave Warsaw and knew he would never see the capital again. Bidding farewell to the clergy, who found it so hard to understand and appreciate him, those were the words he had spoken. Feliński never returned from exile, but his words told Wyszyński that where there was to be life there had to be a mother, and where there was such a Mother there had to be life. If two people whose memory he cherished had said the same thing, that must be the key to the future.

"No, I should not worry that I cannot act," he thought. "She is acting."

Then, suddenly, relief came – he was taken to Komańcza. While he was there, hundreds of thousands of people took the vows at Jasna Góra, reciting a text he'd written for them. He prayed and suppressed all grief in his soul.

"She is to grow," the thought, "so I must diminish. Let everything be the way She wants it."

And then, as She wanted, he had regained his freedom.

The car rounded a bend and entered the town, passed decrepit houses, all of them equally ugly, and turned onto the Avenue of the Blessed Virgin. Long, straight, tree-lined, it had not changed in all those years. At the far end was a dark clump of trees, with the monastery steeple towering above it. The houses along the avenue showed signs of neglect. The new Częstochowa was growing in another direction and everything else had been left to decay. The buildings in Seven Houses Street, which circled the hill, were in an even more pitiful state.

A noisy, dirty bazaar thrived in the vast meadow outside the monastery gates: unsightly religious objects, peasant handicrafts, jugs of homemade lemonade, and repulsive sandwiches scorched by the sun. Seedy looking individuals wandered among the peddlers, offering bottles of vodka and lodgings for the night.

The car circled the monastery wall and entered the compound through the back gate, which faced the fields. As soon as it stopped, a group of monks in white cassocks surrounded it and led Wyszyński to his suite on the third floor.

There was probably no other place that he would have felt so much at home. He stood by the window, from which he could see the upper terrace and below, at the foot of the wall, the meadow. Beyond the park, the straight line of the Avenue divided the town. Factory chimneys, veiled in fog, smoked in the distance. Meanwhile, a few steps away, the Icon lived and kept vigil in the chapel – a visible connection with an invisible presence, a window onto the world of motherly love, a sign of union with the One to whom he had dedicated himself entirely.

For many years, both in Poland and in Rome, ironic smiles had appeared on the faces of the people he met. There were even attempts to prove that his cult of Our Lady ran contrary to theological doctrine and that his love of Her crossed the boundaries of veneration. And, by this token, overshadowed the love of Jesus Christ. Someone had said spitefully that "for the Primate, Mary has taken the place of the third person of the Holy Trinity." He knew that many ears were listening keenly to what he said, trying to catch him in some insufficiently precise statement. Subconsciously, he began to distrust the professors of theology who appeared to belittle the role of Mary, and who in fact seemed to be irritated by Her. It was as if they could not bear his ardent belief that She was there to help people, and especially the faithful of Poland. He did not engage in disputes with them, knowing that they would immediately invoke various authorities, mostly French. In France, faith in Mary's assistance seemed to have died out altogether. People still took their ailing bodies to Lourdes, but not their ailing souls. In Poland, however, Mary was still the Mother. The Poles, who had so often been hurt, ignored, and rejected, needed the One to whom everything could be brought – sorrow and joy, suffering and hope, weakness and willingness. And the Mother would not hide from Her children the One who was the Savior and the Redeemer. On the contrary, She would lead them to Him.

"At the level of motherly trust," he thought, "the Polish cult of Our Lady is certainly perfect. In time it will be necessary to add the next levels. Even so, there are already some germs of profound syntheses. Wasn't that what the black-haired, bearded Franciscan, the founder of Niepokalanów, had attempted to do before he met his death in a bunker in Auschwitz?" He remembered Father Maximilian's arguments – which caused uneasness among some theologians – about Mary being the Intercessor of all Grace, and how everything coming from the people to God and from God to the people passed through Her hands. Grignon de Montfort said the same: "She hands out favors, giving what She wishes to whomever She wishes, however much, whichever way, and whenever She wishes..."

He remembered the Soviet soldier he had met in Lubraniec, who entered the church and looked with interest at a picture of Jesus the Miserable. Seeing Wyszyński pass, the soldier asked, "*Kto takoi?*"

"That's Jesus Christ," he replied. "Didn't you know?"

The Russian shook his head and shrugged his shoulders.

"Don't you know anything about Him?"

The soldier shook his head again.

"Well, have you heard about Our Lady?"

This time the other man nodded yes and smiled.

"Isn't that the simplest, easiest way to Jesus?" he thought. "It is a road open to everyone. Why can't the wise doctors and professors understand this? Why do they look for other paths, convoluted and tortuous ones? If they want to search for them on their own, then let them. But they should leave the common people to follow the road that is accessible to them. I am responsible for those poeple. I want to avoid anything that might expose them to the risk of taking too difficult a road."

There was a knock on the door.

A White Friar asked if he would be coming down to the refectory for lunch.

As they descended the stairs, he joked with the young Paulite. He was rediscovering the fun of jocular conversation. In his boyhood he'd been an avid prankster and often got a talking-to or even quite a painful spank on the hand for his antics.

He hadn't stopped being witty when he became chaplain to a group of fighters from the Warsaw Uprising in the Kampinos forest. Under the alias Radwan the Third, he worked in a hospital and prayed with the wounded, heard their confessions, and also told them funny stories. He was sure they needed humor as well. Then the situation changed and the insurgents withdrew deeper into the woods. Two hospitals were set up: one near the lines and another at the Laski boarding school for the blind, where only those casualties who could pass for civilians were kept because of the Germans' visits. He traveled from one hospital to the other, treking across sand dunes and through woods of young pines that came under German fire. He prayed as he went.

One day, circling a sand dune along the edge of the forest, he heard a faint cry. He saw a girl lying on the dunes out in the open, obviously wounded. In order to reach her, he'd have to leave the wood. He did not hesitate for a moment, telling himself that he was looked after by the Virgin Mary. Bullets whistled overhead and a grenade exploded with a deafening bang thirty or forty paces away. He reached the girl, who grasped him by the arm convulsively.

"Please save me, Father," she whispered. Her leg was bleeding badly.

Kneeling, he pulled her onto his back, supported her with his right arm and held her leg with his left.

"Hold on to me," he said.

She clasped her hands so tightly around his neck that he could hardly breathe. He could not possibly run with such a load. As soon as he got up, his feet sank into the sand. He dragged himself on, unable to keep a straight line, panting heavily, and he made it to the edge of the forest. But that was not the end of his problems: he had to get the girl to the hospital at Łaski. She kept fainting, loosening her grip, and falling to the ground. Then he remembered how the village women carried their babies in scarves, and he took off his cassock and tied the sleeves below his chin.

He was half-conscious with exhaustion after walking the two kilometers to Laski. His step was unsteady, he had black spots before his eyes and he would have fallen down had he not been spotted from a distance. A group of nuns and those pupils who could see a little ran to help.

When he got his breath back, he went to see the girl. Her wound was dressed and she felt better. "Next time, my dear," he quipped, "find yourself a stronger mule. This one wouldn't take you very far."

But when he found himself inside the cold walls of Rywałd, his fondness for jokes disappeared. He could hardly muster enough strength to preserve his peace of mind. He had a fairly impulsive personality and had worked for many years to develop self-control and suppress the militancy awakened in him when he wrote newspaper articles. But he realized that a polemic was often like a duel, and that a blow aimed improperly usually hit the man instead of the real target.

The guards could be quite a nuisance when they wanted to, and he was angered that they lacked the courage to make even a tiny gesture of opposition to the discipline imposed on them. Nothing, he thought, could be worse than such submissiveness. When he looked at them it occurred to him that maybe out there, beyond those walls, that obedience was becoming increasingly widespread; that if he'd been allowed to disappear without a trace and nobody was looking for him it was because the spirit of submission had conquered a nation known for its refusal to bow down to force.

Prior to his arrest, people had come to him and asked whether they were allowed to do this or that. At first he talked softly, but with time he became tougher. "Just do what your conscience tells you to do. Why do you want me to decide for you?" In the end, they stopped coming and he was encircled by emptiness.

He remembered somebody who came to discuss the problem of spiritual assistance for a group of people. "They should know themselves how best to act," he had told him. "Everybody wants international recognition and my blessing as well!" The man had bowed, kissed his hand, and left without a word. He himself was taken aback by his own severity. After all, he thought, these are poor people facing many dangers. They have homes and children. They have to exist. They have to live.

Freedom approached – miraculous and unexpected. He was so overcome with joy that he forgot about his accusations of human servility.

Everything was drowned by his words of gratitude to Our Lady; he had no doubt that he owed the victory to Her. He was returning to his work and his responsibilities, and from the Sinai of his experiences he was bringing the tablets of well-considered thoughts and plans of action.

But then the day came when he had an urge to hurl the tablets to the ground, as Moses had done.

A crucifix hung at a slight angle above the immense refectory. The bishops' table stood below it. He was joined by the father general, the provincial, and the prior. He was surrounded by white cassocks. They told him all sorts of things relating to the monastery and treated him like a member of the family. They talked about repairs and renovation projects, negotiations with the authorities, and the condition of the Icon, which had suffered considerably during the years it was walled up. There was also the problem of the snowballing number of pilgrims coming to Jasna Góra.

He ate and listened. He always ate quickly and sparingly, not caring much about food. On formal occasions, those sitting at the far end of the table were always disturbed to see the Primate ready to get up from the table when the main course had not even reached them. One of his close associates complained: "Your Eminence, have mercy on the hungry..."

The superiors of the congregation thanked him for the assistance they had received on many occasions. Jasna Góra owed a lot to him, but he was deeply convinced he owed more to it. The shrine was the source of the strength which let him rise to do battle again after every wound, for the time of wounds was not over yet. The triumph of his return did not prove to be his final triumph. New objections were being raised and those who'd been full of promises at the time of danger now created difficulties. The idea of a replica of the Icon of Our Lady of Jasna Góra touring the country, one blessed by the Pope, encountered obstruction and harassment. The picture was seized and hidden.

Although Wyszyński could understand the resistance and reconciled himself to the thought that Our Lady did not want to perform a miracle but merely wanted people to discover the truth through their own errors, it hurt him to realize that his own people were a long way from understanding the discoveries he'd made in confinement. To give everything to Mary, dedicate oneself to Her and give oneself into the slavery of love, sounded strange to many Catholics. Years of feverish contestation began. The conviction was born that it was necessary to change everything in the Church and strike an alliance with old enemies, and that this had to be done as quickly as possible, as it was being done in France and Holland. More and more complaints were heard about the Church in Poland being obstinately conservative and failing to keep pace with the changing times. In the West, there were calls for the abolition of celibacy, the acceptance of all birth control techniques, the ordainment of women, homosexual equality, and cooperation with freemasonry. Everything the West offered appeared to be so attractive that, although nobody dared to say what he wanted aloud, there were many people who made it quite clear they were not at all happy with the Primate's "Virgin Mary Catholicism". Some wrote letters of complaint to Rome, others grumbled about "baroque forms of eighteenth century religion in Poland." The Primate wanted the Icon to travel from one parish to another at a time when churches in the West were selling their holy pictures. The Primate wanted to reach even deeper into man's soul, while everywhere there were suggestions that the word "freedom", whatever that meant, should unite all "proper-thinking" people – and woe to those who wanted to define what kind of freedom that was supposed to be.

Along with the complaints came the denunciation of individuals. This fellow had betrayed him, that one had denounced him, another was in the service of the enemy... He was overwhelmed by an avalanche of accusations. In Rywałd and Stoczek he had come to know human frailty through his struggle with himself. Betrayal? Corruption? This definitely happened. But Jesus forgave Judas. After all, were the thirty pieces of silver really what it was all about? Or perhaps people wanted to do good but searched in the wrong places? The important thing was to search for that which united, as the Holy Pope, the man who wanted to change everything around him and succeeded, had once said.

"*Caro filio*," the Pope said to him, strolling in the Vatican gardens, "people are not bad. The only trouble is that they aren't able to love. And how can you teach anyone to love? Only by loving. That's why, right at the start, the good Lord gives us a family. A loving family produces a loving person. I'm sure you know all that. When I was in Częstochowa – that name's so difficult for me to pronounce – and I prayed to the Madonna, it struck me that above all She wants to be a Mother to us. I think, *carissime*, that we should be doing the same – loving people like She does. Slowly, very slowly, we'll win everybody over... You know, sometimes I think that perhaps Joseph might have been too impulsive. He wanted to get angry at other people, but then She would say, '*Piano*, Joseph, *piano*.' It's strange, but when people think something is bad, they talk about it a lot. But when they think something is good, they tend to keep it to themselves."

What he would do then, was love and listen to his conscience. Nothing more than what St. Augustine had taught: do not listen to accusations, close your ears to informers. But this was not easy to do. The people he trusted brought him false information, then they excused themselves, saying they had merely been repeating what others had told them. But who was the first to spread the libel? A poet on whom suspicion had fallen shouted pathetically that if they were going to talk about him that way he was leaving the Church. He died shortly after the outburst, and nobody knew whether he'd really become a renegade or if those were just idle words uttered in anger.

He rose from the table and walked to the desk where a moment earlier a lector had been reading the passage for the day. He said a few warm words to the monks gathered in the refectory and several priests who had come to Jasna Góra with groups of pilgrims. He praised the cook for the excellent meal, then he went to the garden beyond the walls.

He liked to pray while walking. The sun filtered through the canopy of leaves and cast shifting spots of light on the path. The stations of the Cross rose above him; he had to tilt his head back to see which station he was standing beside.

How beautiful the silence was in the canyon of greenery! He loved it so much. Carrying a breviary, he walked slowly. In an hour, he decided, he would say the rosary in front of the miraculous Icon. He could hardly remember his mother's features by now, and in reality knew her best from the photograph on his desk, in which she was sitting with Janka in her lap. Now he often looked for her features in the picture of the Madonna. The faces of all mothers had something in common, an identical tenderness.

He met a monk attending a bed of flowers. "May God give you strength," he said.

"May the Lord thank you." The young Paulite raised a beaming face. "Taking a walk, Your Eminence?"

"I'm partly walking, partly praying."

"We've prepared a surprise for Your Eminence."

"What kind of surprise?"

"My, I shouldn't have said anything. The prior will be angry. I've sinned."

"Well, everybody should watch their tongue, but I wouldn't call it a sin. And I won't tell anybody what you said."

From the garden he went up onto the ramparts.

The monks had pleaded with him not to go out to the pilgrims on his own.

"They'll start shoving and kissing your hands," they said. "They'll be uncontrollably insistent, and who knows what evil idea might cross someone's mind. There are all kinds of people in this world."

"It's all right," he'd reassured them. "Are you afraid of viruses? Haven't you thought that Our Lady also has power over them? If She chooses to protect me from them, She will. As for jostling crowds, Jesus faced them. What else could happen to me?"

There were few people on the ramparts at that time of day, and they did not recognize the priest dressed in the black cassock as the Primate. Most of the women present had never seen him at close quarters, and if they had, they had seen him in purple vestments. Still, here and there he saw looks of surprise and guessing smiles.

A woman, still fairly young, ran up to him.

"Oh, it's you, Your Eminence! I'm so glad. At last I can thank you."

"Thank me for what?"

"You don't recognize me?"

He looked at her round face, straight blonde hair, and blue eyes. Nothing came to mind.

"I'm afraid not," he said. "Who are you?"

She laughed in embarrassment.

"Remember the hospital at Laski? I was the one you brought in with the wounded leg after you found me lying in the woods."

"Julka! Oh, my dear child. How could I have recognized you?" Her face had been covered with mud and tears the last time he saw her. "So what have you done with yourself, Madam?"

"As you promised, Your Eminence, Our Lady took care of me. I recovered completely, earned a degree in medicine, and got married. I have two children now. I come here to thank Her."

"Never stop. She'll certainly not refuse you Her protection." He touched the woman's head with the tips of his fingers and she kissed his hand. Sometimes it occurred to him that strangers whom he'd helped by accident benefited greatly while others who were dear to him, whom he'd tried to help and for whom he prayed, became remote, wasted their lives, or went astray.

A small crowd had gathered during the short conversation with Julka, and soon it began to swell as the identity of the tall, slim priest became known. When Julka withdrew, others formed a tight circle around him. Several hands reached for him.

One of the monks was already wading through the crowd. The people stepped back and Wyszyński blessed them and followed the monk through to the Knights' Hall. At the entrance to the off-limits section of the monastery the General of the Order met them.

"I was beginning to fear they wouldn't let Your Eminence go," he said.

"Trust me, Father General. Nothing will happen to me here."

"What will Your Eminence do after tea?"

"I have some work to do. Or have you got other plans, Father?"

"We'd like to take up a little of your time..."

"Then don't hesitate to do so." He guessed that must be the surprise.

Waiting for the friars to arrive, he stood by the window. Now, in the afternoon, a rather sleepy silence prevailed in the square below the walls. Only a few people moved between the stalls near the gate and the road, which was an extension of the avenue. But, he thought, the day after tomorrow the square would be a sea of human heads. Year after year the ceremonies attracted more people. Such crowds were never seen there in the old days. Neither he nor the other bishops nor the monks had anticipated that development. In the past they'd been proud if tens of thousands of people who came – these days there were hundreds of thousands. Who had caused this to happen? Not me, no – he rejected the idea. She alone was responsible.

"These walls," he thought, "who hasn't camped under them? Jasna

Góra has been besieged by Swedes, Russians, Prussians, and Austrians. The flood of disasters that have .befallen the nation washed over these walls. But the tide always ebbed, while Jasna Góra stayed on, like the evangelical home built on top of a rock. And now multitudes wanting to pay homage and testify to their faith are drawn here. This is no empty demonstration designed to irritate 'the other side.' People come in a mood of solemnity, understanding the seriousness. One might almost get the impression that these millions of Poles, famous for their impetuosity, have now realized that it's necessary to learn self-control. There've been many ideas about how to run the country, yet finally the conviction emerged that man cannot govern anything until he has learned to govern his own actions. In order to teach the nation to work hard, one has to work hard oneself; in order to teach the nation to live in love, one has to learn to love; and in order to give peace to the world one first has to find peace within oneself. Poland is open to enemies on all sides, bounded neither by seas nor impassable mountains. And that's just as well. When poeple feel secure, they often opt for the easy way out. We have to live a hard life and therefore we have to muster a strength of spirit that others don't have."

He was so strongly linked to the nation. Pure Polish peasant blood flowed in his veins. He would never exchange Zuzela for any other place. The time would come when people would find it on maps. If only they managed to stay sober in spirit, all those looking for faith would come there on pilgrimage.

He recalled how he'd traveled to Rome to attend the conclave after the death of Pius XII, and was astonished by the enthusiasm of the crowds that greeted him. Everybody talked about his arrival, and his name and a photograph appeared in all the papers. He, a Pole, attracting so much attention! The votes he received during the early ballots were insufficient to give him a chance of victory, yet they demonstrated that Poland, always underestimated and slighted, had suddenly and unexpectedly become a force to be reckoned with in the Sacred College.

Of all the romantic poets, he prized Norwid the most:

"No Polish king has ever been beheaded,
And so Frenchmen will brand us as rebels.
No Polish monk has ever blasphemed against virtue,

And so the heretic will charge us with heresy.
No Polish plow has ever turned foreign soil,
And so we shall be proclaimed thieves.
No Polish spirit has ever deserted its own kind,
And so they will lecture us on what history is..."

Other works he quoted frequently were: "I long, O Lord, for the land where they pick up crumbs from the ground out of respect for the gifts of Heaven." If he had to leave the country, that was precisely how he would long for it.

Going to Rome for the first time after his release, he'd been apprehensive. What if they didn't let him back in? The suspicion lingered in his heart, and he knew that if it were up to him he would return even if that meant immediately going back to Rywałd or Stoczek.

If I'm elected – the thought had occurred as he sat under the canopy in the Sistine chapel – I don't know if I'd be able to accept. Exchange Poland for the world? Impossible. I couldn't live away from it. *Sic Traba papa – Cracovia Roma. Sic Wyszyński* – No, it's too early. The day will come when someone will take Poland's victories to the throne of St. Peter, but these victories have to grow and mature. We cannot go emptyhanded.

Then the canopies were folded down, and the one that remained upright was above the chair of the Patriarch of Venice.

When he knelt in front of the new Pope, a heavy peasant's hand rested on his shoulder and he heard: *"Mio caro,* Częstochowa, remember Częstochowa..."

Several years later the next Pope said to him: "I want to come to Poland, Your Eminence. Please try to convince them that this would be no political demonstration, that I genuinely wish to pay homage to Our Lady of Częstochowa. Something strange and extraordinary is going on in your country. I can feel it..."

Someone knocked on the door.

"Come in."

It was the general, the provincial, and the prior.

He motioned them to the armchairs but was amazed by their unusual earnestness. They remained standing, the way people did when they brought a particularly important message which they had to pass on before they said anything else.

The general said: "Your Eminence's love of Our Lady is so great, and you have done so much for our monastery, that we jointly decided to help you to talk to Our Lady. In a moment the Icon will be brought to your room and will remain here until the evening service. We thought this would please Your Eminence greatly."

"How could you have doubted that! You've given me the greatest joy possible." He choked with emotion. "If I have ever done anything for the monastery, you are rewarding me a hundredfold."

One of the monks opened the door. Heavy steps could be heard. Although separated from the steel case that secured it, the picture required the considerable efforts of six men to carry it. They deposited it on a couch and everyone genuflected. The general recited a brief prayer, then the monks rose and left the room one by one. The general was the last to go. He bowed deeply before leaving.

They were alone.

He crawled to the Icon on his knees. He'd seen it many times, but always from a distance. Now it was right before his eyes, he could actually touch it. He could see only the face and hands; the rest was hidden by a robe stretched on a steel frame. It glittered with gold and thousands of gems: crosses, holy medals, chains, and miniature votive offerings. From the center of the frame, a familiar face looked out at him.

He tried to pray only after looking at Her until he felt satiated. His lips moved as if muttering words, but his eyes remained locked on Hers, as if seized and held by them.

"Thank You, Mother," he whispered. "Thank You for everything: for life, for the crosses, for the pain and the joy, for being able to come to You and dedicate myself to You, and for Your willingness to accept me as Your own. Thank you for not rejecting us unfaithful ones, who do not remember their promises. Thank You for not being repelled by our sins, hideous as they are, and for agreeing to become our Queen. Thank You for giving back the strength we had lost through our own fault, for having saved us so many times, and for waiting mercifully until we, in our laziness, learn Your lessons at last. Thank You for having chosen us and for leading us to Your Son. You and You alone are the Road that leads to Him. You are the Bridge over an abyss of evil, the Light that shines in the dark, a friendly Hand encountered in a void."

"What you have said is true, My son," the narrow eyes seemed to say.

"Yes, I have chosen you all. Ask not why. The time will come when you will learn how many anonymous hearts are responsible for this choice. You love Me, so I love you and watch over you. He has awakened this feeling in you. Everything you have, you have received from Heaven above.

"And now the moment is approaching. You are happy to see the crowds coming here to pay tribute to me. Yes, I summoned them, but I also entrusted the matter to you. You have done well. You have called out as ardently as the one whose severed head is in your coat-of-arms. Thank you my son. I need your work. I will give you enough strength to last until your final moment.

"You will not find your work easy. Once again, there will be objections from your own people and others. Enthusiasm will lead to errors. To many the triumph will appear to be the ultimate victory, but you know that it can only take place on the Cross and must be born of love. Our triumph must be expressed by open hands, not clenched fists.

"You must desire only that which I desire. You must forget about yourself. Others will pass you by, but you will be the source of their strength. Summon all those from whom you have grown distant. Forgive the guilty, comfort the weak, forget the lies.

"The moment is near. The world around you will rage on. You will be the one who will shield other men with the sacrifice of your life. And I will give you a power even greater than that you enjoyed when your words moved thousands of thousands of people."

He lay flat on the floor, his arms outstretched, as he had done half a century earlier when he was preparing to be admitted into the priesthood in the chapel of Our Lady of Częstochowa in Włocławek. He had been so weak then. He had begged for just one year, and She had given him so many. He closed his eyes.

He seemed to see all of Warsaw shrouded in black. He saw a procession of hundreds of thousands of people, those who had loved him and those who had failed him, those who were faithful to him and those who were against him. They were following a coffin. It passed from shoulder to shoulder. Everybody wanted to touch it... The bells rang in the churches where he'd said Mass and spread the Gospel so often.

Through the tolling of the bells he heard the poem: "Great is the man

who only needs to lower his head to triumph, without spear nor shield...
And if people boast that they have known great men, it is only because the
little do not recognize the great until they die."

The bells continued to toll and Warsaw's Royal Way opened out before
the procession, laying itself at the feet of the one who deputized for
kings.

He wanted to leap to his feet and cry: "Mother, and what about
Poland?" But his mouth and his heart remained silent.

Hadn't he written during his imprisonment: "Everything I shall do
with Your assistance, Immaculate Intercessor of all Grace, I dedicate to the
glory of the Holy Trinity – *Soli Deo*"?

·Hadn't he entrusted everything to Her completely?

He was sure he would see Her with his own eyes. He was sure that his
desire had become Her desire. But then, Her wishes were always his
wishes. Was there any need to worry about the days to come?

CHAPTER 14

THE POLISH POPE

The white helicopter flew in a wide circle above rectangles of green fields, square patches of dark woods, roads where cars scurried like ants rushing to repair a damaged mound, and houses scattered as if they were blocks discarded by a bored child. It skimmed a bare mountain ridge that thrust up from the forest like the skeleton of an ancient reptile, then the grey blot of the town spread below: smokestacks, boilers, and ugly buildings searching vainly for the sun. An immense crowd moved along a broad tree-lined avenue – a human rainbow of colors made more vivid by the recurrent rainshowers. When the copter crossed the railroad tracks, one of the passengers leaned against the window and searched for the landmark he knew would come into view any moment. Then the monastery emerged from behind the wooded park, and the steeple pierced the sky.

The pilot headed towards the spire and circled it like a returning stork orbits the tree in which he'd nested the previous spring. People waved from the balcony. The helicopter flew in tighter and tighter arcs to allow the visitor a view of the building that was both the holiest of shrines and a fortified castle guarding the national tradition. The surrounding hillside was packed with people from the fortress walls to the park. Flags were everywhere: red and white, yellow and white, blue and white. The visitor's heart pounded and he was so moved by the enormous amount of love that had brought the thousands of people there, that he felt he might weep for joy.

No one had needed to teach him to love Our Lady, She had been part of him from his youngest years. He had loved the Virgin Mary of the church in Wadowice, the Mary of Kalwaria Zebrzydowska, the Mary of the poor church at Niegowić, the Mary of St. Floryan Church in Cracow, and the Mary kneeling among the Apostles in Wit Stwosz's altarpiece in Cracow Church of Our Lady. But he had also come to Jasna Góra often. He had a particularly vivid memory of the night during the Nazi occupation when he traveled to Częstochowa with a group of young men who, like himself, concealed their true intentions under soiled workers dungarees. They had come to repeat the unforgettable vows of 1936. He had every right to include the words *"totus Tuus"* in his coat-of-arms.

Later he had returned as a priest, lecturer, and traveler, then as a bishop, and finally as a cardinal.

The sight of the crowds below brought back the memory of the man who had tied him inseparably to the place.

From the upper terrace –"the summit" as it was called in Jasna Góra – two cardinals had once surveyed the meadow below the walls. It teemed with people. As always, Karol Wojtyła had looked with a mixture of respect and admiration at the tall, slim, older man with fair hair and blue eyes. The gap of twenty years that separated them was not the only cause for respect. The decisive factor was the man's personality, which was so immense and multi-hued. There was his disarming smile, which revealed exceptional goodness, but also the severe glint in his eyes as they suddenly turned the color of steel; was his manly, sonorous, unyielding voice, but also his soft words, those a mother whispers to her child. For some time the old cardinal had been taking the younger one aside and asking him many questions. He listened patiently to the answers as they strolled together in the monastery garden. He liked to talk and listen while he walked.

Cardinal Wojtyła felt that he was closer to the Primate with every passing year, despite the fact that they differed so vastly and came from totally different environments. Subconsciously, Wojtyła sensed that the other man was trying to peer inside him, to get to know him fully, and that there was more than curiosity involved. It was the prelude to saying something extremely important. Or was it perhaps a desire to confide something?

Karol's life had been a string of successes; the old cardinal had had a different life, and he watched this rapid progress with amazement. But experience had taught him that the divine wind blew in whichever direction it wanted to. He did not want to prejudge anything, so he simply watched, studied, and observed.

"See those crowds, Your Eminence," Wyszyński once said. "I watch them every year, and every year they're bigger. It's like a river emptying into this meadow. Jasna Góra is our heart, and the tired blood of the nation flows through it, to be pumped out, purged and rejuvenated. This reminds me of the Greek legend of the son of Mother Earth who could not be defeated because as soon as he was thrown to the ground he regained his strength. She, too, is our Mother. Through Her Grace She consented to join our lives in order to heal us. We are safe as long as this process goes on. Nothing can threaten us and evil will always be turned into good. But this means we have to be alert. And that is a task for you, Your Eminence."

"Jasna Góra has always enjoyed your protection," Wojtyła said.

"Yes, we've been running the roost around here for some time," he conceded with his slightly jocular smile. "But now it'll be different. This is Your Eminence's see. A short while ago I was approached about a plan to organize a meeting of men of letters in Jasna Góra. I sent the organizers to you."

"Yet Your Eminence has so many artists in Warsaw –"

He ended all argument with a gesture of his hand.

"You know best who should be invited to that meeting." The tone of his voice changed. "I haven't felt very well lately," he said. "Quite bad, in fact."

"Is it your old ailment again?", Wojtyła asked shyly.

The old cardinal was reluctant to speak about his health.

"Yes," he admitted. "I know I'm not going to break free of it." He paused and added, "But I would like to carry on until the end of our time of expectations. I think She promised me that."

He never used to speak like that before, Wojtyła reflected.

"During my imprisonment," Wyszyński continued, "I often thought about the presence of the Blessed Virgin in the mystery of the faith in Poland. I'm afraid not many people think about it, yet it's extraordinary. Why is it that we survived? We were no better than others then, and we're no better now either. Our nation has grave sins on its conscience, and yet it did not perish. People often think that it's got to be that way forever. And I believe, Your Eminence, that they expect something from us, that they want us to do something. The world is headed for great decisions..." He stopped and smiled. Then he asked: "Perhaps you think that I'm succumbing to mysticism? I've heard that accusation many times. Especially in France. There they say I'm too old fashioned in my love of Mary... Some people in Poland say the same. *Inimici hominis domestici eius.*"

What the old cardinal said was true. How many times had Wojtyła heard such views?

Both in the West and at home, people tried to contrast the two cardinals: "Oh, that Primate of yours! He's a brave man, there's no denying that. When the time came he knew how to say no. But his cult of Our Lady is a throwback to Medieval mysticism. That's out of date now, after the Second Council. It's just as well he's getting on in years. He should step down, then Your Eminence would take matters into his own hands."

In the past, he, too, had sometimes thought that some of Wyszyński's statements were exaggerated. But now he felt that the man was drawing him onto his own path.

"She's watching over us," Wyszyński went on, without taking his eyes off the crowd gathered outside the walls, "but then She's watching over the whole Church. Maybe it's still too early to speak about it? And yet there's something to it: Nuncio Ratti prayed here, and when he became Pope he asked for a copy of the Black Madonna of Jasna Góra, John XXIII always remembered that he had been here, and when he was elected Pope he asked me to make sure that he wasn't forgotten here. And Paul VI, too, prayed before the Icon when he was a young priest. He wanted to come here very much, and he would have, had it not been for the blind resistance of certain people... But that's not so important. Mary will wait. We just have to remain alert. That's up to you, Eminence. Perhaps you'll be the one to whom She'll confide her secret."

"What secret?" he wanted to ask, but he changed his mind. "Why ask?"

Wyszyński didn't know the answer either. He'd waited for it all those years and now he was passing the vigil on.

Some years later Karol Wojtyła heard the old cardinal's broken voice on the telephone: "Holy Father... When you come back – because you will come again – Holy Father, She'll tell you Herself..."

The helicopter began its descent. Its whining rotor blades generated a wind that jerked small branches off nearby trees and sucked leaves and bits of grass into the air. A chaplain leaned over Wojtyła's seat and in a subdued monotone he reminded the Pope of the order of appointments for the remainder of the day: the welcoming ceremony, the drive to the cathedral, and, finally, the visit to the monastery.

Wojtyła listened absently, staring down at the waiting crowd that surged forward as the copter descended. A cordon of police held them in check. Only a small group – bishops in purple vestments, Paulists in white habits, priests in black soutanes, and laymen in dark suits – was permitted close to the landing marker. The people, he thought, were being kept at a greater distance than ever before. The situation had been different four years ago – flowers had fallen on his shoulders, and children had run freely to him and he'd stroked their heads and kissed them. Everyone had been united by one emotion, without exception. Today that was no longer true. Each side wished to welcome him for their own purpose, as if what was really at stake did not concern him at all. Perhaps the shots fired in St. Peter's Square had signaled the approaching division.

What he had heard that day in the square had not sounded like gunfire. There was only a cracking noise, as if someone had snapped a whip. Simultaneously, a terrible pain like a sharp thorn being forced deep inside him wracked his entire body. He fell at once... Someone held him up by his arms... Pain mixed with shock as he realized what had happened. The car accelerated madly and careened away from the scene of the assault, and every jolt of the wheels was like a fresh blow to him. Before he lost consciousness he whispered, "Why? Why? I forgive..."

The helicopter dipped low and hovered above the flat, green expanse as if trying to decide between heaven and earth.

"He had been in a similar position a few times himself," Wojtyła thought.

When he was still a young lad, a friend had once stood in front of him waving a gun. Inadvertently, he pulled the trigger. The bullet narrowly missed Karol's ear. Nothing happened, he did not even have to go to the hospital.

He landed there later, when he was already a seminarian and was hit by a German truck one night. He tumbled into a roadside ditch. The Germans did not even stop. He lay unconscious until morning, when he was found and taken to a hospital.

He finally recovered consciousness in the Gemelli Clinic. They didn't need to tell him that he had been brought there at the last moment, only minutes away from dying from loss of blood. He found it hard to come back to life. When he knew that he would live, a new worry formed in his mind: would he be crippled for life? Would his life, saved miraculously, be one in the full sense of the word?

Incurably ill people who died a slow death spread over years – that had been a deeply felt experience for him in the period when his future was being decided. As a healthy, energetic boy who played a number of sports, he was repelled by people twisted by disease. Being a good altar boy, he often helped an elderly lady to rise from her knees, but he did so out of innate helpfulness rather than dedication. His friends were youngsters like himself, bursting with life, kicking balls and running about. Over the years his acquaintances were always young and full of the joy of life.

A move to Cracow with his father had been a turning point in Karol Wojtyła's life. He'd been attracted to poetry and the theater in high school and he already knew that both meant a great deal to him. He joined a circle of artistically talented people, took part in their amateur theatrical productions, listened to their works, and read his poems to them. When Tadeusz Kudliński set up the Drama School in 1939 and produced a play by Niżynski about the legendary Polish figure Pan Twardowski, young Karol was one of the actors. His performance received liberal doses of applause and praise, both of which could be powerful drugs. Around that time he considered merging his two passions and, like Shakespeare, writing for the theater and playing his own heroes.

It was probably purely accidental that he thought about Brother Albert, the painter who rejected art in order to serve people. He was thought of by many people torn between the temptations of artistic creation and their attachment to the faith. Chmielowski was an artist, but he was also aware of a threat to something that was the most important thing in his life. Could art exist side by side with religion? Art absorbed men so easily, became a tyrant and demanded to be served. But could a man serve two masters at the same time? Karol Wojtyła reflected on that dilemma as well.

Some time earlier, Mauriac had wrestled with the same problem and his books were just beginning to reach Poland. "The defender of the holy cause, the soldier of God," he wrote, "demands that everybody serve and often thinks that to serve means to refuse to write anything that does not produce immediate benefits... And yet even the most modest of us thinks he would not deserve to be called an artist if he did not approach his literary work in an atmosphere of purity and independence, and detachment from everything else."

While in Munich, Chmielowski had already realized that if man did not love God, he would worship art. So was it necessary to desert art in order not to desert God? – the young Wojtyła asked himself. That seemed impossible. Art had to remain itself, yet serve... How could that be done? How could art be forced to serve the Lord?

Karol tried to trace the line of Brother Albert's thoughts. He was interested in Chmielowski's meeting with Rafał Kalinowski and then with the down-and-outs in the shelter. The decisive moment came somewhere. The young student began to sneak into places where he could meet the sick and the infirm, the sight of whom he'd once found repulsive. He fought to overcome that revulsion. He looked at faces distorted by sickness, deformed limbs, various kinds of disabilities. Sometimes he noted with terror that these were young people doomed to die a slow death, people for whom there was no place left in life. And yet there must have been some reason for their existence!

The spell cast by Chmielowski bound him more and more strongly. The more he looked at the suffering, the more he had to think about it. Meanwhile, a disaster was taking place around him. The German invasion seemed to have put an end to the dream of independent statehood that was barely twenty years old. For his father it was indeed a bolt of lightning that struck a healthy tree and reduced it to a dead stump. Karol had to go underground with his problems, hopes and passions, but the young were bursting with energy. Mieczysław Kotlarczyk, the man steadily leading Wojtyła in the direction of the stage, set up the underground Rhapsodic

Theater. Clandestine though it was, Karol could at least perform and recite his poems there.

He was attracted to the theater, but something pulled him in the opposite direction. There were meetings with members of the Revival Group and there was the Living Rosary, to which Wojtyła was introduced by the pious tailor Tyranowski. Added to this was his exhausting and dangerous work in the quarry of the Solvay Chemical Works, a very instructive encounter with the working class. And then came the death of his father, for whom the Nazi occupation was beyond endurance.

Wojtyła was left to himself and had to cope with all his problems alone. He heard a new calling in his heart, one that became louder with every passing day. In order to be able to answer it, he decided to go to Częstochowa. Travel by rail was perilous at the time, as even the best papers were often not enough to secure safe passage. Germans were billeted in Jasna Góra and the guards kept a watchful eye on people heading for the church. Only when they got inside the chapel could they forget about the dangers that threatened them.

He had looked into Our Lady's face above his clasped hands. As always, Her eyes were fixed on him.

They gazed at him, studiously and piercingly, as if they wanted to say: "I am here, I know all about you, I am waiting for you." Our Lady of Jasna Góra was the Waiting Mother of them all.

When he left the chapel, he knew that he had a difficult conversation with Kotlarczyk ahead of him in Cracow. He did not yet know how the relationship between art and service would work out, but his decision was final.

"What do you mean, Lolek, you want to give up the stage?" Kotlarczyk asked. "But that's nonsense. You're a born actor. You're even more – a born artist. You know what art is. I know how intense your faith is, and I realize what a calling means. I respect that, I really do. But for heaven's sake, you've already got a calling. We artists also have a vocation." Warmly, he laid a hand on Karol's shoulder. "You've every right to be depressed: your father's death, the loneliness, the hard labor. For all our friendship, there isn't much we can do for you. But don't make your decision final yet. I've got a part that's just made for you."

"No, please. Don't try to talk me out of it. I've already made up my mind. I'll be a priest and monk, best of all a Carmelite like Kalinows-ki –"

270

"A monk as well! Do you want to give up writing altogether?"

"No, not quite. I'll write while I'm in the Order. After all, both the Theresas wrote, and so did John of the Cross."

"If you don't mind my saying so, that wasn't art. Those two women saints deserve admiration, but not for their poems. If you really insist on doing this, you'll stop being an artist."

"Not necessarily. I'll find a way for my art to serve God yet still remain art."

"Nothing will come of it, Lolek. Believe me."

Wojtyła would not be diverted from the road he had chosen. While in the seminary he still kept in touch with Kotlarczyk's theater, wrote poetry, and worked in the quarry. Although he had made his choice, he'd not given up anything.

One August night, shortly after he left the hospital after being hit by the German truck, old Konstancja, a kitchen maid at the Archbishop's residence, came to the house at 10 Tyniecka Street. Wojtyła had just returned from work in Borek Fałęcki. The workers were excited, passing around news about the reported outbreak of fighting in Warsaw.

"Mr. Wojtyła," said the old woman, "His Excellency the Archbishop asked me to tell you to report to his palace first thing in the morning."

"But I have to go to work, Konstancja."

"I don't know about that. His Excellency said: 'Tell him to take the barest essentials and come at once. Tell him not to waste time.' You know, Mr. Wojtyła, that our men are fighting the Germans in Warsaw?"

"I heard something, yes."

"They say they've launched an uprising. There's terrible fighting going on. There'll be fighting here too, soon, don't you think?"

"Who knows? But what will happen if I don't report to work tomorrow?"

"His Excellency will think of something, Mr. Wojtyła, don't you worry."

The following morning, the seminarian Karol Wojtyła vanished. Only a handful of people knew the truth, others made wild guesses. Archbishop Sapieha, afraid for his seminarians and wanting them close by, hid them in his place. He had his own ways of concealing Karol's disappearance from the German authorities.

Six months later Cracow was not only liberated but also saved from destruction, and a year later Wojtyła was ordained. The Archbishop believed he showed great promise, and almost immediately afterwards sent him to Rome. During the trip Wojtyła also had an opportunity to see some of France and Belgium. He came across the Young Catholic Workers movement and learned of the shocking discovery made by young French priests: France had become so pagan that it qualified for missionary work. After almost fifteen centuries of Christianity, the land of St. Louis and St. Joan was sapped of its religious and moral strength. Yet Christianity meant perpetual renewal, renewal which always assumed new forms. Finding those new forms meant pouring enriched yet unchanged contents into a new evangelic wineskin that would withstand the process of fermentation. That was the task facing the young priest.

He was filled with a youthful zeal, a drive to discover new things, but he still longed for artistic creativity. It was perhaps the memory of Chmiel-owski's experiences that made Karol select the works of John of the Cross, the mystic and poet, as the subject of the thesis he wrote while in Rome.

He returned to Poland in a feverish mood, full of enormous discoveries and experiences. Sapieha, a wise shepherd, sent him to the rural parish of Niegowić near the salt-mining town of Bochnia to cool down. Niegowić was a remote village which had changed little since the nineteenth century. Someone there, no doubt discreetly, observed the behavior of the young curate and reported his impressions to the newly appointed cardinal, who had great hopes for Wojtyła; the young priest had first caught his eye when he was taking his final exams at Wadowice High School. The impressions must have been positive. After a very short time Father Wojtyła was called back to Cracow and started work as curate at St. Floryan's parish in the district of Kleparz.

Wojtyła's return to Cracow was a return to the old friends and acquaintances he'd abandoned. They were all in the mainstream of Cracow's artistic life now. The Rhapsodic Theater was open to the public and art flourished in one of the few Polish towns to emerge from the war unscathed. Literary journals were beginning to appear. The young curate again tried his hand at poetry, publishing under the pen name of Andrzej Jawień. He could not stop thinking about writing for the stage.

And then one day he once again came face to face with Chmielowski and his sufferers.

While at St. Floryan, he was asked to meet a young woman who was confined to a wheelchair for the rest of her life. He treated the request as a professional duty. Meetings with the sick had always been difficult for him. In an attempt to arouse his interest in the meeting, someone told him that the girl wrote poetry and prose. To be precise, she did not actually write, and her throat would only emit sounds that were unintelligible to the average person. But she was surrounded by friendly women, some of whom had learned to understand what she said and to take dictation from her.

The woman lived in an apartament in a typical Cracow courtyard with its narrow gateway and wooden galleries running along the walls. She had a young face full of charm, but the charm diminished when she tried to speak: she moaned as if uttering every word took the greatest of effort. When she spoke, almost choking, she raised one hand, her bent fingers trembling in the air. She stretched out the shaking hand to the priest and uttered a few words he could not understand. Her friend sitting beside her translated: "Zosia wants to thank you, Father, for coming to see her."

At first he was so nervous he didn't know what to say. The feeling soon left him and he realized that any words of consolation, any assurances that the Lord might restore her health, would be out of place. In the girl's dark eyes he read the certainty she must have felt: no cure awaited her, things would stay the same for many years. What could he say to her?

He sighed and then he began: "The Lord has selected you, Zosia, and entrusted you with the great task of serving Him with your suffering. Every day must become more deserving of the choice He has made. Christ did not save the world with His words, but on the Cross. Similarly, Man carries on the sacrifice of Jesus not with words, but with the suffering of his body. The world would perish if it were not constantly being saved through suffering together with Jesus Christ. This is a great cause and you have been called on to take part in it."

Once more her trembling hand grasped his and tried to press it to her lips. He embraced her shrunken body and touched her forehead with his lips. He was sure he had been properly understood.

Zosia's friends gave him some of her writing. Casting an eye over the pages, he was surprised by the depth of her observations. He studied them carefully in his room that night. The poems and fragments of prose were strangely mature, and he decided to see about having them published.

He visited the young woman a number of times. At first he talked to her through "interpreters," then he tried to decipher her words himself. He was right: he'd been understood. She had wished to offer up her suffering even before he had told her to do so. His words had given her joy because they were like an answer to her prayers.

Later responsibilities prevented him from seeing Zosia again. All he knew was that she was alive, amazed others with her peace of mind, kept writing, and that her works appeared in Catholic periodicals.

The young vicar became a scholar, a professor, and a lecturer. His lectures abounded in interesting philosophical concepts, and Wojtyła devoted particular attention to the great issue of man's dignity, duties, and responsibilities. Only twelve years after he'd been ordained he received the bishop's miter. Four years later, after the death of Archbishop Baziak, he was granted on an interim basis – the throne of Bishop Metropolitan of Cracow. A year later the Pope confirmed him as the legitimate successor to the unforgettable Cardinal Sapieha. Four more years passed before he was made a cardinal. At 47, he was then the youngest cardinal in the Church.

Wojtyła was reputed to have a rare gift for winning over the youth, being able to talk to them despite all his titles and offices, and sharing their joys and leisure activities. He remained an active sportsman, practiced skiing, canoeing and climbing, and he was the foremost singer in any group of young people.

At the same time, his popularity among churchmen abroad grew rapidly. His great gift for languages earned him friends everywhere. He visited exotic countries and gradually his name became well known on all continents. The boy from Wadowice had grown into a citizen of the world.

It was then that Cardinal Wyszyński began to look closely at the Cracow Metropolitan. Could he have felt that some day his vote would be decisive in electing a Polish Pope?

Wojtyła remembered perfectly the moment when he had to say yes to the choice made by the cardinals. He was concentrated in prayer. Somewhere in the tangle of his thoughts he saw the sick, the bedridden, people confined to wheelchairs, their bodies twisted by pain, and he saw Chmielowski's down-and-outs too. He heard the words – like an echo, it seemed – about those who "complement what is missing in Christ's suffering." In a sudden flash he realized that there was a certain link between him and the people he visualized; that, if had not been for them, he would not be sitting there in an armchair under the only canopy that would not be folded down in a while. He said yes, convinced that this link had not been severed, that it was actually being reinforced.

He found that link again in his reflections in the Gemelli Clinic, and in the quiet, broken voice of the old cardinal who was dying in Warsaw.

The landing skids touched the grass and the helicopter settled to earth, and with one last whoosh the rotor blades stopped spinning. Wojtyła rose and left the cabin. The crew stood in formation outside the door, and the welcoming officials walked towards the Pope the moment he emerged. It had started to rain again and the ceremony was brief.

The security car was parked a few steps away: a squat, ugly box equipped with bulletproof glass, the only automobile he was permitted to travel in now. A jeep carrying members of the anti-terrorist brigade in full battle gear preceded him on the way to the cathedral, while his personal bodyguards clung to the car. The crowds that lined the narrow streets waved excitedly, but they were kept away from the curb by a wall of policemen whose backs were turned towards the cavalcade and the flower-carpeted pavement. Nowhere did he find the forced separation from the people as painful.

Częstochowa Cathedral might have seemed more beautiful at another location. Situated at the foot of Jasna Góra, the church was overshadowed by the shrine and the strange glow that seemed to emanate from the monastery walls and draw all eyes toward the top of the hill.

The cathedral was less crowded that day then was usual during the Pope's visit to a church in Poland. The scene reminded him of Chmielowski's sufferers: people in wheelchairs or other special devices, some of them incurably ill; the injured and the suffering, their arms outstretched in tragic gestures, their faces contorted with pain. He had seen them before – in Cologne, at Lourdes, in the Gemelli Clinic, in Third World countries. He'd seen lepers and people deformed by horrible tropical diseases that often went hand in hand with poverty, and always with despair. It was not easy to look at it all; to walk among the people, smile amid the smell of disease and poverty, touch the ailing bodies, dispense the words of faith. Most tragic of all were the children. Their suffering touched his heart profoundly: children locked in rigid body corsets, children missing arms or legs, children with vacant looks or mindless smiles on their young faces. He saw them as he imagined Chmielowski had seen them, pitiful and beautiful.

I could be one of them, he thought, remembering his stay in the Gemelli Clinic after the hit-and-run accident during the occupation.

He walked down the aisle towards the pleading eyes and the raised hands disfigured by disease. He looked into the faces and saw their joy and sorrow, and he felt a lump of emotion in his throat. Some of the faces were illuminated by the desire for sacrifice, like the face of the girl he had seen in Cracow many years before. He smiled, touched outstretched hands, hugged heads to his chest, and made the sign of the cross.

"Thank you," he whispered to the Bishop. "Thank you so much. You couldn't have arranged a better meeting for me."

Father Stanisław passed him a sheet of paper, but he found it difficult to read throught his tears. He put the prepared words aside and spoke direct to the people.

"I'm going to Jasna Góra now, that heart of Catholic Poland, from this cathedral, the heart of the Częstochowa Church. This place has moved me extraordinarily because I have been able to meet you, my suffering brothers and sisters. This meeting evokes an emotion that I would call evangelical. Those who suffer as you do are in a sense an extension of the suffering Jesus, and the suffering Jesus is the source of our strength. In meeting you, I am meeting Jesus crucified. Our meeting is like a station of the cross along the road to Jasna Góra. It is purifying. I had to meet you before I stand before Our Lady of Jasna Góra, the Mother and Queen of this nation. I needed this meeting because you, with your prayer and especially with your suffering, are assisting me in my pilgramage to the shrine which holds the history of our motherland. If I once dared to say yes when asked to take up the duties of pope, it was because you helped and supported me. It is with your help that I have found the strength of Christ. You are the most valiant detachment of our army, the one which tips the scales of victory."

The glass cage took him to Jasna Góra along the avenue he knew so well. People chanted constantly: "We are with you." The car stopped at the bottom of the stairs leading to the monastery. He walked up the steps with the heavy foot of a weary worker. There was no end to the chanting. Again and again he turned back and raised his arms in a gesture of greeting. Down below stood an army of young pilgrims from every corner of Poland. Night was falling – one of the shortest nights of the year – when he addressed them.

"I am vigilant! What a good thing it is that these words were included in the Jasna Góra Appeal. They are rooted in the Gospel, and it is from the Gospel they were adopted by the scouting movement. 'I am vigilant' – this is a response to the word *Love*. 'I am vigilant' means I am responsible for our common heritage, called Poland. It is a costly heritage. But that which costs much has great value. Let us not yearn for a Poland that would cost us nothing!"

He bade them good-bye again and again, and yet again. It was hard to part with those whose company he valued so much. The night had spread its canopy of stars over the monastery, which seemed to be lit by thousands of candles and lamps.

He pressed his fingers to his closed eyes. There he was, he had reached the goal of his pilgrimage. In a moment he would see Her, the Mother of God with the scarred face. The difficulties which had been piling up around him had not disappeared. But as he had often said, it was difficulties that created a man, and the things that cost most were the most precious of all. Love of Our Lady was difficult and costly. Our love of Her had to overcome obstacles and entailed huge costs; but one had to put one's trust in Her. As the old cardinal had said, one had to offer Her one's sufferings. He felt Wyszyński's presence strongly there, "below the summit."

Although the sky was still lit with stars, clouds had gathered on the horizon and surrounded Jasna Góra. That's unimportant, he thought. Beyond the clouds is Our Lady, and where She is, is hope. We have to trust Her and dedicate ourselves to Her over and over again. Her triumph is the triumph of the Cross. Our Savior comes to the heart of very sufferer through the heart of His Mother. And the Cross always triumphs. The strength of God flows through us like a river, whose source is in the rock of human weakness.

CHAPTER 1. QUEEN JADWIGA

JADWIGA (1373?–1399), the youngest daughter of Louis d'Anjou, King of Hungary and Poland, and Bosnian Princess Elisabeth. Crowned in 1384, marriage to Władysław Jagiełło in 1386, leading to Lithuania's baptism and its union with Poland. Beatified.

WŁADYSŁAW OPOLCZYK (Władysław of Opole), (?–1401), Duke of Opole from 1456, Palatine of Hungary from 1367, Governor of Red Ruthenia: close associate of Louis d'Anjou and Poland's Viceroy on his behalf 1377; took part in negotiations with Jagiełło concerning the latter's marriage to Jadwiga. In 1396, Jagiełło forced him into submission and confiscated his estate.

LOUIS d'ANJOU (Ludwik Węgierski) (1326–1382), son of Charles Robert, King of Hungary, and Elisabeth, daughter of Polish King Władysław Łokietek. Ascended to the Hungarian throne in 1342. Crowned himself as King of Poland 1370. At Košice, 1374, granted additional privileges to the gentry in return for the assurance of one of his daughters succesion to the Polish throne.

DYMITR OF GORAJ (1340?–1400), crown treasurer 1364–70 and 1377–1391, Marshal of the Realm 1390–1400, adviser to King Casimir the Great. Took Jadwiga's side in the dispute over the succession of Louis d'Anjou. Co-founder of the Polish-Lithuanian union.

BODZANTA of the house of Szeliga (1320?–1386), Cracow Governor 1350–82, Gniezno archbishop from 1382; supported the candidacy of Ziemowit IV of Mazovia and then of Jagiełło for the Polish throne; co-founder of the Polish-Lithuanian union.

SIGISMUND OF LUXEMBOURG (1386–1437), Brandenburg elector from 1378, King of Hungary from 1387, of Germany from 1410, Emperor from 1433; son of Emperor Charles IV. Opposed to Poland, supported the Teutonic Knights. Married Mary, sister of Jadwiga.

JAN RADLICA (?–1392), bishop of Cracow, physician; studied in France. One of Cracow's most prominent dignitaries.

DOBIESŁAW OF KUROZWEKI (?–1387), Cracow voivode from 1368 and castellan from 1371. In 1385 promoted Jagiełło's marriage with Jadwiga.

SPYTEK OF MELSZTYN (?–1399), Marshal of the Court. Cracow voivode, Cracow starost until 1390, supported the succession of Jadwiga to the Polish throne and her marriage with Jagiełło.

ELISABETH the BOSNIAN (1340?–1387), wife of Louis d'Anjou from 1353, mother of Catherine, Mary and Jadwiga. Regent of Poland after Louis's death. Kept the Hungarian throne for Mary and decided to put Jadwiga on the Polish throne. Consented to her marriage to Władysław Jagiełło. Murdered during internal strife.

MARY (1370–1395), Queen of Hungary 1382–87, sister of Jadwiga. Married Sigismund of Luxembourg in 1385 and ceded to him her right to the throne.

ELISABETH (1305–1380), Queen of Hungary 1320–1342, daughter of Polish King Władysław Łokietek (1260–1333). Mother of Louis, Regent of Poland 1370–1379.

WILHELM HAPSBURG (1370–1406), Duke of Styria and Carinthia, Jadwiga's fiance.

WŁADYSŁAW II JAGIEŁŁO (1351?–1434), Grand Duke of Lithuania 1377–1401, Poland's King from 1386. In 1388 received baptism and married Jadwiga. Defeated the Teutonic Order at the Battle of Tannenberg 1410, led to the conclusion of the Polish-Lithuanian Union in Horodło. Awarded broader privileges to the gentry.

WITOLD (1352?–1430), Grand Duke of Lithuania from 1410. Władysław Jagiełło's brother-in-law.

CHAPTER 2. THE WOODCARVER

JADWIGA, Duchess of Niemodlin, daughter of Elżbieta and Spytek of Melsztyn, god-daughter of Queen Jadwiga.

JAN ŽIŽKA (1360?–1424), leader of a radical faction of the Taborites which fought wars against the imperial forces over religious and national issues in 1419–1434.

ZBIGNIEW OLEŚNICKI (1389–1455), Bishop of Cracow from 1423, cardinal from 1449, politician and statesman. Fought against Hussite influence in Poland. Removed from power by King Kazimierz Jagiellończyk.

CHAPTER 3. NICHOLAS COPERNICUS

NICHOLAS COPERNICUS (1473–1543), astronomer, mathematician, economist, physician and priest. Author of the heliocentric theory. Brought up by his mother's brother, Bishop of Warmia Łukasz Watzenrode. Studied at Cracow Academy 1491–1495, later in Bologna, Padua and Ferrara. Returned to Poland in 1503. Most important work, *De revolutionibus orbium coelistium*, not published until 1543.

ŁUKASZ WATZENRODE (1447–1512), Bishop of Warmia from 1489. Adviser to Kings Jan Olbracht, Aleksander and Zygmunt Stary (Sigismund the Old) on matters of policy toward Prussia. Adversary of the Teutonic Order. Uncle and protector of Copernicus.

JAN I (John I) Olbracht (1459–1501), King of Poland from 1492.

PAWEŁ WŁODKOWIC (1370?–1435?), lawyer, religious and political writer, diplomat; Cracow Academy rector 1414–1415, member of the Polish delegation to the Council of Constance 1414–1418, where he disputed the Teutonic Order's claim to the lands it occupied and questioned the Order's goals.

KAZIMIERZ IV JAGIELLOŃCZYK (1427–1492), of the Jagiellon dynasty, Grand Duke of Lithuania from 1440, King of Poland from 1447. Son of Władysław Jagiełło. Waged wars against the Teutonic Order, granted privileges to the gentry.

ALEKSANDER JAGIELLOŃCZYK (1461–1506), King of Poland from 1501.

WOJCIECH OF BRUDZEWO (1446–1495), astronomer, professor of mathematics, philosophy and theology at the Cracow Academy. Was one of the first to note the inconsistencies of the geocentric theory: devised tables for calculating the postion of planets.

ALEXANDER VI, Rodrigo Borgia (1439?–1503), Pope from 1492. Sought to strengthen the Church State. Protector of arts and sciences.

THEOPYLACTUS SIMOCATTES, 7th century Byzantine historian.

BERNARD WAPOWSKI (1470?–1535), historian, astronomer and Poland's greatest cartographer of the 16th century, priest. Involved in the Rome publication of Ptolemy's Geopraphy.

CHAPTER 4. **BISHOP HOZJUSZ**

STANISŁAW HOZJUSZ (1504–1579), Bishop of Chełmno from 1549, Bishop of Warmia from 1551, cardinal drom 1561, anti-reformation leader, chairman of the Council of Trent. Brought Jesuits to Poland. Author of many theological treatises.

STANISŁAW OPOROWSKI, provincial of the Paulite Order.

ANDRZEJ KRZYCKI (1482–1537), humanist and poet, secretary to King Zygmunt Stary (Sigismund the Old), referred to in the chapter as the "old King", from 1516, Bishop from 1522, Primate from 1535.

ALBRECHT HOHENZOLLERN (1490–1568), last Grand Master of the Teutonic Order, first Duke of Prussia. Defeated by Poland in 1519–1521, paid homage to Zygmunt Stary.

BONA SFORZA d'ARAGONA (1494–1557), Queen of Poland from 1518, second wife of Zygmunt I Stary, daughter of ruler of Milan, promoter of Italian culture in Poland.

REGINALD POLE (1500–1558), cardinal, resided in Rome, from 1553 Papal Legate in England, then Archbishop of Canterbury. Deposed by the Pope in 1555.

ZYGMUNT II August (1520–1572), here referred to as the "young King", King of Poland from 1548, son of Zygmunt I and Bona, married Elżbieta, daughter of Frederick I, and after her death, Barbara Radziwiłł. The last king of the Jagiellonian dynasty. His reign was a period of economic prosperity and the development of culture. Since his death, Polish kings were elected by the gentry.

ST. AUGUSTINE (354–430), early Christian Church father and author. His philosophy constituted the official doctrine of the Church in the 13th century. Leading representative of the patristic trend.

CHAPTER 5. FATHER MĘCIŃSKI

WOJCIECH MĘCIŃSKI (1598–1643), Jesuit, misionary in south-east Asia, the Philippines and Japan, where he was martyred.

MANUEL DIAZ (1574–1659), missionary, worked in India and China and lectured in theology there.

AUGUSTYN KORDECKI (1603–1673), prior of the Paulite monastery at Jasna Góra. In 1655 organized the defense of the monastery against Swedish forces. Described the siege in his diary.

CHAPTER 6. KING JAN III SOBIESKI

JAN (John) III SOBIESKI (1629–1696), King of Poland from 1674. Grand Marshal from 1665, Field Hetman from 1666. Grand Hetman from 1668. Defeated Turks at Chocim in the Ukraine in 1673. Famous for his part in the 1683 relief if Vienna, then besieged by Turkish forces.

STANISŁAW JAN JABŁONOWSKI (1634–1702), Field Hetman, Cracow castellan from 1692. Attempted to marry queen Marysieńka after Jan III death. Backed Augustus II in the 1696 royal election. One of the ablest military commanders in Polish history, credited with developing hussar formations. Helped to build the Holy Trinity trenches (a chain of forts around Chocim in the Ukraine, designed to protect Poland and Christianity – hence the name) from Turkish attacks – compare the chapter about Pulaski.

LEOPOLD I (1640–1705), Holy Roman Emperor from 1658, of the house of Hapsburg. Fought wars against Cossacks and Turks, killed in the battle of Batoh.

MAJOR HISTORIC CHARACTERS APPEARING IN THE BOOK

MARYSIEŃSKA (Marie Casimire) (1641–1716), Queen of Poland from 1674; previously married to Lublin voivode J. Zamoyski; married Jan Sobieski, 1665.

STANISŁAW PAPCZYŃSKI (1613–1701), priest, founder of the Order of Marians. Jan Sobieski's confessor.

KARA MUSTAFA (ca 1620 or ca 1634–1683), Turkish Grand Vizier, took part in many victorious campaigns. Promoted admiral 1662 and Vizier 1676. Pursued a policy of military expansionism, in 1683 set out for Vienna and laid siege to it; after being routed there by Jan III Sobieski fled to Belgrade, where he was executed at the Sultan's order.

LOUIS XIV (1683–1715), King of France from 1643, reigned for 72 years.

JAN ANDRZEJ MORSZTYN (1621–1693), poet, from 1668 Crown Treasurer; leading member of the pro-French party, opposed Jan III. Accused of treason in 1683, fled to France.

MICHAŁ KORYBUT WIŚNIOWIECKI (1640–1673), King of Poland from 1669. Married Archduchess Eleonor Maria 1770. Considered an incompetent ruler.

IMRE THÖKÖLY (1657–1705), leader of the anti-Hapsburg uprising (1677–1685), Duke of Hungary and Transylvania. Died in Turkey, where he had sought refuge after the defeat of the uprising.

WŁADYSŁAW IV WARNEŃCZYK (Władysław of Varna) (1420–1444), King of Poland from 1434 and of Hungary from 1440, son of Władysław Jagiełło. In Poland, Bishop Zbigniew Oleśnicki (q.v.) ruled on his behalf. Killed at Varna in a poorly organized expedition against the Turks.

WESPAZJAN KOCHOWSKI (1633–1700), poet and historian, Sobieski's historiographer from 1683.

STEFAN CZARNIECKI (1599–1665), Kiev castellan 1655, voivode of Ruthenia from 1657. Crown Field Hetman from 1665, outstanding commander. Fought in Swedish wars and in battles against Chmielnicki. Mentioned in the Polish national anthem.

MICHAŁ KAZIMIERZ PAC (?–1682), Lithuanian Hetman from 1667. Supported the candidacy of Michał Korybut Wiśniowiecki to the throne, opposed Sobieski.

LUDWIKA MARIA of the house of Gonzaga de Nevers (Marie Louise) (1611–1667), Polish Queen, wife of Władysław IV from 1646, of Jan Kazimierz from 1649. During second marriage gained influence in the affairs of state.

CHAPTER 7. CASIMIR PULASKI

CASIMIR PULASKI (1747–1779), general, one of the most prominent figures in the armed struggle of the Confederation of Bar; when it collapsed, went into exile in Saxony, France and Turkey. Left for America in 1777, became national hero of the United States fighting for its independence. Killed in the siege of Savannah.

FRANCISZKA KRASIŃSKA, Duchess, niece of Stanisław Lubomirski and Bishop Adam Krasiński, Married Karol Duke of Courland.

KAROL (1733–1796), Duke of Courland, son of King Augustus III, secretly married Franciszka Krasińska in 1760; forced to leave Courland by Catherine II in 1763. Supported by the Confederation of Bar as a possible candidate for the Polish throne.

ADAM STANISŁAW KRASIŃSKI (1714–1800), Bishop, one of the organizers and leaders of the Confederation of Bar, co-organizer of the Generality.

JÓZEF PUŁASKI (1704–1769), father of Kazimierz (Casimir) and Antoni. Co-founder and marshal of the Confederation of Bar, jointly with Hetman Branicki. After the seizure of Bar by the Russians escaped to Turkish territory and died there in prison.

NIKOLAI REPNIN (1734–1801), general, Russian ambassador to Warsaw 1764–1769. Opposed reforms launched by the King and the Czartoryski family, initiator of the anti-Polish Confederation of Targowica.

CHARLES FRANCOIS du PERIER DOUMOURIEZ (1739–1823), French general and politician. Arrived in Poland in 1770 on a military and political mission to help the Bar confederates. Became foreign minister and commander-in-chief of the French Army. Wrote diaries dealing with his stay in Poland.

STANISŁAW AUGUST PONIATOWSKI (1732–1789), King of Poland 1764–1795, protector of the arts and sciences; lover of Tsarina Catherine II. Abdicated after the third partition of Poland.

ALEKSANDER SUVOROV (1730–1800), Russian field-marshal, victorious in the war against Turkey and France. In 1794 commanded the Russian army in Poland during an attack against the Praga suburb of Warsaw.

FRANCOIS ETIENNE CHOISEUL (1719–1785), Prince, French statesman, foreign minister and minister of war.

ANTON WENZEL KAUNITZ (1711–1794), Prince, Austrian statesman, chancelor 1753–92; supervised Austria's foreign policy; opponent of Prussia, inspired Austria's involvement in the first partition of Poland.

284

CHAPTER 8. **PRINCE PONIATOWSKI**

JÓZEF PONIATOWSKI (1763–1813), Prince, nephew of King Stanisław August, minister of war and commander-in-chief of the Duchy of Warsaw, Napoleon's marshal. Fought many battles. Mortally wounded while retreating across the Elster during the battle of Leipzig.

JÓZEF CHŁOPICKI (1771–1854), general, took part in the 1792 war, the 1794 Rising and the campaigns of the Polish Legions abroad; leader of the armed forces 1830–31, commander of the Uprising.

KAROL KNIAZIEWICZ (1762–1842), general, took part in the 1792 war and the 1794 Uprising, fought with the Legions; took part in Napoleon's 1812 campaign, representative of the National Government in Paris, 1830–31.

DOMINIQUE de FOURT de PRADT (1759–1837), French diplomat and political writer, Archbishop of Malines; Napoleon's representative in Warsaw 1812.

CHAPTER 9. **ARCHBISHOP FELIŃSKI**

ZYGMUNT SZCZĘSNY FELIŃSKI (1822–1895), Archbishop of Warsaw from 1862; took part in the Wielkopolska Uprising 1848. In 1863, opposed the outbreak of the January Uprising 1848. In 1863, opposed the outbreak of the January Uprising, then joined the "white" (moderate) fraction.

EWA FELIŃSKA (1793–1859), mother of Zygmunt, author of novels and precious memoirs, written also in exile.

ALEKSANDER WIELOPOLSKI (1803–1877), Margrave, conservative politician, sought an accomodation with the Tsar; head of the Government of the Congress Kingdom od Poland 1862–63; supported polonization of education, introduction of pensions fo the peasants, conscription; exiled 1863.

SZYMON KONARSKI (alias Janusz Hejbowicz) (1808–1839), revolutionary activist, member of the Young Poland movement, organizer of a radical plot for independence in Byelorussia, Ukraine and Lithuania in 1835; executed by the Russians.

ANDRZEJ TOWIAŃSKI (1799–1878), philosopher, founder of religious and mystic movement, representative od Polish Messianism; influenced poet Adam Mickiewicz.

LUDWIK MIEROSŁAWSKI (1814–1878), leader of liberation struggle, emigré activist, political writer, took part in the 1830–1831 insurrection. First dictator of the 1863 Uprising.

LUIS EUGENE CAVAIGNAC (1802–1857), French general and politician; as minister of war suppressed June 1848 workers' revolt in Paris.

ALEXANDER LUDERS (1790-1874), Russian general, Viceroy of the Congress Kingdom of Poland; applied tactics of terror, target of an unsuccessful assassination attempt.

JÓZEF ALEKSANDER MINISZEWSKI (1823–1863), writer and journalist, supporter of Wielopolski; stabbed to death by conspirators.

KAROL MIKOSZEWSKI (Father Sykstus) (1831–1886), activist of the 1863 Uprising, supporter of „red" (radical) faction; insurgents' chaplain.

HIERONIM KAJSIEWICZ (1812–1873), preacher, religious writer, co-founder of the congregation of Resurrectionists, opponent of Towiański.

JULIUSZ SŁOWACKI (1809–1849), Romantic poet and playwright, went into self-imposed exile in Paris after defeat of the November 1830 Uprising.

ROMUALD TRAUGUTT (1826–1864), last dictator of 1863 Uprising, executed in Warsaw Citadel.

CHAPTER 10. JOHN

JOHN XXIII (Angelo Giuseppe Roncalli) (1881–1963), Pope from 1958. Founder of Second Vatican Council, responsible for Church reforms.

PIUS XI (Achille Ratti) (1857–1939), Pope from 1922; signed Lateran Treaty with Mussolini.

CHAPTER 11. FATHER MAXIMILIAN

RAJMUND KOLBE (Father Maximilian) (1894–1941), Franciscan founder of Niepokalanów, center of cult of the Virgin Mary, missionary in Nagasaki; murdered in Auschwitz concentration camp, where he offered his life to save a fellow inmate. Canonized.

CHAPTER 12. THE OLD MAN AND THE CHILD

JÓZEF PIŁSUDSKI (1867–1935), politician and statesman. Founded Polish Military Organization in 1914 and the Polish Legion. Poland's leader 1918–1922. Marshal of Poland. Staged coup d'etat in 1926 and headed government until his death in 1935.

CHAPTER 13. THE PRIMATE OF POLAND

STEFAN WYSZYŃSKI (1901–1981), Archbishop of Gniezno, and Warsaw Cardinal, Primate of Poland from 1948.

MICHAŁ KLEPACZ (1893–1967), Bishop of Łódź, Professor of Wilno University, theologian, philosopher and educator.

ZYGMUNT CHOROMAŃSKI (1892–1968), Bishop, secretary of the Polish Episcopal Conference.

MIKOŁAJ TRĄBA (1358–1422), Archbishop of Gniezno from 1412, first Primate of Poland. Counselor to Władysław Jagiełło.

AUGUST HLOND (1881–1948), Archbishop of Poznań and Gniezno, from 1946 Archbishop of Gniezno and Warsaw, Cardinal and Primate.

PIUS XII (Eugenio Pacelli) (1876–1958), Pope from 1939. Proclaimed dogma of the Assumption of Mary.

Chapter 14. THE POLISH POPE

PAUL VI (Giovanni Montini) (1897–1978), Pope from 1963. Carried out the reforms of Second Vatican Council. Advocate of peaceful coexistence and Church reform.

TADEUSZ KUDLIŃSKI (b. 1898), writer and theater critic.

JOHN PAUL II (Karol Wojtyła) (b. 1920), Archbishop of Cracow from 1963, Cardinal from 1967, Pope from 1978.

ADAM CHMIELOWSKI (Brother Albert) (1845–1916), painter and social worker, founder of the Congregation of Albertines, beatified.

RAFAŁ KALINOWSKI (1835–1907), Carmelite friar, patriot and participant in 1863 insurrection, prior of Wadowice monastery, beatified.

MIECZYSŁAW KOTLARCZYK (1908–1978), actor and director, founder of Rhapsodic Theater.

ADAM SAPIEHA (1867–1951), Archbishop Metropolitan of Cracow from 1946, Cardinal.

ISBN 83-7021-066-X